A84-C3043

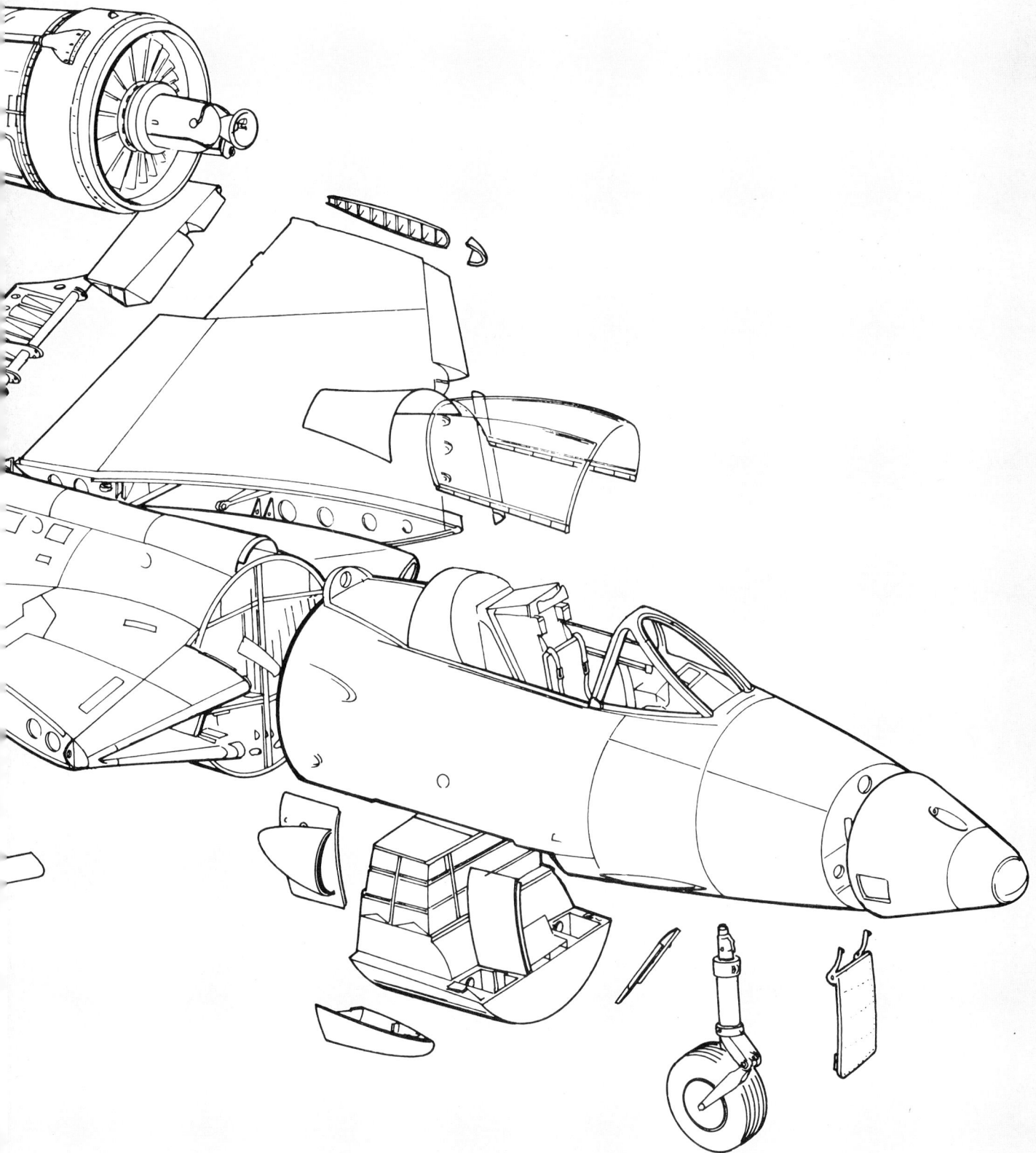

The Illustrated Encyclopedia of 20th Century

WEAPONS AND WARFARE

VOLUME 13

Holt/Inva

The Illustrated Encyclopedia of 20th Century

WEAPONS AND WARFARE

COLUMBIA HOUSE/New York

Editor: Bernard Fitzsimons
Consultant Editors: Bill Gunston (Aviation)
                    Ian V. Hogg (Land Weapons)
                    Antony Preston (Naval)
Deputy Editor: Suzanne Walker
Copy Editor: Michael Maddison
Assistant Editors: Will Fowler, Richard Green,
                   Corinne Benicka, John
                   Liebmann, Michael de Luca
Editorial Assistant: Julie Leitch
Art Editor: David Harper
Assistant Art Editor: John Bickerton
Design Assistants: Jeff Gurney, John Voce
Production: Sheila Biddlecombe
Picture Research: Jonathan Moore
Contributors: Chaz Bowyer, David Brown,
              Mark Hewish, Ian V. Hogg, Bill
              Gunston, Hugh Lyon, Pamela D.
              Matthews, Kenneth Munson,
              Antony Preston, John A. Roberts,
              John S. Weeks, Anthony J. Watts
Illustrator: John Batchelor

Cover Design: Harry W. Fass
Production Manager: Stephen Charkow

"We shall prevail."
—King George VI on declaration
of war, 3 September 1939.

INTRODUCTION

Among the entries in Volume 13 of *The Illustrated Encyclopedia of 20th Century Weapons and Warfare* are a number which demonstrate the increasingly diverse roles filled by one of the more recent developments in military hardware, the helicopter. Those covered include the Soviet Mil Mi-12 **Homer,** able to lift almost 30 tons and easily the biggest helicopter in the world; the Mi-6 **Hook,** Homer's predecessor both technologically as well as in size; the Kamov Ka-25 **Hormone,** standard antisubmarine helicopter of the Soviet navy; the Yakovlev Yak-24 **Horse** assault helicopter and its predecessor, the Mi-4 **Hound.** In addition, two American machines represent contrasting roles, the Kaman **Huskie** being a utility type used for firefighting, photographic and rescue work, while the awesome Bell AH-1 **HueyCobra** has been developed through a number of variants as a battlefield weapons platform.

Although the first tentative helicopter flights were made as early as 1907, and the less sophisticated autogyro was widely used between the world wars, by 1933 the flight endurance record for helicopters was less than ten minutes, and it was not until the Second World War that the helicopter became established as a useful military vehicle, the limited performance of the early types being compensated for by the rotary-wing aircraft's unique versatility. The first armed helicopters were the wartime German Focke-Achgelis Fa 223 transports, which usually mounted a machine gun in the nose, and by the early 1950s both the U.S. armed forces in Korea and the French in Indo-China were experimenting with armed helicopters—mainly Bell OH-13s carrying bazookas or machine guns and rocket-armed military derivatives of the Sikorsky S-55.

One of the early devotees of armed helicopters was Brigadier General Carl Hutton, US Army, who in 1957 formed an experimental unit, the Aerial Combat Reconnaissance Platoon, under the command of Colonel Jay Vanderpool, to develop Hutton's ideas for an integrated airborne force: infantry landed by air in the combat zone and supported there by "aerial cavalry" and air-mobile artillery. Though they soon became known as "Vanderpool's Fools," the platoon made substantial progress with the idea, and in July 1962 the first armed helicopter company was formed for service in Vietnam.

During the Vietnam war the helicopter came into its own, and by the end of the 1960s the Air Cavalry had become an integral part of the Infantry Division. The basic unit of the Air Cavalry was the troop, comprising one platoon of light scouts, a second of UH-1 ("Huey") Iroquois transports, a weapons platoon of Cobra gunships, and an Aero Rifle Platoon—the airborne infantry. Standard procedure was for a hunter-killer team of OH-6 Cayuse scout and HueyCobra gunship to reconnoiter and mark the landing zone, deliver suppressive fire while the infantry was landed by the Hueys and remain in the area to relay information on enemy movements to the ground troops and provide the heavy supporting fire envisaged in Hutton's original scheme.

The main weapons of the Cobras in Vietnam, where the opposition did not normally include heavily armored vehicles, were high-speed Gatling-type machine guns, grenade launchers, and spin-stabilized rockets. The more recent AH-1Q and -1S versions are equipped with Tow wire-guided antitank missiles (while European antitank helicopters carry the Buromissile **Hot**) and have been developed with tanks as their primary target. As a result, in 1975 the US Army created the 6th Cavalry Brigade (Air Combat) as an, initially experimental, independent unit. Provided with AH-1S antitank machines, OH-58 Kiowa scouts, Huey transports and Chinook heavy-lift helicopters, the Air Combat Brigade is scheduled to receive the first AH-64 Advanced Attack Helicopters in the early 1980s. The AAH, firing Hellfire launch-and-leave laser-guided missiles, will have an even greater antitank capability, and in spite of its enormous cost may well establish the helicopter as the prime battlefield weapon of the future.

Holt

US military tractor manufacturers. The Holt Manufacturing Company was an American firm with factories in Peoria, Illinois and Stockton, California, which in the early years of the twentieth century pioneered the development of tracked agricultural vehicles. This work was aided by the purchase, from the British firm of R Hornsby & Sons, of several patents relating to tracked vehicles. Hornsby had hoped to interest the British Army in tracked vehicles, but became discouraged at the lack of support (particularly financial) from the War Office, and abandoned their projects. The Holt company subsequently developed a range of gasoline-engined tracked tractors which were sold throughout the world prior to 1914.

At the outbreak of war, numbers of these vehicles were purchased by the British and French armies for hauling artillery and other heavy loads, while the German and Austrian armies commandeered the few Holt tractors that were in use in their countries, for similar purposes. It was the sight of a Holt tractor which led Colonel E D Swinton to think of an armoured machine-gun destroyer on tracks, and the track and suspension units from Holt tractors were of considerable value in the development phase of early British tanks. Holt tractors also formed the inspiration for the French St Chamond and Schneider tanks, whose suspension units were basically copies of the Holt system. Similarly, an Austrian-owned Holt tractor formed the basis of the first German tank, the A7V.

As soon as European development of the tank became publicly known, the Holt company began their own development programme. Their first design was a one-man tank propelled by a motorcycle engine, but this was soon dropped and in January 1917 work began on two larger models, one of which featured two revolving gun turrets. In April 1917 the Holt Gas-Electric Tank was designed, a 25-ton vehicle in which a gasoline engine drove a generator to provide power for two electric motors, one driving each track. This tank was armed with a Vickers 2.95-in (75-mm) Mountain gun in the front plate and two Vickers M1917 machine-guns in sponsons in the sides. It was not adopted

for service, however, and the company next evolved the Holt Steam Three-Wheel Tank. This had similar armament but, as the title suggests, it was an impractical device and got no further.

None of the Holt designs was taken for production, nor was the company ever employed on tank manufacture, other than as suppliers of components. Their production facilities were devoted to the manufacture of tractors for artillery and other applications, and this was considered to be too important to be interrupted—there were other firms available for tank manufacture. The Holt company did not pursue tank development after 1918.

Holy Moses, NDRC/Caltech

US air-to-surface rocket. The 12.7-cm (5-in) HVAR (high-velocity aircraft rocket), known as Holy Moses because of its tremendous blast, was developed by the NDRC (National Defense Research Committee) in conjunction with the California Institute of Technology. The weapon was sponsored by the US Navy, which by 1944 was ordering rockets for various applications at the rate of $100-million-worth a month, and was also adopted by the US Army Air Force.

Holy Moses could penetrate 3.8 cm (1.5 in) of armour plating and nearly 1.2 m (4 ft) of high-grade reinforced concrete, making it an excellent weapon for use against ships, pill-boxes, bunkers and other fortifications during an amphibious assault. The ability to fire the rocket at varying dive angles, combined with its flat trajectory, allowed Holy Moses to destroy targets which were invulnerable to ship-launched rockets or conventional artillery. The weapon also had a good underwater trajectory and was very effective against submarines attempting to dive after being caught on the surface.

USAAF fighter-bombers based in England and Italy used 11.4-cm (4.5-in) rockets against industrial targets and railway networks for several months before D-Day, and Holy Moses, with its extra punch, was adopted by the Army Air Force initially for use against V-1 flying-bomb sites. Development was completed at Caltech by June 1944, and the first 2000 rounds were ferried across

the Atlantic daily as each hundred rolled off the production line. The US Ninth Air Force battered railway marshalling yards near Paris in its first Holy Moses attack, and by the end of July USAAF P-47 Thunderbolts and RAF Typhoons were flying repeated strikes to support the St Lô breakthrough of the US Third Army under General Patton. The German armoured counter-offensive the following month was blunted by fighter-bombers firing Holy Moses against tanks and the formidable German 88-mm (3.46-in) antiaircraft artillery.

Having been blooded in Europe and the Pacific, Holy Moses graduated to arm the early jet fighters such as the F-84E Thunderjet, and the weapon saw widespread service on several aircraft types in the Korean War. The drag caused by 16 or 24 rockets carried in clusters was enough to knock 160 km/h (100 mph) off the top speed of a jet fighter, however, and the weapon was eventually superseded by a combination of pod- or canister-mounted rockets, high-velocity guns and guided missiles.

Length: 183 cm (6 ft) *Weight:* 63.5 kg (140 lb)
Speed: 420 m/sec (1380 ft/sec)

Homer, Mil Mi-12

Soviet transport helicopter. The Mi-12, also often referred to as the V-12, is by far the world's largest helicopter and is employed on both military and civil duties when outsize loads have to be moved rapidly or to areas where surface transport is unavailable. Homer, which made its maiden flight in the autumn of 1968, uses the dynamic components of the Mi-6 Hook mated to a new fuselage. The Mil design bureau forsook the normal tandem layout for the powerplant, and mounted pairs of engines on the tips of an inverse-taper wing. The four Soloviev D-25VF turboshafts are uprated to 6500 shp each—1000 shp more than is available in the Mi-6—by adding a zero stage to the compressor and by raising operating temperatures.

In its military role Homer is intended to supply front-line forces with equipment flown into rear bases by An-22 Cocks or Il-76 Candids; the main cargo cabin, which measures 28.14 m (92 ft 4 in) long by 4.42 m (14ft

The ungainly but effective configuration of the Mi-12's four Soloviev D-25VF turboshafts which give a load lift comparable to the An-22

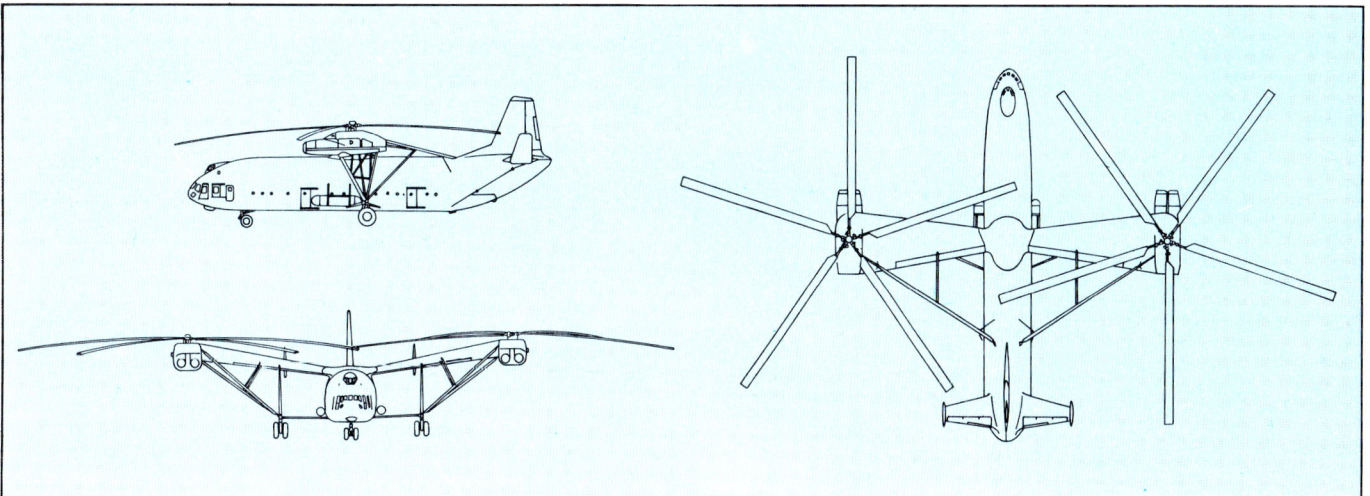

6 in) square, is of the same dimensions as the An-22's hold apart from being 4.85 m (15 ft 11 in) shorter. An electrically powered gantry is slung from two rails running the length of the cabin, and each of the four loading points can lift 2500 kg (5500 lb); non-mobile items weighing up to 10000 kg (22000 lb) can thus be handled, and a rear loading ramp is available for vehicles. An Ivchenko AI-8V auxiliary power unit is used to start the engines without a ground power supply at remote bases. Seats for up to 120 fully-equipped troops can be installed, and the normal maximum payload for a vertical takeoff is 25000 kg (55000 lb); this rises to 30000 kg (66000 lb) when a rolling takeoff is employed. Homer holds the world record for helicopter weightlifting, with more than 40000 kg (88000 lb) having been hauled up to a height of 2260 m (7400 ft) in 1969.

Rotor diameter: (each) 35 m (114 ft 10 in) *Length:* 37 m (121 ft 5 in) *Gross weight:* 105000 kg (231500 lb) *Maximum speed:* 260 km/h (160 mph)

Honest John, Douglas

US artillery rocket. Honest John achieved the distinction of being the longest-serving missile-type system with the US forces by the time it was replaced by the guided Vought Lance battlefield-support weapon in the mid-1970s. The original MGR-1A was developed by Douglas under the technical supervision of the US Army's Redstone arsenal. Firing trials began only a year after the initial contract was awarded in 1950. Production was shared by Douglas and Emerson Electric, the shorter and improved MGR-1B entering service in 1960, seven years after the MGR-1A.

Honest John is unguided but is spin-stabilized by means of small rockets, and is fired from a truck-mounted launch rail which is elevated to produce the desired range, and aimed off to compensate roughly for the prevailing wind. Accuracy is correspondingly low, but this is less important when the weapon is fitted with a nuclear warhead. Honest John was deployed widely by the US and its allies, many of whom replaced it with Lance or, in the case of France, Pluton.

Length: 7.57 m (24 ft 10 in) *Span:* 1.37 m (4 ft 6 in) *Diameter:* 76 cm (2 ft 6 in) *Weight:* 2140 kg (4720 lb) *Range:* 7.4-37 km (4.6-23 miles) *Warhead:* Nuclear or high-explosive, 680 kg (1500 lb)

An Honest John MGR-1B tactical bombardment missile lifts off from its mobile launcher during training at Fort Sill Artillery Range

The Mil Mi-12, V-12 (Homer in NATO identification), the largest helicopter in the world. It is capable of lifting 30 000 kg (66 000 lb) on a STOL takeoff or 25 000 kg (55 000 lb) vertically. When a Mi-12 lifted 40 000 kg (88 000 lb) up to 2260 m (7400 ft) during a test flight in 1969 it lifted roughly double the gross weight of any Western helicopter. The two sets of engines and rotors are arranged side by side linked by high-speed cross-shafting and with the tips intermeshing so that the left rotor is fitted with blades of reversed profile and turns in the opposite direction. Homer was first seen in the West at the Paris Air Show in 1971

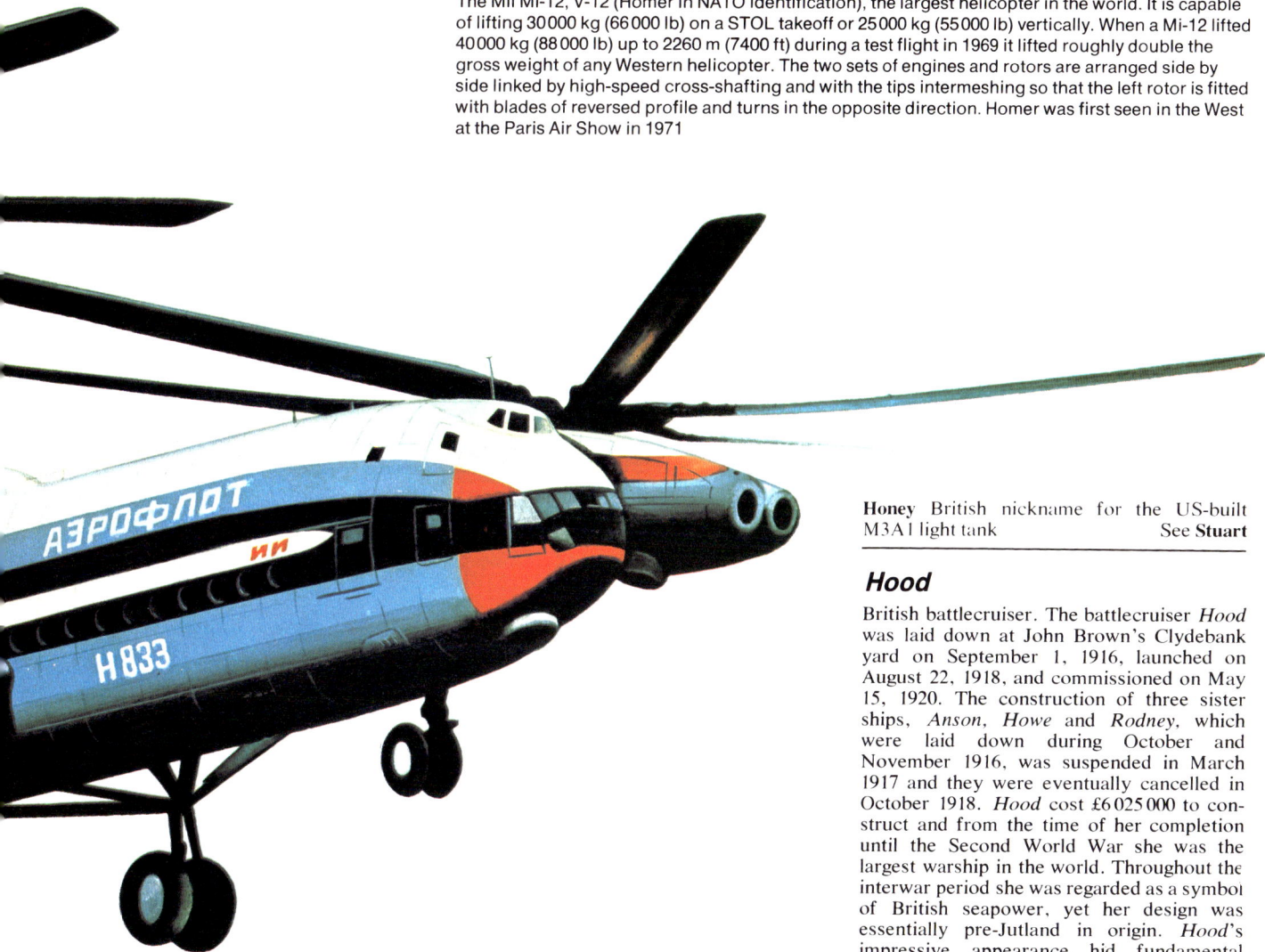

Honey British nickname for the US-built M3A1 light tank See **Stuart**

Hood

British battlecruiser. The battlecruiser *Hood* was laid down at John Brown's Clydebank yard on September 1, 1916, launched on August 22, 1918, and commissioned on May 15, 1920. The construction of three sister ships, *Anson, Howe* and *Rodney*, which were laid down during October and November 1916, was suspended in March 1917 and they were eventually cancelled in October 1918. *Hood* cost £6 025 000 to construct and from the time of her completion until the Second World War she was the largest warship in the world. Throughout the interwar period she was regarded as a symbol of British seapower, yet her design was essentially pre-Jutland in origin. *Hood*'s impressive appearance hid fundamental weaknesses, and these were eventually to bring her career to an abrupt end.

The design of *Hood* originated in 1915 with a proposal to build 25-knot fast battleships incorporating recent war experience, but by early 1916 it had been decided that 31-knot battlecruisers would be of greater value to the fleet. The design finally accepted in April 1916 was for a 32-knot ship of 36 300 tons, protected by 8-in (203-mm) side armour and armed with eight 15-in (381-mm) guns, 16 5.5-in (140-mm) guns and ten torpedo tubes (8 surface, 2 submerged). Orders were placed almost immediately, but after the Battle of Jutland (Skagerrak) work on the new ships was suspended pending the results of investigations into the material aspects of the action. After a rearrangement of the armour the ship's construction was restarted, but for several months improvements in the design of the protection continued to be made. The thickness of vertical armour was increased in general by 50% at the suggestion of the Director of Naval Construction. Later, the deck protection was substantially increased following examination of the lessons learned from Jutland. The changes increased the designed displacement to 41 200 tons and the draught by 3 ft (0.91 m) with a loss in speed of only one knot.

In 1917, work on *Anson, Howe* and *Rod-*

Honest John in 1957. Trials began in 1950 and it was not replaced until the mid-1970s

Hood

HMS *Hood* during her trials. Her design was of pre-Jutland vintage and proved disastrously vulnerable to shell fire during the Second World War

ney was suspended never to be resumed, and *Hood* was the only ship of the projected class to be completed. Further additions to the deck protection over *Hood*'s magazines were made in 1918, and in part compensation four of the 5.5-in (140-mm) guns were omitted. Nevertheless firing trials in 1919 against a target representing *Hood* revealed that her magazines were still vulnerable to long-range gunfire, and proposals were made to increase the deck protection further by the addition of 6-in (152-mm) and 5-in (127-mm) armour over the magazines. In partial compensation for the added weight, four of the above-water torpedo tubes mounted on the upper deck were omitted, together with the protection to the warheads of the remaining four. Unfortunately the ship was completed before the deck armour became available, and this was never fitted.

As completed, the load displacement of *Hood* was 42 670 tons, exceeding the original design figure by 6000 tons. This led to a number of disadvantages. Firstly, the stability was lower than originally intended; secondly, the reduction of freeboard affected her seakeeping qualities and made her wet, particularly aft where in anything but a flat calm the sea continually washed over the quarterdeck; lastly, the additional weights greatly increased the stress on the hull structure and reduced its margin of safety. She was however comparatively successful on trials, achieving 32 knots with 155 280 shp at load draught and proving to be a steady ship and a good gun platform.

Hood served most of her peacetime career with the Atlantic and Home Fleets but also operated with the Mediterranean Fleet during 1936-39. She was employed extensively to show the flag and represent the British Empire on various cruises. Between November 1923 and October 1924 she sailed on a round the world tour of 48 300 km (30 000 miles) with the battlecruiser *Repulse* and the 1st Cruiser Squadron. In 1927 the question of improving her deck protection was raised but this required reconstruction, and the older capital ships of the fleet enjoyed priority. Towards the end of the 1930s, it was decided that she should be taken in hand for major reconstruction after *Queen Elizabeth* but this plan was cancelled following the outbreak of war in 1939. The work was to have included the provision of new machinery, deck armour, a dual-purpose secondary armament and a new bridge structure.

The main alterations and additions made to the ship up to the time of her loss were as follows:

1931—Sixteen 2-pdr pom-poms (2×8) fitted abreast funnels. AA director fitted on after superstructure. Aircraft catapult added on quarterdeck. Oil-fuel stowage increased from 3900 to 4600 tons.

1932—Catapult removed. Eight 0.5-in (12.7-mm) AA guns (2×4) added abreast bridge structure.

1937—Eight 2-pdr pom-poms (1×8) and eight 0.5-in (12.7-mm) AA guns (2×4) added at after end of shelter deck. Two 4-in (102-mm) (2×1) AA guns added amidships.

1938—Two 5.5-in (140-mm) guns on shelter deck replaced by two 4-in (102-mm) (2×1) AA guns.

1939—Eight 4-in (102-mm) (4×2) AA guns added and single 4-in (102-mm) AA removed, two 5.5-in (140-mm) guns replaced, two AA directors mounted abreast of the bridge.

1940—All 5.5-in (140-mm) guns removed, six 4-in (102-mm) (3×2) AA guns and five multibarrel AA rocket projectors fitted. Air-warning radar fitted.

1941—Gunnery radar set fitted.

By 1940 the ship's displacement had risen to 48 360 tons full load, 42 462 tons light, compared with 46 680 tons and 41 000 tons respectively at the time of her completion. This great increase in weight further increased the stress on the hull and reduced her freeboard and stability.

At the outbreak of the Second World War *Hood* was serving with the Home Fleet, and in September 1939 received minor damage from a bomb which struck the port bulge during the first air attack on the fleet. In June 1940 she transferred to Force H at Gibraltar and in the following month took part in the destruction of the French fleet at Oran. She returned to the Home Fleet in August 1940.

On May 23, 1941, *Hood,* flying the flag of Vice-Admiral Launcelot Holland, together with the battleship *Prince of Wales* and four destroyers was patrolling to the southwest of Iceland when a sighting report of the German battleship *Bismarck* and the cruiser *Prinz*

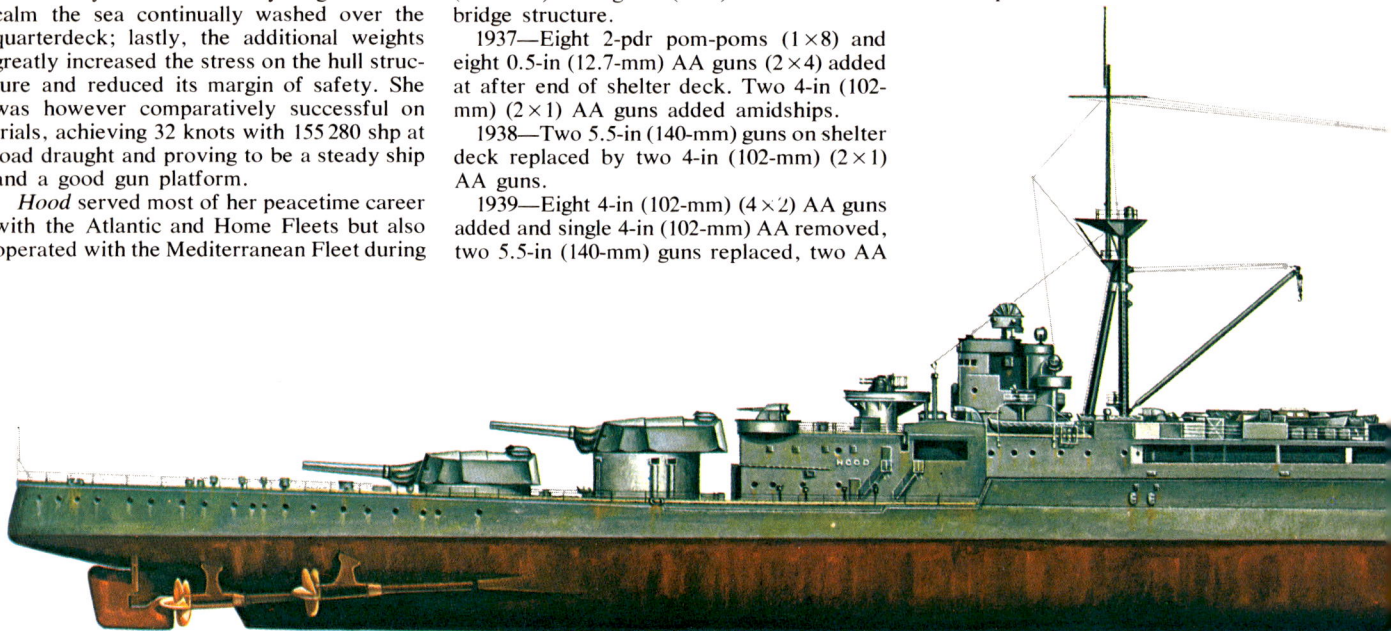

The *Hood* flying a Rear-Admiral's pendant during a courtesy visit between the wars. *Hood* became a symbol of British naval power in the 1920s

Eugen was received from the cruiser *Suffolk* patrolling with her sister ship, *Norfolk,* in the Denmark Strait. Admiral Holland ordered speed to be increased to 27 knots and steered an interception course in response to regular reports from the British cruisers which shadowed the enemy ships through the night. At 0537 hrs on May 24, *Bismarck* was sighted from *Prince of Wales* at a range of 27 km (17 miles) and the British force altered course to close the enemy, with *Hood* leading *Prince of Wales* in an end-on approach. Although this meant only the forward guns could be brought into action it served to close the range quickly to a point where the deck protection of *Hood* would be less vulnerable to plunging shells. At 0552 hrs, *Hood* opened fire, and three minutes later the enemy vessels replied. The third salvo from *Bismarck* straddled the British flagship. About this time an 8-in (203-mm) shell or shells from *Prinz Eugen* struck *Hood* in the vicinity of the boat deck, starting a fire which spread among the many ready-use ammunition lockers carried on the shelter deck. At 0600 hrs at a range of 13260 m (14500 yards) the British ships began to turn to bring their full broadsides to bear. As *Hood* turned she was straddled by

Bismarck's fifth salvo, and a sheet of flame was seen to shoot up from the vicinity of the mainmast, followed by a heavy explosion which broke the ship in two. The after part sank almost immediately and the forward part in about three minutes, leaving three survivors from her crew of 1477.

The generally accepted theory of how *Hood* was lost is that one of the 15-in (381-mm) shells from *Bismarck*'s fifth salvo penetrated the battlecruiser's decks and detonated in the after 4-in (102-mm) AA magazines causing sympathetic explosions in the 15-in (381-mm) magazines which they surrounded. There is, however, a certain amount of evidence to suggest that this was not the case. The centre of the explosion was observed at the base of the mainmast 20 m (65 ft) forward of the 4-in (102-mm) magazines. Although the explosion could have vented itself through the engine room to the forward engine room vents, the detonation of the main magazines would certainly have been visible further aft. It has been suggested that the fire on *Hood*'s shelter deck was the external manifestation of a much greater conflagration below that deck, which either spread to the after magazines or

caused the detonation of the warheads of the upper-deck torpedo tubes mounted abreast the mainmast. Given the highly stressed state of *Hood*'s hull, the explosion of these warheads (each containing 227 kg [500 lb] TNT) could have weakened the upper strength deck sufficiently to cause her to break in two.

Unfortunately, the actual details of the incident are remembered vaguely since the majority of those present were watching the enemy and not *Hood*. Given the speed at which events occurred there must always be some doubt as to the accuracy of the observers' reports.

See also *Bismarck*.

Displacement: 42670 tons (load), 46680 tons (full load) *Length:* 262.31 m (860 ft 7 in) oa *Beam:* 31.75 m (104 ft 2 in) *Draught:* 8.94 m (29 ft 4 in) *Machinery:* 4-shaft geared steam turbines, 144000 shp=31 knots *Protection:* 305-127 mm (12-5 in) sides, 381 mm (15 in) turrets, 305 mm (12 in) barbettes, 76-25 mm (3-1 in) decks *Armament:* 8 15-in (381-mm) (4×2); 12 5.5-in (140-mm) (12×1); 4 4-in (102-mm) AA (4×1); 6 21-in (53-cm) torpedo tubes (4 surface, 2 submerged) *Crew:* 1477

The British battlecruiser *Hood,* commissioned in August 1920, had a brief but disastrous wartime career after peacetime operations that included a cruise around the world in 1923-24. In May 1940 during the pursuit of the German battleship *Bismarck* and battlecruiser *Prinz Eugen* she was straddled by a salvo from the *Bismarck.* Observers saw a sheet of flame near the mainmast and a huge explosion followed which split the ship in half. The stern section sank almost at once while the bows followed three minutes later. Out of a complement of 1477 only three men survived. With so few survivors it is hard to establish what happened. The explosion may have been the 15-in (381-mm) magazines or more likely the explosion of the upper-deck torpedo tubes caused by fierce internal fires from an earlier hit by the *Prinz Eugen*

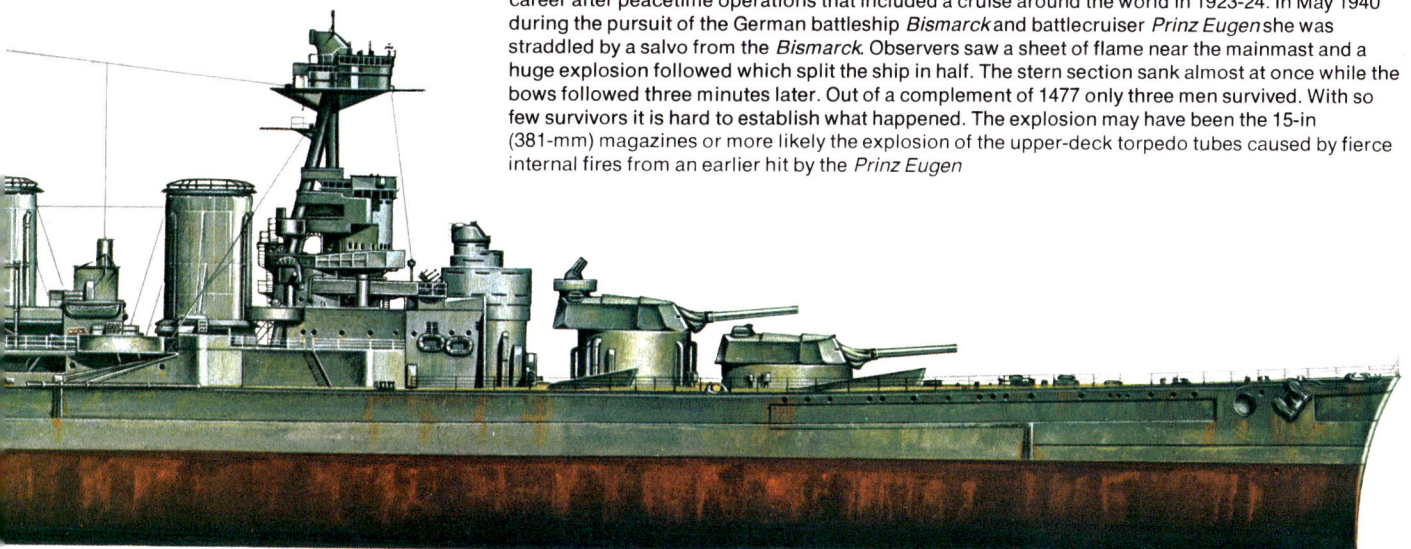

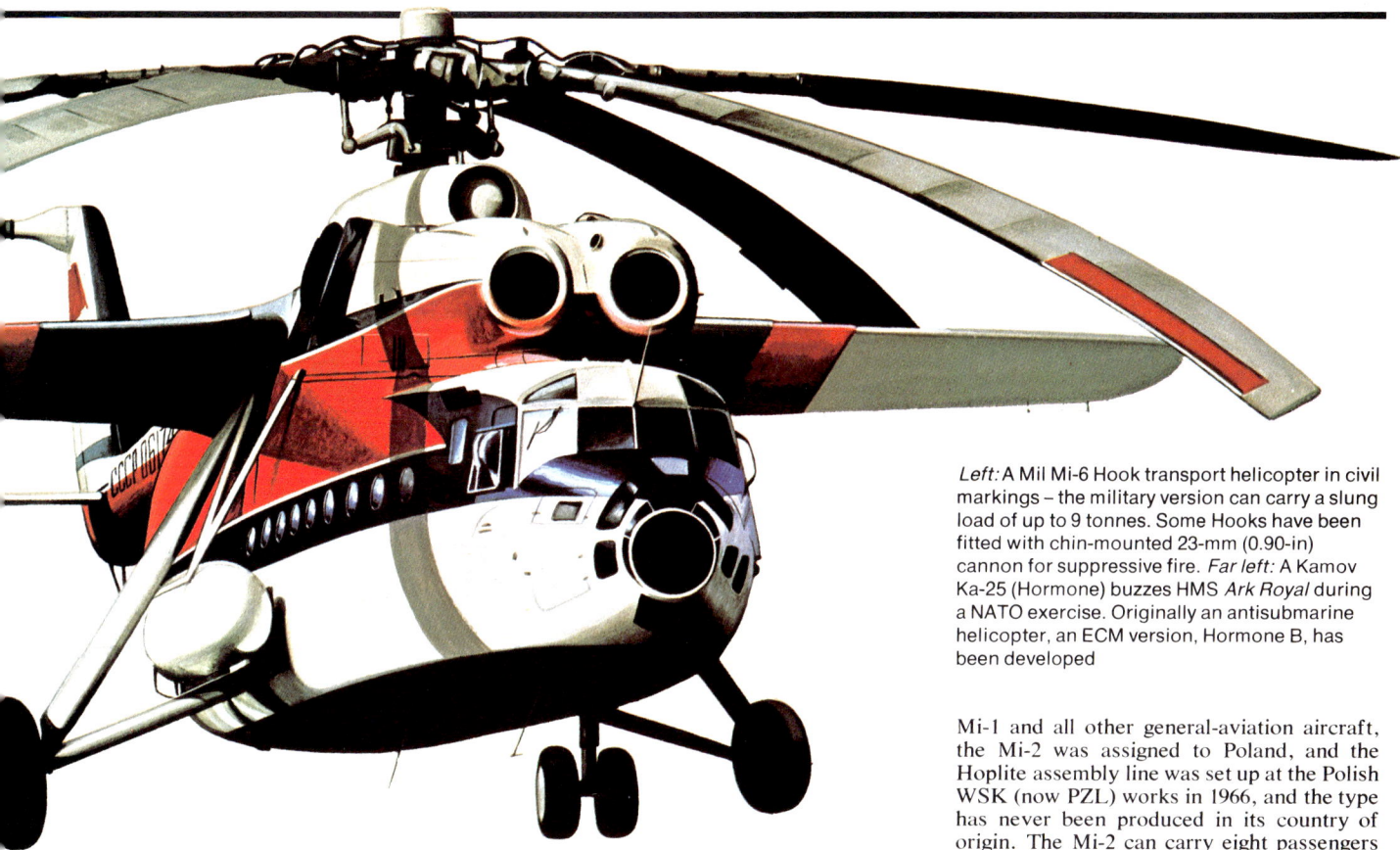

Left: A Mil Mi-6 Hook transport helicopter in civil markings – the military version can carry a slung load of up to 9 tonnes. Some Hooks have been fitted with chin-mounted 23-mm (0.90-in) cannon for suppressive fire. *Far left:* A Kamov Ka-25 (Hormone) buzzes HMS *Ark Royal* during a NATO exercise. Originally an antisubmarine helicopter, an ECM version, Hormone B, has been developed

Hook, Mil Mi-6

Soviet transport helicopter. Just as the later Mi-12 Homer was developed to complement the An-22 Cock transport aircraft, so was the Mi-6 Hook designed to integrate with operations of the An-12 Cub military freighter. Hook was the world's largest helicopter until the introduction of Homer, and it was also the first to exceed 300 km/h (186 mph). Design of the Mi-6 began towards the end of 1954, and the first of five prototypes made its maiden flight in the autumn of 1957. The general layout which had proved successful in the Mi-1 and Mi-4 was retained, but the availability of comparatively small and light turboshaft engines allowed the powerplant to be mounted on top of the fuselage. This reduced transmission weight and allowed the cargo space to be increased.

Production Hooks are powered by a pair of Soloviev D-25V turboshafts with a takeoff power of 5500 shp each. The flexible metal main rotor has five blades, and auxiliary wings are normally fitted to take some 20% of the load during cruise. The cargo hold, which measures 12 m by 2.65 m by 2.5 m (39 ft 4 in by 8 ft 8 in by 8 ft 2½ in), is slightly smaller than that of the An-12 Cub, but outsize items weighing up to nine tonnes can be slung externally. Any payload transported into rear airfields by an An-12 can be delivered to the front line by a pair of Hooks.

Three Mi-6s can transport a pair of vehicle-mounted battlefield-support missiles and their ancillary equipment, the vehicles being loaded via the rear clamshell doors and a ramp. The standard flight crew comprises two pilots, a navigator and a radio operator, with accommodation for 65 troops on tip-up seats along each side of the hold together with supplementary seats which can be installed in the centre of the cabin. The Mi-6 can also be fitted out as an ambulance, carrying two medical orderlies and 41 stretchers. Some Hooks have been fitted with a chin-mounted 23-mm (0.90-in) cannon for defence suppression during assault landings.

A trolley-mounted auxiliary power unit is normally carried for engine starting, and the built-in fuel capacity of 6315 kg (13 920 lb) can be augmented by two 1745-kg (3850-lb) tanks strapped externally to the fuselage sides and a further 3490 kg (7700 lb) in two tanks in the cabin.

More than 700 Hooks are reported to have been built, most of them being supplied to the Soviet armed forces. Military examples have also been exported to Vietnam (where they were used to transport SA-2 Guideline missiles amongst other loads), Bulgaria, Egypt and Indonesia.

Rotor diameter: 35 m (114 ft 10 in) *Length:* 33.18 m (108 ft 10 in) *Gross weight:* 42 500 kg (93 700 lb) *Max speed:* 300 km/h (186 mph)

Hoplite, Mil Mi-2

Soviet/Polish utility helicopter. Hoplite is a turboshaft-powered derivative of the piston-engined Mi-1 Hare, in much the same way as the Mi-8 Hip succeeded the Mi-4 Hound. The introduction of gas-turbine propulsion radically increased payload. The Mi-2's two Isotov GTD-350 turboshafts, each developing more than 400 shp for takeoff, produced 40% more power than the Mi-1's single piston engine for only half the dry weight, more than doubling the maximum load.

The first prototype Mi-2, which made its maiden flight in 1962, was little different from its predecessor, although a number of changes have since been introduced. Like the Mi-1 and all other general-aviation aircraft, the Mi-2 was assigned to Poland, and the Hoplite assembly line was set up at the Polish WSK (now PZL) works in 1966, and the type has never been produced in its country of origin. The Mi-2 can carry eight passengers or 700 kg (1540 lb) of freight, or 800 kg (1760 lb) slung externally in the special cargo version. The modified 11-passenger Mi-2M, with plastic rotor blades and a skid undercarriage, made its maiden flight in 1975.

Rotor diameter: 14.5 m (47 ft 7 in) *Length:* 11.86 m (38 ft 11 in) *Gross weight:* 3550 kg (7825 lb) *Maximum speed:* 210 km/h (130 mph)

Hormone, Kamov Ka-25

Soviet antisubmarine helicopter. Hormone as such made its first appearance as late as 1967, although the basic type had been flying since 1961 or before, in the form of the Ka-20 Harp. The helicopter which eventually emerged as Hormone was developed to meet the Soviet naval air force's requirement for a twin-turbine successor to the Mi-4 Hound for both shipboard and shore-based antisubmarine warfare. The Kamov bureau extrapolated its tried and tested formula of coaxial contrarotating rotors, pod-and-boom fuselage, multi-fin tail unit and four-wheeled undercarriage, as developed through the Ka-15 and Ka-18 series. The adoption of gas-turbine propulsion in the form of two 900-shp Glushenkov GTD-3 turboshafts mounted on top of the fuselage conferred a useful payload-range performance on this comparatively small helicopter, optimized for operation in confined spaces aboard ship.

Sensors include radar, dipping sonar, a towed magnetic-anomaly detector and an electro-optical device, either infrared or low-light television. The antenna of the search radar is mounted in a radome under the chin, and has been seen in two forms: one with a diameter of 1.25 m (4 ft 1 in) and the other much larger. The second version may be a high-power set for long-range target acquisition for mid-course guidance of antiship mis-

Hormone, Kamov Ka-25

siles launched by surface vessels, submarines or aircraft. Weapons carried in Hormone's internal bay include torpedoes and nuclear depth-charges. The air-to-surface missiles mounted on the prototype Harp were almost certainly dummies, and there is no evidence that Hormone is equipped to carry external weapons.

A collar surrounding each wheel can be inflated from gas bottles if the helicopter is forced to ditch. A modular approach to construction has been adopted to ease maintenance at sea, and the rotors, engines, transmission and auxiliaries form a single unit which, it is claimed, can be removed in an hour. Auxiliary fuel tanks can be attached to the fuselage sides.

The *Moskva* Class helicopter carriers each carry about 20 Hormones, and 25 to 30 are carried on *Kiev* Class large antisubmarine cruisers; *Kresta* and *Kara* Class cruisers operate Hormones from platforms at the stern. Nine Hormones have been supplied to Syria for shore-based coastal patrol.

In addition to its self-contained role, the Ka-25 also provides target information for the parent ship's antisubmarine rockets and for the SS-N-14/FRAS-1 missile/rocket system fitted to the Soviet navy's more modern large ships; the type is expected to have an increasing part to play in mid-course missile

Above: **One Hormone lands as a second hovers near the stern of a Soviet cruiser during exercises**

USS *Hornet* (CV-8) after her launch in late 1941. She lasted one year in service, but during that time launched the first carrier strike against Japan in 1942

guidance. It fulfils a secondary plane-guard role aboard the *Kiev* Class vessels. An electronic-warfare version, Hormone-B, has recently joined the ASW Hormone-A.

Rotor diameter: 15.74 m (51 ft 8 in) *Length:* 9.83 m (32 ft 3 in) *Gross weight:* 7300 kg (16 100 lb) *Maximum speed:* 220 km/h (137 mph)

Hornet

US aircraft carrier, built 1939-41. A *Yorktown* Class carrier, *Hornet* was authorized several years after her sister ships and was the first US carrier ordered after the ending of treaty restrictions on total carrier tonnage. She was laid down in September 1939, launched on December 14, 1940, and commissioned on October 20, 1941, just seven weeks before the Japanese attack on Pearl Harbor.

Hornet worked up her air group in the Caribbean during January 1942, and on her return to Norfolk, Virginia, she embarked a pair of North American B-25 Mitchell bombers for a deck takeoff trial. The trial, which was successful, was in preparation for one of the most dramatic operations of the Second World War—a carrier-based strike against the Japanese mainland. The next two months were taken up with further training, and

Above: As two torpedo bombers streak over the *Hornet* a Japanese dive-bomber screams down amidships. *Below:* A B-25 takes off from *Hornet* during the 'Doolittle Raid' in April 1942

Hornet

USS *Hornet* (CV-8) after her attack on Tokyo in April 1942. She launched B-25 Mitchell bombers against the Japanese capital in a raid which began as a propaganda gesture and became the preliminary to the major carrier battles of Coral Sea and Midway. *Hornet* was sunk in October 1942, a little over a year after her commissioning. Her sister *Enterprise* participated in every major action in the Pacific, while *Yorktown* (CV-5) was lost on June 7, 1942. For several weeks in 1942 *Enterprise* was the only carrier in the Pacific until she was joined by HMS *Victorious*. She survived battle damage twice and two kamikaze attacks in 1945. The class could carry 100 aircraft and later in the war *Enterprise* switched from naval targets to attacking Japanese land installations and supporting landings by the US Army and Marine Corps. *Hornet* was slightly heavier than her 19 900-ton sisters, weighing 20 000 tons

passage to San Francisco. Here, *Hornet* took on board 16 US Army Air Force B-25s, and left on April 2 to rendezvous to the north of Midway Island with her sister ship *Enterprise* on April 13.

President Roosevelt had been interested in the idea of an air attack on the Japanese capital since the beginning of the war in 1941. An initial report on the projected operation recommended carrier transport of B-25s to within 640 km (400 miles) of Japan. Since B-25s were too large for flight-deck landings, it was planned that they should fly on to friendly areas of China after completing their mission. After the aircraft had taken off, their carrier would head away from Japan at top speed to avoid retaliatory attacks.

Early on April 18, when they were still 1075 km (668 miles) to the east of Tokyo, *Hornet*, *Enterprise* and their escort were sighted by Japanese picket boats. Vice-Admiral William Halsey, commander of the carrier force, decided to start the mission at this point. At 0800 hours, Colonel James Doolittle led the 16 B-25s as they took off from *Hornet*'s deck for the first air raid on Tokyo. Flying at treetop height, the bombers crossed the Japanese coastline at 16 different points, and despite the sighting of the carrier force Japanese defences were caught unprepared.

Doolittle's lead aircraft dropped 910 kg (2000 lb) of incendiary bombs over downtown Tokyo. A further nine bombers hit steel plants and oil refineries in north Tokyo, and the docks to the south of the city. Factories and oil tanks in Yokohama were the targets for three of the B-25s, and another three raided the industrial town of Nagoya while en route to Kyoto. One aircraft bombed Kobe and severely damaged the Kawasaki aircraft plant. The raid was over by 1300 hours. Ninety factories had been gutted and a fuel-tank farm and six fuel tanks destroyed. Slight damage was also caused to the light carrier *Ryuho* undergoing conversion at Yokosuka dockyard. None of the B-25s was lost over Japan, and most of Doolittle's bomber crews reached safety in China, although three died in a crash-landing. One aircraft crash-landed near Vladivostok and the crew of five were detained by the Soviets, and eight airmen were taken prisoner in Japanese-held China and were eventually put on trial for alleged war crimes. Three of them were executed. *Hornet* and *Enterprise* withdrew to Pearl Harbor and arrived there a week after the raid.

Five days later, on April 30, the two carriers sailed again with two dozen Marine Corps fighters destined for delivery to Espiritu Santo. The mission was cancelled when the ships were near Fiji, and they returned to Pearl Harbor to prepare for what was to be the first clear-cut US fleet victory of the war—Midway.

On June 4, 1942, the day on which four Japanese carriers were sunk, the only aircraft from *Hornet* to sight the enemy were the 15 Douglas Devastators from the ship, together with six Grumman TBF Avengers detached to Midway Island. Torpedo Squadron 8 lost all the Devastators and five Avengers, as well as 59 of the 63 aircrew, without scoring a hit. The Douglas SBD Dauntless dive-bombers and Grumman F4F fighters failed to find the enemy. All ten F4Fs ditched after running

out of fuel, as did two of the SBDs. Sixteen SBDs later attacked *Hiryu* but scored no hits. On June 6, *Hornet*'s dive-bombers made up for their earlier undistinguished performance by finishing off the damaged heavy cruiser *Mikuma* and severely damaging *Mogami*.

Hornet returned to Pearl Harbor to embark a new torpedo squadron and to carry out the further air group training which was so necessary. She thus missed the battle fought off Guadalcanal on August 24, 1942, although at the time en route for the south-west Pacific, ferrying Marine Corps fighters. Once these were unloaded at Guadalcanal, *Hornet* joined the patrols to the east of the island, covering the reinforcement convoys. On September 6, the carrier was narrowly missed by a torpedo and a submarine. Nine days later *Wasp*, in company, was sunk by a submarine. *Saratoga* had already been damaged by torpedo in the same area, on August 31, and the one remaining undamaged carrier was withdrawn to Espiritu Santo.

On October 2, *Hornet* sortied to attack the Japanese advanced base at Shortlands in the Solomon Islands. The raid, which took place on October 5, was unsuccessful due partly to poor weather, and a strike on Rekata Bay, Santa Isabel Island, found no worthwhile targets. The carrier remained at sea, covering Guadalcanal reinforcement shipping and was joined to the north of the Solomons on October 24 by the recently repaired *Enterprise*, on the eve of the fourth and last carrier battle of 1942.

The action at Santa Cruz began with the two sides locating and assessing one another's forces. On the next day, October 26, *Hornet* and *Enterprise*, with 158 aircraft between them, engaged the enemy fleet of four carriers (*Zuikaku*, *Shokaku*, *Junyo* and *Zuiho*) which had 207 aircraft. *Hornet* launched 39 out of her 50 attack aircraft, but before they reached the enemy, 27 dive- and torpedo-bombers from *Zuikaku* and *Shokaku* broke through the US fighter patrols and, in the space of 11 minutes, scored six bomb hits and two torpedo hits on *Hornet*. Two aircraft also made successful suicide attacks. *Hornet* was left dead in the water, with a 12½° list and many fires.

Ten minutes after the end of the attack on *Hornet*, her aircraft fought their way through defending Zero fighters and scored six direct hits on *Shokaku*, putting her out of action for months. Three hits were also scored on the heavy cruiser *Chikuma*, resulting in severe damage. Air Group 8 had been successful at last, but were unable to return to their own ship and had to return to *Enterprise*.

Hornet was taken in tow by a heavy cruiser at noon, after her fires were under control. The list was reduced and prospects of saving her were fair when, four hours later, a strike launched by *Junyo* scored another torpedo hit and two more bomb hits. The decision was taken to scuttle *Hornet*, but hits from torpedoes and 430 rounds of 5-in (127-mm) HE shells failed to finish her off. It was left to the Japanese destroyers *Makigumo* and *Akigumo* to provide the coup de grâce in the early hours of October 27, 1942, following an unsuccessful attempt to take the still-blazing carrier in tow.

Hornet's career had been brief and relatively unsuccessful. Although she was present at Midway, her contribution was limited,

and at Santa Cruz her aircraft had only scored hits after she had been incapacitated. But she will always be remembered as the ship which launched the 'Doolittle Raid' on Tokyo, an operation which raised American civilian morale at a time when it was most needed. Her name was revived for the eighth ship of the *Essex* Class (CV.12), which distinguished herself during the last 18 months of the Pacific War.

See also *Enterprise*, *Yorktown*.

Displacement: 20 000 tons *Length:* 232 m (761 ft) wl, 246.7 m (809 ft 6 in) oa *Beam:* 25.4 m (83 ft 3 in) *Draught:* 6.6 m (21 ft 9 in) *Machinery:* 4-shaft geared turbines, 120 000 shp=34 knots *Aircraft:* 100 *Armament:* 8 5-in (127-mm) *Crew:* 2200

Hornet, de Havilland

British fighter and fighter-bomber. The last and fastest piston-engined fighter to serve with the RAF, the de Havilland Hornet was designed as a private-venture successor to the Mosquito, to which it bore a strong resemblance, being powered by two 2030-hp Merlins mounted below the wings, though the Hornet's wings were stepped and with slightly swept leading edges outboard of the engines. An Air Ministry specification was produced to cover the design, and the first prototype flew on July 28, 1944.

Deliveries of 60 F.1s to the RAF began in April 1945, and these were followed by 130 F.3s, which introduced the filleted tail also used on Sea Hornets, and by 12 F.R.4s. The Royal Navy's Sea Hornet was a navalized version of the Hornet, with arrester gear, catapult attachment point and folding wings. Deliveries of the Sea Hornet F.20 began in June 1947, and a total of 77 were delivered, as well as 23 of the P.R.22 photo-reconnaissance variant. One other naval version, the only two-seat Hornet, was the N.F.21 night-fighter, with an ASH scanner in

The second prototype de Havilland Hornet, a long-range single-seat fighter developed for use in the Far East at the close of the Second World War. Development ended with VJ Day

the nose, flame-damping exhausts and a second cockpit for the navigator midway along the fuselage. Armament on all versions was four 20-mm (0.79-in) cannon in the nose, plus up to 907 kg (2000 lb) of bombs or rockets under the wings.

Span: 13.72 m (45 ft) *Length:* 11.18 m (36 ft 8 in) *Gross weight:* 9480 kg (20 900 lb) *Maximum speed:* 760 km/h (472 mph)

Hornet, F-18 McDonnell Douglas/Northrop

US carrier- or land-based fighter and attack aircraft. In April 1974 the US Navy's proposal to develop a new multirole combat aircraft, the VFAX, was accepted by the US Department of Defense. But in August of that year the navy was directed by Congress to use a version of one of the LWF (light-weight fighter) prototypes built for the US Air Force. Although the USAF chose the F-16, the navy finally selected an alternative proposal from McDonnell Douglas based on the other LWF, the twin-engined Northrop YF-17. McDonnell Douglas subsequently received the prime contract to develop the NACF (navy air combat fighter) with the designation F-18, later named Hornet. Northrop's status was reduced from sole supplier of the YF-17 to associate contractor handling 30% of development and 40% of production.

Compared with the YF-17, and earlier P.530 Cobra, the F-18 is larger, has greater fuel capacity and is much heavier. Its several versions include the F-18A Hornet for the navy, the A-18 land-based attack versions for the US Marine Corps, and the TF-18 tandem-seat mission trainer with less fuel and long one-piece canopy. Eleven development aircraft were planned, followed by 800 production aircraft for the US forces. Throughout the Hornet programme detail design has been aimed at increasing reliability and reducing operating cost, and it is claimed that the new aircraft will be far superior in performance to the two main types it will replace, the F-4 Phantom and A-7 Corsair.

The powerplant consists of two General Electric F404 two-shaft augmented bypass jets (low bypass-ratio turbofans), each rated at 7260 kg (16 000 lb) thrust with maximum afterburner. Each engine is fed by a fixed plain inlet under the long fixed wing-root strake alongside the fuselage. The unswept wing, which like the whole airframe makes extensive use of graphite/epoxy composite structures, has leading-edge manoeuvre flaps and trailing-edge flaps which, with drooping ailerons, extend from tip to tip. There are large leading-edge dog-tooth notches, immediately outboard of which the wings fold for carrier stowage. The slab tailplanes are mounted halfway down the rear fuselage;

An artist's impression of the F-18 Hornet naval strike fighter. Two versions are planned to replace the role of the F-4 and the A-7

Hornisse

A camouflaged Hornisse SP antitank gun in an ambush position in a ruined building—the tank kills are marked with rings on the gun barrel

ahead of them, above the wing trailing edge, are the twin outward-canted vertical tails.

In the nose is a Hughes radar with 711-mm (28-in) planar reflector, immediately above which is an M61 Gatling 20-mm (0.79-in) gun. Up to 6215 kg (13 700 lb) of weapons, tanks or ECM pods can be carried on nine external pylons, including wingtip rails for Sidewinder AAMs. The F-18A is also intended to carry the AIM-7F Sparrow medium-range AAM, with continuous-wave guidance. Litton provides an inertial navigation system, and Kaiser an advanced HUD (head-up display), which is omitted from the rear seat of the trainer version. The ejector seat is the zero/zero (zero-height zero-speed capability) Martin-Baker Mk 10, and the flight-control system has electric fly-by-wire signalling. The A-18, and possibly some F-18 sub-types, will have provision for FLIR (forward-looking

infrared) and laser tracking and marked-target seeking. They will also carry such air-to-surface weapons as the three chief versions of AGM-65 Maverick.

Although not competing with the F-14A Tomcat in the task of defending the US battle fleet against air attack at long range, the Hornet will be able to undertake all forms of escort and air combat. However, it is too early to predict the extent to which it will be used for defence rather than offensive roles, such as it is to perform with the Marine Corps. Its mission radius with typical weapon loads will exceed that of the A-7E or F-4J, and in interdiction roles the CEP (circular error probable: an estimate of accuracy, used to determine probable damage to target) is expected to be better than for any other seagoing aircraft. The first of the 11 test aircraft was expected to fly in July 1978.

Production deliveries are planned to begin in 1981-82.

Span: (over Sidewinder missiles) 12.41 m (40 ft 9 in) *Length:* 17.07 m (56 ft) *Gross weight:* 22 710 kg (50 067 lb) *Maximum speed:* (clean, high altitude) 1915 km/h (1190 mph, Mach 1.8)

Hornisse Popular name for Messerschmitt Me 410 German fighter-bomber   See **Me 410**

Hornisse

German self-propelled antitank gun, in service 1943-45. The Hornisse (hornet) was among the first German tank destroyers to be anything like purpose built, and used a chassis derived from components of the PzKpfw III and IV tanks. The principal change was

The Hornisse combined the mobility of the PzKpfw III or IV chassis with the powerful 88-mm (3.46-in) PAK 43/1 antitank gun. However, it suffered from a high silhouette and thin, incomplete armour protection for the crew

that the engine was moved forward to a position alongside the driver, leaving space at the rear for a large fighting compartment. The hull sides were raised to enclose this compartment, and an 88-mm (3.46-in) PAK 43/1, L/71 antitank gun was mounted in the front plate.

About 470 of these vehicles were built during 1944, and the majority were used on the Eastern Front. In general they were highly effective as guns, but the silhouette was high and only poor protection was afforded by the thin and substandard armour. During 1944 the name Hornisse was dropped, and they were subsequently known as Näshorn (rhinoceros).

Weight: 24 tonnes *Length:* 8.44 m (27 ft 8 in) *Width:* 2.95 m (9 ft 8 in) *Height:* 2.94 m (9 ft 8 in) *Armour thickness:* 10 mm (0.39 in) *Armament:* 88-mm (3.46-in) PAK 43/1, L/71 *Powerplant:* Maybach V-12 gasoline, 300 bhp at 3000 rpm *Speed:* 40 km/h (25 mph) *Range:* 200 km (125 miles) *Crew:* 4

Horsa, Airspeed

British transport glider. Following the dramatic success of German assault gliders in the reduction of the Belgian fort of Eben-Emael on May 10, 1940, the British Ministry of Aircraft Production issued orders for the manufacture of troop-carrying gliders. In December 1940, Airspeed (1934) Ltd was instructed to build a prototype to Specification X.26/40. The specification was rather general, the only specific requirements being for all-wood construction, jettisonable landing gear and seating for 26 troops with a paratroop door at each end and a wide freight door at the front. The work was carried out under the direction of Hessel Tiltman.

The A.A.51 Horsa prototype, serial DG597, was flown by Squadron-Leader (later Group-Captain) 'Willie' Wilson, a world speed record holder, on September 12, 1941. Early flying was carried out using Armstrong Whitworth Whitley bombers as tugs. Both tug and glider had diagonal black-and-yellow striped undersides. The main burden of development was borne by Flight-Lieutenant 'Nick' Carter, with company test-pilots George Errington and Ron Clear. The most difficult task was learning how to ride blind (in cloud, for example), and even the addition of an 'angle-of-dangle' tow-rope indicator was not successful because it was discovered that the motion of the visible part of the rope gave no indication of the tug's position. Fortunately the Horsa was almost unbreakable, although it creaked loudly in turbulent conditions.

Two pilots sat side by side in the extremity of the nose, and often needed their combined strength to handle the controls. The fuselage was circular in section, and the thick wing was mounted on top and provided with very large flaps, depressed by stored air pressure, to enable unusually steep descents to be made. On a combat mission the tricycle undercarriage was jettisoned and the landing made on a belly skid. After coming to rest, the whole rear fuselage could be detached, and the left cargo door slid back. On the Mk II the bifurcated tow rope was changed to a single line pulling under the nose, which could swing open for loading and unloading a Jeep, a 17-pdr gun, Bailey bridge parts, a Bofors gun, and many other loads. A vital quality of the glider was excellent control down to speeds around 80 km/h (50 mph).

Production was handled not only by Airspeed at Christchurch but also by Elliots of Newbury, and a Horsa Group which included Harris Lebus, The Gramophone Co, Boulton Paul, H H Martin, Waring & Gillow, Radio Cabinets and many other companies. A total of 3655 aircraft were built, of which at least 3000 were erected by 41 Group RAF. A plan for Tata Industries to build Horsas in India was cancelled.

The first operation, on a Norwegian heavy-water plant, was carried out by two Horsa Mk Is towed by Halifax tugs on November 19, 1942. The mission was disastrous, although this was no fault of the tugs or gliders. On July 10, 1943, Horsas were involved in operations in Sicily, having been towed three days earlier non-stop from Britain to North African bases. Early on D-Day, over 250 Horsas arrived in Normandy. One group was fitted with arrester parachutes for very short landings at the Orne bridges, and on the battery commanding the left flank of the seaborne landing. At Arnhem, 320 gliders carried out the first lift and 296 the second, while in the Rhine crossing some 440 carried the British 6th Airborne Division. The Horsa was an excellent machine, and in terms of achievement can be considered the leading Allied assault glider of the Second World War. Apart from the Halifax III, V and VII the main tugs were the Albemarle, the C-47/Dakota and the Stirling IV.

British airborne troops wait by their D-Day striped Airspeed Horsa gliders. A tough and versatile aircraft, it carried troops or cargo

Horsa, Airspeed

A British Airspeed Horsa cargo and personnel glider with a typical load during a pre-D-Day exercise. In action the glider was unloaded by removing the tail section which gave access to the cargo area. Gliders were a cheap and efficient way of delivering a section of fully-armed men onto a target like a bridge or artillery position, in complete silence

Horse, Yakovlev Yak-24

Factory-fresh Horsa gliders. The Horsa was used throughout Europe in all the major airborne assaults and a host of minor operations

Span: 26.8 m (88 ft) *Length:* 20.4 m (67 ft) *Gross weight:* 6917 kg (15 250 lb) *Towing speed:* (typical) 204 km/h (127 mph)

Horse, Yakovlev Yak-24

Soviet assault helicopter. The Yak-24 was the 'doubled up' counterpart of the Mi-4 Hound, both types having been launched following a meeting at the Kremlin in 1951. The Yak-24 was intended to meet the requirement for a *Letayuchy Vagon* (flying boxcar) which could transport 24 passengers or freight, and the first of four prototypes took to the air in July 1952. The Yakovlev team had adopted an ambitious tandem-rotor layout, and duplication of effort was minimized by the use of the rotor hub and pitch-change mechanism developed for the Mi-4 Hound, although the blades themselves were slightly modified. The powerplant comprised a pair of ASh-82V radial engines producing 1700 hp each for takeoff.

Production did not begin until 1955, as a result of serious vibration problems, and the four helicopters demonstrated at the Soviet Aviation Day display in that year were to preproduction standard only. Typical loads comprised 30-40 troops, up to 4000 kg (8800 lb) of cargo, three M-20 staff cars, two GAZ-60 command vehicles, or antitank guns and their crews. The more capacious Yak-24U, with structural modifications and autostabilization, made its maiden flight at the end of 1957 and the design was tinkered with for several more years. A commercial version, the 30 passenger Yak-24A (Aeroflotsky) was evaluated by Aeroflot but was rejected. Horse never entered widespread service, however, and production did not exceed 100 units (some sources put the total as low as 40).

Rotor diameter: 21 m (68 ft 11 in) *Length:* 21.3 m (69 ft 11 in) *Gross weight:* (Yak-24U) 15 830 kg (34 900 lb) *Maximum speed:* 175 km/h (109 mph)

Horsley, Hawker

British bomber and torpedo bomber. The Hawker Horsley was produced to meet a 1923 specification which called for a two-seat long-range day bomber powered by a single 650-hp Rolls-Royce Condor III, and was selected in preference to the Bristol Berkeley, Handley Page Handcross and Westland Yeovil. The last all-wooden Hawker aircraft, the Horsley was an unequal-span biplane armed with a single synchronized Vickers and a ring-mounted Lewis.

The prototype first flew in 1925, and in March 1926 a first production batch of 38 were ordered, though to a revised specifica-

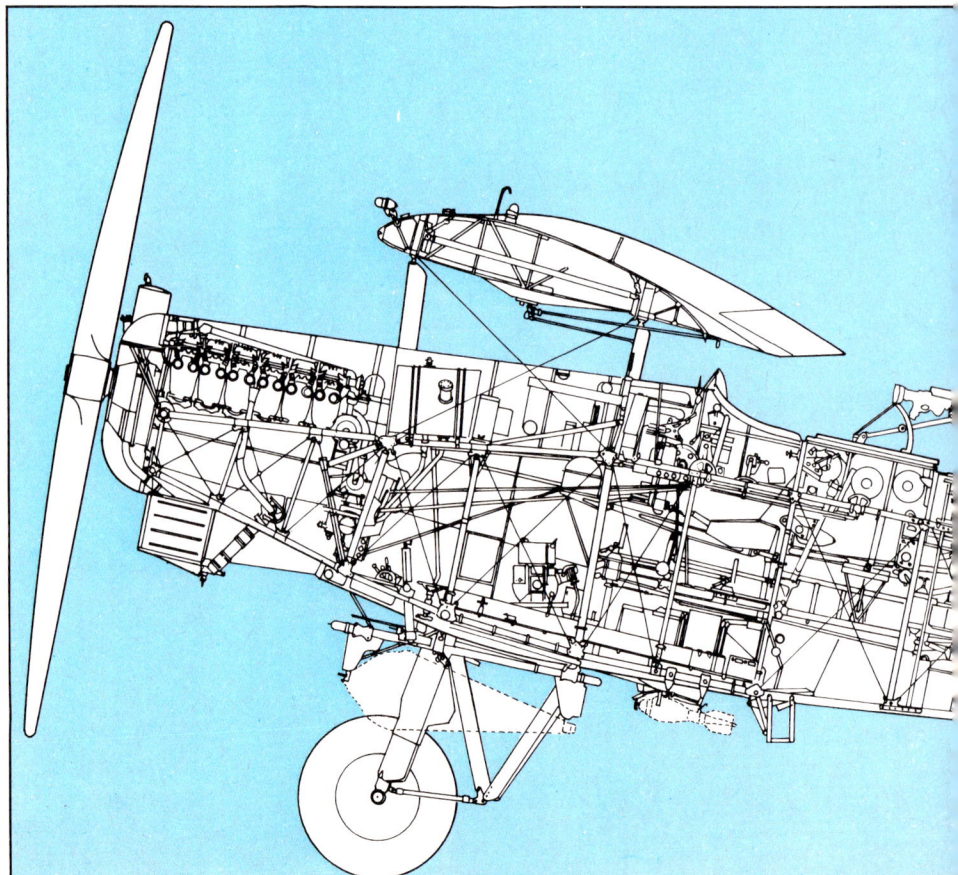

The figure by this Hawker Horsley II shows the substantial size of the aircraft (S1452), used in trials for the Rolls-Royce Condor III

tion calling for increased load-carrying ability. A second prototype introduced slightly swept wings, and after the first few Mark Is the Mark II of composite construction was introduced, the 665-hp Condor IIIA being substituted. Later, all-metal Horsleys were completed as land-based torpedo bombers. An eventual total of 128 Horsleys were produced, deliveries beginning in 1927, and six being sold to the Greek navy in 1927. The last to be retired from front-line service were the torpedo bombers with 36 Squadron in Singapore, which were replaced by Vickers Vildebeests in 1935. Two Horsley derivatives, three-seat torpedo bombers known as Dantorps and powered by 805-hp Armstrong Siddeley Leopard IIIA engines, were sold to the Danish navy in 1932.

Span: 17.22 m (56 ft 6 in) *Length:* 11.84 m (38 ft 10 in) *Gross weight:* 3538 kg (7800 lb) *Maximum speed:* 203 km/h (126 mph)

The Hawker Horsley—named after the designer T O M Sopwith's home of 'Horsley Towers'—was built in wood and metal as a bomber and torpedo bomber. The pilot was armed with a synchronized Vickers machine-gun, while his observer had a Lewis. The first flight was made from Brooklands in 1925 with Sydney Camm in the observer's cockpit and subsequently orders were placed by the RAF

Hosho

Japanese aircraft carrier, built 1919-22. *Hosho* was the third flat-top aircraft carrier to be completed, and Japan's first flat-top carrier. Like her predecessors, the British *Argus* and the US *Langley*, she was converted for the role, having been laid down in late 1919 as the naval oiler *Hiryu*. She was taken over for conversion in 1921 and completed on December 27, 1922.

The carrier design was worked out in collaboration with British officers of a technical mission to Japan. The British also had an involvement in the design of the aircraft which she was to embark during the first ten years of her service. However, several features of her aviation facilities were never to appear in British ships. A 130-m (430-ft) long hangar was built over the oiler's tank deck, the flight deck being supported by the hangar walls. Forward of the hangar, the flight deck sloped downwards over the open forecastle. Amidships, the hangar sides were closed off from the open air only by light screens, though this American-style arrangement later proved unsatisfactory and the apertures were plated over. No arrester gear was fitted at first, but electrically-controlled transverse wires were later installed. Two rectangular lifts connected the hangar with the flight deck.

Triple-expansion reciprocating engines were to have been installed in the oiler, but the carrier needed a higher speed and destroyer-type turbines were substituted, giving a maximum speed of 25 knots. The exhaust was led to the starboard side of the hangar deck amidships and trunked into three short funnels which could be swung downwards through 90° to carry smoke clear of the deck during flying operations. A small island navigating bridge was sited on the starboard deck-edge when *Hosho* was first completed, but although it was a negligible obstruction it was disliked by the pilots and was removed in 1923. Thereafter, command was exercised from open sponsons on either side of the deck.

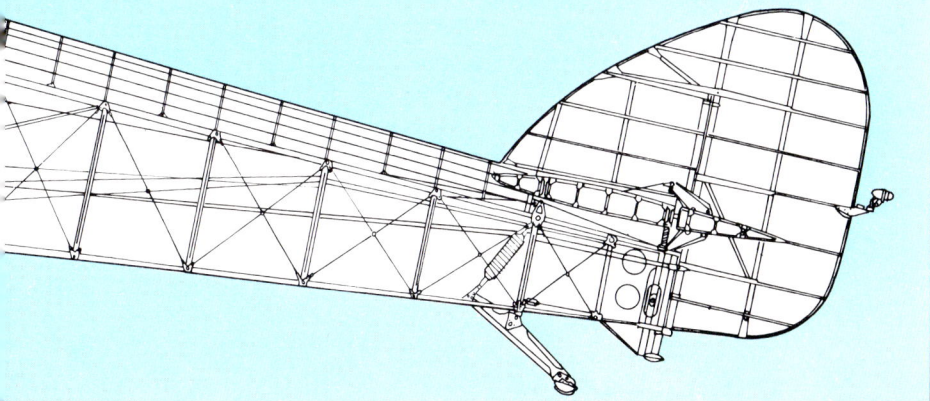

Hot, Euromissile

The Japanese carrier *Hosho*, employed for advanced training during the Second World War

As was common in Japanese ship designs, *Hosho* was very narrow in relation to her length (the fineness ratio being 1:9 compared with 1:8.5 in *Hermes*) in order to obtain high speed on modest power. *Hosho*'s high slab-sided hangar would have resulted in loss of stability had Sperry-designed active stabilizers not been installed. Despite this, the problems of topweight were never completely overcome; on the later addition of modern communications equipment and strengthened aircraft-operating machinery, compensating reductions could only be made in the armament and the aircraft complement. Originally armed with four 140-mm (5.5-in) low-angle guns and two 76-mm (3-in) AA guns, *Hosho* was finally fitted with eight twin 25-mm (1-in) AA mountings. In 1923, 21 aircraft could be operated but by 1942 she was carrying only a dozen larger and heavier aircraft.

Like her British and US opposite numbers, *Hosho* was classed as an experimental carrier for the purposes of the Washington Treaty, and so her 7500 tons did not count against the national limit. Experience gained with this small ship was applied to the larger conversions, such as the 36 000-38 000-ton *Akagi* and *Kaga*, and the weight-reduced but unstable 8000-ton *Ruyjo*, the first Japanese purpose-built carrier.

Hosho saw action off China during the successive 'incidents' of the 1930s, and she was also involved in ferrying aircraft from Japan. By 1940, the Japanese navy had sufficient larger carriers to spare *Hosho* for training duties, but at the outbreak of the Pacific war in 1941 she was teamed with *Zuiho* in Carrier Division 3. Short-ranged and with few aircraft, *Hosho* was held at the advanced base in the Palau Islands while *Zuiho* operated off the Philippines and the East Indies. In April 1942, Carrier Division 3 was disbanded and *Hosho* resumed training duties until required for the Midway operation in late May. This was her last fleet employment and she was included in Admiral Yamamoto's battleship group to provide long-range reconnaissance with her 11 Nakajima B5N Kates.

Thereafter, *Hosho* was employed exclusively for training carrier aircrews, operating in the Inland Sea for the 50th Air Flotilla. In these waters she was safe from enemy interference, but was damaged when she ran aground in September 1944. On March 19, 1945, she was at Kure when American carrier aircraft attacked this major naval base. She suffered only slight damage, but because of Japan's inability to rebuild a carrier force she was decommissioned into reserve on April 20. While laid up under camouflage near Kure, she was again slightly damaged by US carrier aircraft on July 24, but survived as one of the few Japanese carriers afloat on VJ-Day. Subsequently, she was taken into service for repatriating Japanese servicemen, but was finally withdrawn in August 1946. She was taken to Osaka in April 1947 to be scrapped.

Displacement: 7470 tons (standard), 10 000 tons (full load) *Length:* 168.1 m (551 ft 6 in) oa, 158.2 m (519 ft) flight deck *Beam:* 18 m (59 ft) wl, 22.7 m (74 ft 6 in) flight deck *Draught:* 6.2 m (20 ft 4 in) *Machinery:* 2 sets geared steam turbines, 2 shafts, 30 000 shp=25 knots *Aircraft:* 21 (later 12) *Armament:* 4 140-mm (5.5-in) LA; 2 76-mm (3-in) AA *Crew:* 550

Hot, Euromissile

French/German antitank missile. Hot (*Haut-subsonique optiquement téléguidé*—high-subsonic optically-guided missile) has been developed by Messerschmitt-Bölkow-Blohm in Germany and Aérospatiale in France to replace earlier vehicle-mounted and helicopter-borne antitank missiles such as the Harpon and SS.11. A range of 4000 m (4370 yards) was specified so that the launch platform would be safe from the heaviest foreseeable tank gun. The German army also demanded development of an automatic

Hot antitank missiles mounted in a sextuple tube installation on a BO105 multirole helicopter. Hot can hit targets up to 4000 m (4370 yards)

launcher for its tank destroyers, enabling the weapon to be operated continuously in NBC (nuclear, biological, chemical) condition.

Hot is intended to provide long-range support for armoured formations and protection for their flanks during an attack, and to cover a retreat by preventing enemy forces from approaching within gun or missile range of friendly tanks. Hot is a semi-automatic system. The operator keeps his optical sight aligned with the target, and an infrared sensor detects the off-boresight angle of flares on the rear of the missile in flight. A computer in the launch vehicle calculates the steering commands necessary to bring the round back onto the sight axis, and these are transmitted automatically along training wires. The missile is supplied in a sealed glass-fibre launcher/container which needs no inspection and which is discarded after use.

The German army plans to install Hot on 316 Raketen Jagdpanzer tank destroyers; the French army's principal mounting will be the VAB wheeled vehicle carrying a four-round Méphisto turret. The weapon can also be installed on a wide variety of other vehicles and on helicopters such as the BO105, Gazelle, Lynx and Hirundo. Hot has also been sold to a growing number of export customers, especially in the Middle East.

Length: 130 cm (4 ft 3 in) *Span:* 30 cm (1 ft)
Diameter: 14.2 cm (5.6 in) *Weight:* 21 kg (46 lb)
Minimum/maximum range: 75/4000 m (82/4370 yards) *Time to maximum range:* 17 sec
Warhead: 6 kg (13 lb)

The Hotchkiss Portatif Model 1909 on its tripod mount. It was adopted by France, Britain, the US and by the Indian Army in the 1930s

John Weeks

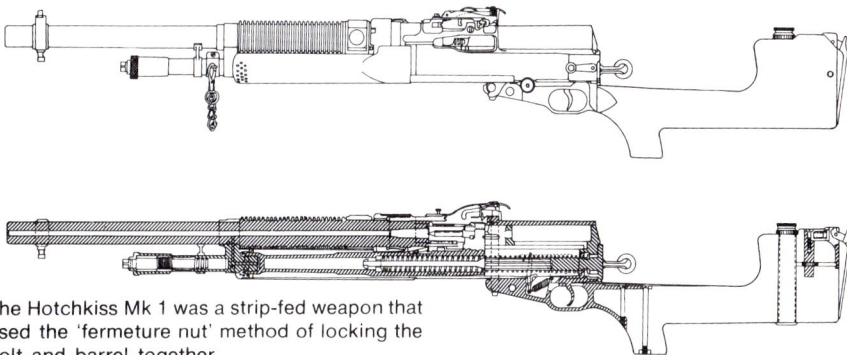

The Hotchkiss Mk 1 was a strip-fed weapon that used the 'fermeture nut' method of locking the bolt and barrel together

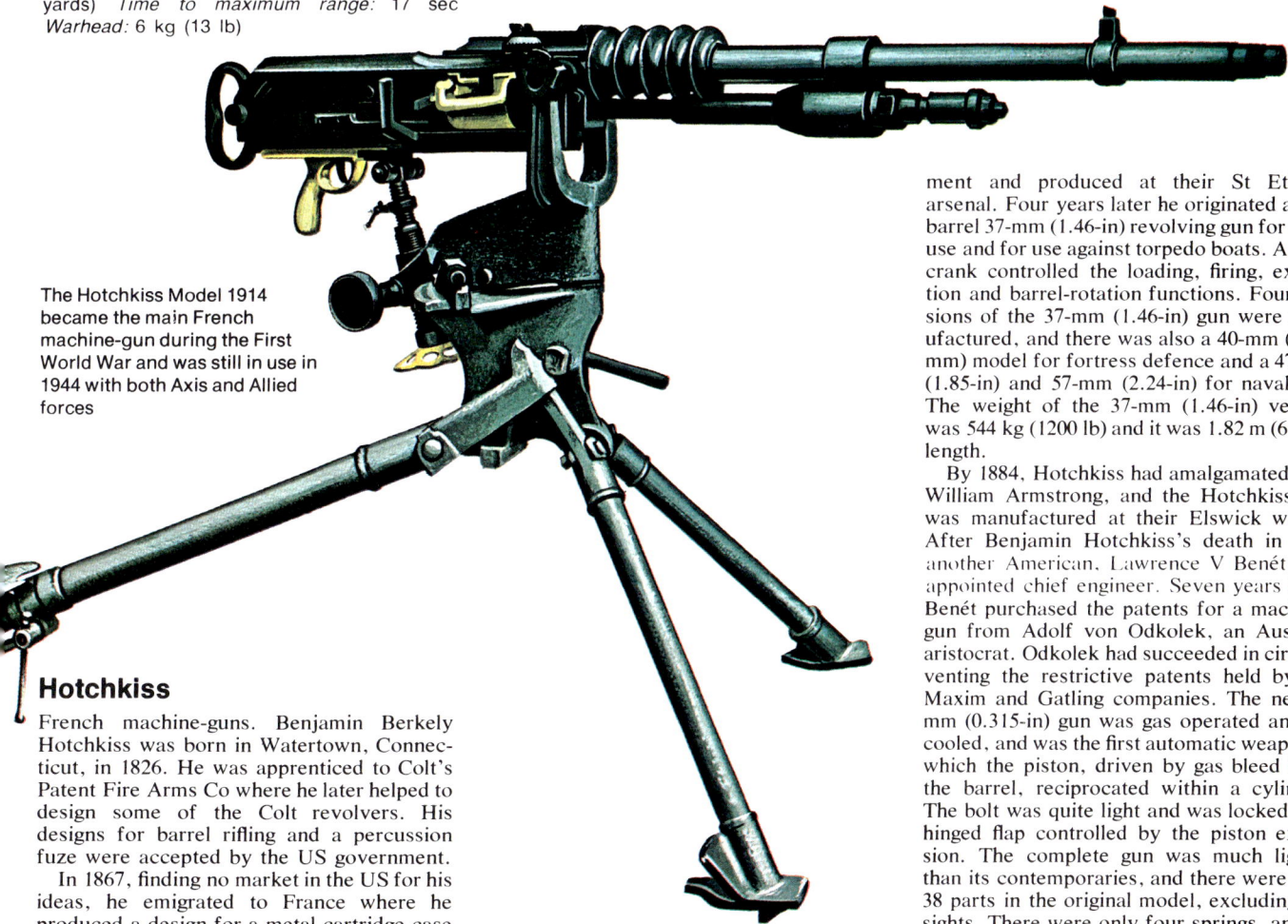

The Hotchkiss Model 1914 became the main French machine-gun during the First World War and was still in use in 1944 with both Axis and Allied forces

Hotchkiss

French machine-guns. Benjamin Berkely Hotchkiss was born in Watertown, Connecticut, in 1826. He was apprenticed to Colt's Patent Fire Arms Co where he later helped to design some of the Colt revolvers. His designs for barrel rifling and a percussion fuze were accepted by the US government.

In 1867, finding no market in the US for his ideas, he emigrated to France where he produced a design for a metal cartridge case which was adopted by the French govern-

ment and produced at their St Etienne arsenal. Four years later he originated a five-barrel 37-mm (1.46-in) revolving gun for army use and for use against torpedo boats. A hand crank controlled the loading, firing, extraction and barrel-rotation functions. Four versions of the 37-mm (1.46-in) gun were manufactured, and there was also a 40-mm (1.57-mm) model for fortress defence and a 47-mm (1.85-in) and 57-mm (2.24-in) for naval use. The weight of the 37-mm (1.46-in) version was 544 kg (1200 lb) and it was 1.82 m (6 ft) in length.

By 1884, Hotchkiss had amalgamated with William Armstrong, and the Hotchkiss gun was manufactured at their Elswick works. After Benjamin Hotchkiss's death in 1885 another American, Lawrence V Benét, was appointed chief engineer. Seven years later, Benét purchased the patents for a machine-gun from Adolf von Odkolek, an Austrian aristocrat. Odkolek had succeeded in circumventing the restrictive patents held by the Maxim and Gatling companies. The new 8-mm (0.315-in) gun was gas operated and air cooled, and was the first automatic weapon in which the piston, driven by gas bleed from the barrel, reciprocated within a cylinder. The bolt was quite light and was locked by a hinged flap controlled by the piston extension. The complete gun was much lighter than its contemporaries, and there were only 38 parts in the original model, excluding the sights. There were only four springs, and no screws had to be touched in stripping the gun

Hotchkiss

down. The feed system consisted of a sprocket which drew metal strips holding the rounds through the weapon. When required, the 30-round strips could be joined to form a continuous belt. This feed system could have been altered after the Maxim patents expired. Although later models of the Hotchkiss could take a conventional belt, this was not often used since users apparently preferred the strip system.

The prototype was tested in 1895, and although it worked well, there was excessive overheating. As a remedy, the mass of metal surrounding the chamber was increased, and the cooling area vastly increased by the addition of five brass fins at the breech end. Even with these changes, the unloaded weight did not exceed 24 kg (52 lb), a low figure for a medium gun. This was the weapon adopted by the French army in 1897. Improvements in the design resulted in the Modèle 1914, used successfully by the French during the First World War. The weapon proved to be reliable and robust, although after prolonged firing the barrel could still overheat. It stayed in service until 1940, when some were taken over by the Wehrmacht for mounting on the Atlantic Wall, but by 1945 it remained in use only in a few French colonies.

There were two significant attempts from outside the Hotchkiss company to improve the design before 1914. During 1905, the Puteaux arsenal made a heavier, less reliable gun which later had to be taken out of service on the Western Front and relegated to garrison use. Two years later, the St Etienne arsenal produced a weapon which was even more unreliable and scarcely of use even in a garrison role.

In 1917, Hotchkiss developed an 11-mm (0.433-in) variant of their 8-mm (0.315-in)

An Indian Hotchkiss team with Model 1908 guns practising near Querrieu in 1916. The gunner has unfolded the butt strap which enables him to rest the butt against his shoulder leaving both hands free for stoppages. Indian troops retained the Model 1908 into the 1930s

Men of the King's Own Scottish Borderers use a captured Hotchkiss machine-gun against German positions in the streets of Caen in 1944

weapon, later known as the Balloon Model. It was originally planned as an infantry weapon, but in practice was used to fire incendiary bullets to destroy German observation balloons at long range. Few were produced, but nevertheless they inspired the US 0.5-in (12.7-mm) Browning M2.

At the beginning of this century the French army, who were then involved with tactical theories of 'assaulting at the walk', wanted an automatic weapon which was light enough to be carried and fired by advancing infantrymen. In response, Benét and his assistant Mercié designed the Fusil Mitrailleur Hotchkiss Modèle 1909 or the Hotchkiss Portatif. The gun, in 8-mm (0.315-in) Lebel calibre, differed from the normal Hotchkiss models in the design of the locking mechanism (as a result the new gun was often known as the Hotchkiss-Mercié or the Benét-Mercié) which replaced the usual locking flap by a fermeture nut. This locked the bolt and barrel together and was rotated out of alignment by gas pressure. The feed unit was reversed so

that the rounds were now on the underside of the feed strip. The mechanism was relatively simple, although not as efficient as some competing designs. The gun was adopted by the US as 'Machine Rifle, Benét-Mercié, Caliber .30 M1909'. In Britain, where it was employed in 1916 as a cavalry and tank weapon, it was designated 'Gun, Machine, Hotchkiss Mark 1'. The calibre was adapted to 0.303-in (7.7-mm). It was retained by the British Army until the Bren gun replaced it in the late 1930s, but was not declared obsolete until 1946. Some Hotchkiss guns remained in service with the Home Guard and on merchant ships during the Second World War.

The Japanese bought numerous 1900-model guns and used them in the Russo-Japanese war of 1904. They subsequently took out a manufacturing licence, but found that it was better to adapt the design to their own production methods and to suit their

lower-powered standard issue 6.5-mm (0.255-in) round. Colonel Nambu, an ordnance officer, gave his name to the modified weapon, otherwise known as the 3 Nen Shiki Kikanju, or the Taisho 3. In changing the Hotchkiss design Nambu had introduced some undesirable features, among them a rather loose tolerance in the fit of the bolt and barrel, which caused the cartridge cases to rupture if they were not oiled. An oiler was therefore incorporated. The Taisho 3 had cooling fins along the entire length of the barrel, but was otherwise scarcely distinguishable from a Hotchkiss.

In 1932, the Taisho 3 was rechambered for the new 7.7-mm (0.303-in) round, and redesignated Type 92. Like its predecessor it employed the Hotchkiss strip feed.

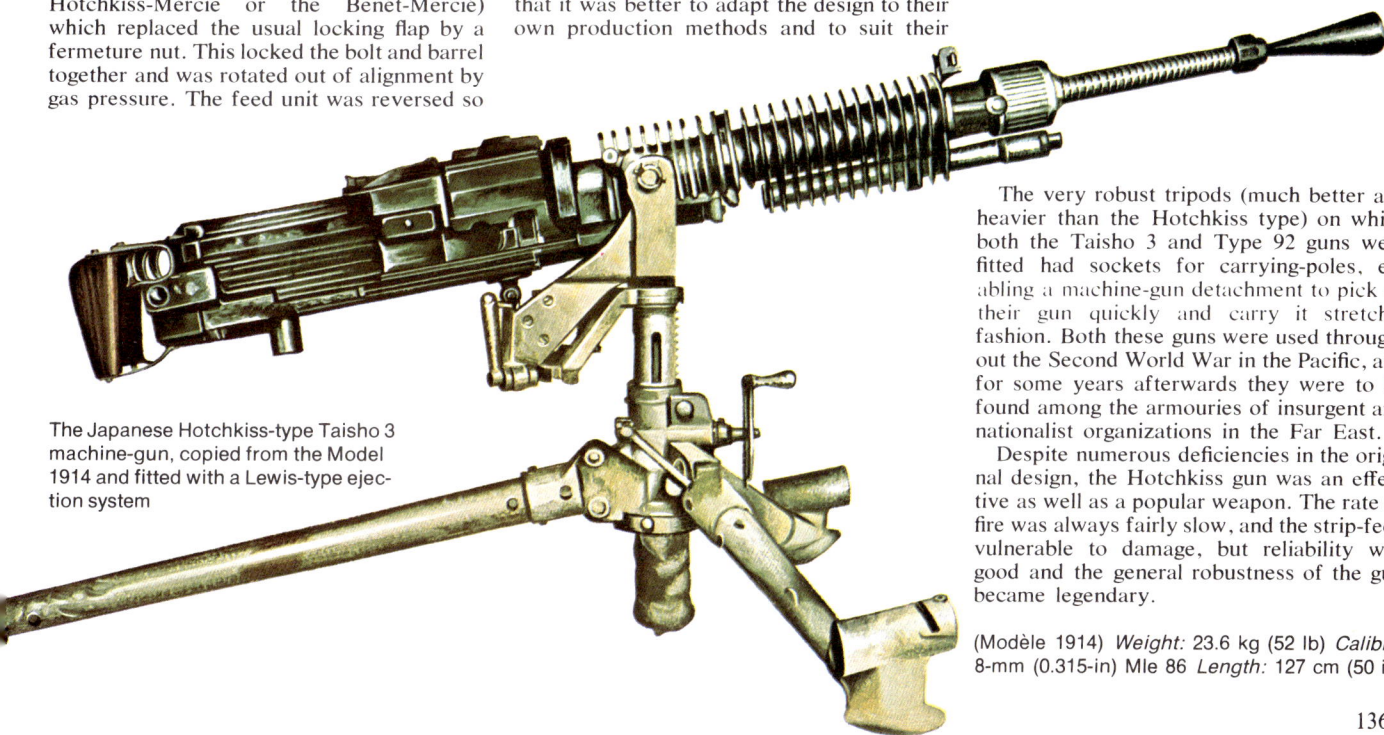

The Japanese Hotchkiss-type Taisho 3 machine-gun, copied from the Model 1914 and fitted with a Lewis-type ejection system

The very robust tripods (much better and heavier than the Hotchkiss type) on which both the Taisho 3 and Type 92 guns were fitted had sockets for carrying-poles, enabling a machine-gun detachment to pick up their gun quickly and carry it stretcher fashion. Both these guns were used throughout the Second World War in the Pacific, and for some years afterwards they were to be found among the armouries of insurgent and nationalist organizations in the Far East.

Despite numerous deficiencies in the original design, the Hotchkiss gun was an effective as well as a popular weapon. The rate of fire was always fairly slow, and the strip-feed vulnerable to damage, but reliability was good and the general robustness of the gun became legendary.

(Modèle 1914) *Weight:* 23.6 kg (52 lb) *Calibre:* 8-mm (0.315-in) Mle 86 *Length:* 127 cm (50 in)

Hotchkiss

Barrel length: 77.5 cm (30.5 in) *Magazine:* 30-round metal strip feed *Rate of fire:* 500 rds/min (cyclic) *Muzzle velocity:* 725 m/sec (2380 ft/sec)

(Portatif Model 1909) *Weight:* 12.2 kg (27 lb) *Calibre:* 0.303-in (7.7-mm) SAA, Britain; 8-mm (0.315-in) Mle 86, France; 0.30-in (7.62-mm) M1906, US *Length:* 118.7 cm (46.7 in) *Barrel length:* 59.6 cm (23.5 in) *Magazine:* 30-round metal strip feed *Rate of fire:* 500 rds/min (cyclic) *Muzzle velocity:* 739 m/sec (2425 ft/sec)

(Taisho 3) *Weight:* 28.1 kg (62 lb) *Calibre:* 6.5-mm (0.255-in) Meiji 30 *Length:* 115.6 cm (45.5 in) *Barrel length:* 74.9 cm (29.5 in) *Magazine:* 30-round metal strip feed *Rate of fire:* 400 rds/min (cyclic) *Muzzle velocity:* 730 m/sec (2400 ft/sec)

Hotchkiss

French armoured vehicles. The Hotchkiss company began as an armaments firm and built up a sound reputation for machine-guns and quick-firing guns. In the early years of this century it began manufacturing motor cars and trucks which achieved considerable success. (Hotchkiss cars won the Monte Carlo Rally in 1933, 1934 and 1939.) They built a number of trucks for the French army, and in the late 1920s began developing armoured vehicles, and by 1934, when the French army requested a light tank, Hotchkiss were able to put forward a suitable model for consideration.

This was a 12-ton vehicle, with cast armour and turret, mounting a 37-mm (1.46-in) gun. It was a sound design, but the infantry refused it. It was then adopted by the cavalry as the Modèle 35H, and shortly before the Second World War the infantry relented and took several of the vehicles. Between 1938-39 the design was improved by having slightly heavier armour, a more powerful engine and a longer-barrelled 37-mm (1.46-in) gun. About 1000 of these tanks were made in all, and they were used in action in the 1940 campaign. During the war the German army used them in considerable numbers, either in as-built form or as a basis for self-propelled guns. After the end of the war the Israeli army employed them until the mid-1950s.

The Hotchkiss company began development work again after 1945, and in the early 1950s offered a tracked armoured personnel carrier to the French army. This was the Modèle TT-6, which was turned down by the French after extensive testing. At that time, however, the newly reformed German army was in need of a reconnaissance vehicle and tested the Hotchkiss. After some modifications to suit its new role, they adopted it in 1957. The Modèle TT-6 entered German service as the Spähpanzer 11-2. Production was carried out by Hotchkiss in France and, under licence, by Klockner-Humboldt-Deutz in Germany, and continued until 1962. Some 2400 vehicles were built. The basic model was fitted with a turret carrying a 20-mm (0.79-in) Hispano-Suiza cannon. The mortar carrier Spz 51-2 carried an 81-mm (3.19-in) mortar inside the hull, firing over the front of the vehicle. The Spz 22-2 was a command vehicle with additional communications equipment, the Spz 2-2 was an armoured ambulance, and the SpzKN was a cargo carrier. These were phased out in the late

A Japanese officer watches as a Taisho 3 puts down fire during fighting in China in 1932

1970s, and replaced by new German designs.

Hotchkiss next produced a number of experimental vehicles for the French army. These included the Hotchkiss-Rive Light Fighting Unit, a tracked chassis based on the TT-6, fitted with a turret which could mount either a 90-mm (3.89-in) smooth-bore gun, twin 30-mm (1.18-in) Hispano cannon, or four SS-11 antitank missiles. Another venture was the VP90 Light Fighting Vehicle, a tiny tracked carrier with a two-man crew who lay prone inside the low-slung hull. Propelled by a Porsche engine, this vehicle could carry a variety of light weapons, such as recoilless guns, rocket launchers, machine-guns or cannon. Finally came the TT-12 APC (armoured personnel carrier), another improvement on the original TT6 design. This added an amphibious capability, improved suspension, better ballistic shaping of the armour, and room for 12 fully equipped infantrymen. Ambulance, mortar-carrying and cargo variants were produced, as were turreted versions mounting either the 90-mm (3.89-in) gun

or twin Hispano cannons. After long trials the French army decided against adoption of any of the designs, and since there seemed little prospect of worthwhile overseas sales, Hotchkiss abandoned the vehicle business and once again concentrated on weapon development.

(H-35 light tank) *Weight:* 12 tonnes *Length:* 4.23 m (13 ft 10 in) *Width:* 1.85 m (6 ft 1 in) *Height:* 2.14 m (7 ft) *Armour thickness:* 40 mm (1.57 in) *Armament:* 1 37-mm (1.46-in) gun; 1 7.5-mm (0.29-in) machine-gun *Powerplant:* Hotchkiss 6-cylinder gasoline, 120 bhp at 2800 rpm *Speed:* 35 km/h (22 mph) *Range:* 150 km (93 miles) *Crew:* 2

(Spz 11-2 reconnaissance vehicle) *Weight:* 8.2 tonnes *Length:* 4.52 m (14 ft 10 in) *Width:* 2.28 m (7 ft 6 in) *Height:* 1.97 m (6 ft 6 in) *Armour:* 15 mm (0.59 in) *Armament:* 1 20-mm (0.79-in) Hispano-Suiza *Powerplant:* Hotchkiss 6-cylinder gasoline, 164 bhp at 3900 rpm *Speed:* 60 km/h (37 mph) *Range:* 400 km (250 miles) *Crew:* 5

A German-crewed Hotchkiss tank fords a river in Russia during the Axis advance in 1941

A Mil Mi-4 Hound in Aeroflot markings. It is capable of lifting 14 troops or freight loads of up to 1600 kg (3530 lb) though the specialized Mi-4A can carry more

Hotel

Soviet nuclear ballistic missile submarine class. The class made use of the ballistic missile launching system developed for the conventionally-powered *Zulu V* Class, and of the hull and propulsion system of the nuclear-powered *Echo* and *November* Class submarines, in order to produce some sort of counter to the US Polaris SSBN force as soon as possible.

Nine were built between 1958-62, and they were originally armed with the 480-km (300-mile) ranged SSN-4 Sark in three tubes at the aft end of the fin, but during 1963-67 these were replaced by three SSN-5 Serbs with a range of about 1125 km (700 miles). This marginally improved the survivability, but since they have to surface to launch their missiles, they are still very vulnerable to countermeasures even before they have revealed their position by firing a missile. Like all Soviet submarines of this period, the *Hotels* are extremely noisy by Western standards.

The Sark-armed boats were classified as the *Hotel I* Class, and these were redesignated *Hotel II* when they were rearmed with Serbs. One *Hotel II* was used as a test ship for the SSN-8 used in the *Delta* Class SSBN, and became the sole *Hotel III*. Their remaining armament consists of six bow 21-in (53.3-cm) and four stern 16-in (40-cm) torpedo tubes. The aft tubes are used to fire A/S torpedoes.

By 1978 the class was totally obsolete, but it is possible that they may be rearmed with a medium-ranged MIRVed tactical ballistic missile, which would enable them to be used to great effect against Western Europe or China. However, the hull and machinery is old, and such a move may not be justified.

Displacement: 4500 tons/5500 tons (surfaced/submerged) *Length:* 115.2 m (378 ft) *Beam:* 8.6 m (28 ft 2½ in) *Draught:* 7.6 m (25 ft) *Machinery:* 2-shaft nuclear steam turbines, 30 000 shp=20 knots (surfaced), 23 knots (submerged) *Armament:* 3 SSN-5 Serb; 6 21-in (53.3-cm) torpedo tubes; 4 16-in (40-cm) torpedo tubes *Crew:* 90

Hound, Mil Mi-4

Soviet transport and antisubmarine helicopter. Soviet helicopter designers were not allowed the luxury of time in the early 1950s: in 1951 the Kremlin instructed Mil and Yakovlev to build single-engined 12-passenger and twin-engined 24-passenger machines respectively for delivery 12 months later. Both design bureaux responded admirably, although the Mi-4 met with more suc-

cess than the Yak-24 and came to be built in larger numbers than any other Soviet helicopter. Hound was Mil's second machine to reach production status, and in some respects it was a scaled-up version of the earlier Mi-1 Hare. Design work began in October 1951, and the first preproduction Mi-4—no prototype as such was built—is reported to have made its maiden flight the following May, although other sources give the date as August 1952. In any event, the type sailed through its initial tests and entered production before the end of that year, despite persistent problems with rotor-blade flutter, which were to take several years to eliminate.

Hound's four-blade main rotor (of all-metal construction in later aircraft) was driven by a Shvetsov ASh-82V air-cooled radial engine developing 1700 hp for takeoff, with a Soloviev two-stage compressor maintaining the cruise rating of 1070 hp up to a height of 4500 m (14 760 ft). The flight crew comprised two pilots, and an observer/navigator who was accommodated in a ventral gondola. Hound carried up to 14 troops, 1600 kg (3530 lb) of freight, a GAZ-69 or M-20 staff car, a 76-mm (3-in) antitank gun and crew, or two motorcycle-and-sidecar combinations, the vehicles being loaded through rear clamshell doors. A specialized freight version, the Mi-4A, carried up to 2000 kg (4410 lb) in its hold, or 1500 kg (3310 lb) slung externally.

A close-support development was fitted with air-to-surface rockets on fuselage pylons and a single gun in the front of the observer's gondola, and machine-guns could

also be mounted at the cabin windows. A naval derivative had a search radar with a chin-mounted radome, dipping sonar deployed from the rear of the fuselage, and sonobuoys dropped from racks on the fuselage sides. Production ended in the mid-1960s after a run of several thousand Hounds, many of which were exported. Licence-production in China began in 1959, and the type continued in widespread service through the late-1970s despite having been largely superseded by the Mi-8 Hip.

Rotor diameter: 21 m (68 ft 11 in) *Length:* 16.8 m (55 ft 1½ in) *Gross weight:* 7800 kg (17 200 lb) *Maximum speed:* 210 km/h (130 mph)

Hound Dog, North American

US strategic air-to-surface missile. The AGM-28 (formerly GAM-77) Hound Dog was the missile element of the United States Air Force Strategic Air Command's Weapon System 131B and was carried by late-model B-52 intercontinental bombers to increase their stand-off range. North American Aviation, later to become part of Rockwell International, was selected in preference to 12 other contractors to develop Hound Dog under a contract awarded in August 1957. An initial production contract followed in November 1958, and the first powered flight was made in April 1959. Fully guided flights began in November of that year, and the following month the missile was delivered to SAC's 4135th Wing at Eglin AFB, Florida.

AGM-28 Hound Dog missiles undergoing IRAN (Inspect and Repair As Necessary) at Tulsa

Howa

An AGM-28 Hound Dog is winched up from its trailer onto a USAF B-52. The Hound Dog can be replenished in flight from the B-52 fuel tanks

Hound Dog was declared operational in 1960, and by September 1963 it equipped 29 SAC wings of B-52Gs and B-52Hs. Hound Dog production ceased in 1963. In March 1974, the US Secretary of Defense announced the decision to phase out Hound Dog with the B-52G/H force by fiscal year 1976. In early 1977 the makers confirmed that activity on Hound Dog had ceased.

Hound Dog, of which two could be carried by a B-52, was attached to an underwing pylon which contained an astro-tracker to supplement data fed from the aircraft to the missile's inertial-navigation system before launching. The weapon's long range was achieved by using an air-breathing engine—a Pratt & Whitney J52-P-3 turbojet producing 3400 kg (7500 lb) of thrust. The missile's motor could be run during takeoff to augment the bomber's main engines on a heavily laden mission, the Hound Dog's tanks then being replenished from the aircraft in flight. The missile was designed to navigate accurately even after prolonged carriage on the bomber, and in April 1960 a B-52 flew a 22-hour mission covering 17 300 km (10 750 miles) before launching a Hound Dog on a preset path which included evasive terminal man-oeuvring. The mission profile and target could be changed by the bomber's crew while in flight, before the missile was fired. A thermonuclear warhead of at least 1 megaton (possibly as much as 4 megatons) was carried. In 1972 Bendix was awarded a contract to develop a passive radiation seeker. Missiles equipped with the new system were to be designated Hound Dog II, but in view of the decision to phase Hound Dog out of service use no long-term contracts were awarded and the project was abandoned.

Length: 12.95 m (42 ft 6 in) *Span:* 3.71 m (12 ft 2 in) *Diameter:* 71 cm (27.5 in) *Weight:* 4340 kg (9600 lb) *Range:* at least 965 km (600 miles), possibly 1255 km (780 miles) *Speed:* Mach 2

Hovea Danish submachine-gun
See **Huskvarna**

Hoverfly RAF name for Sikorsky R-4, R-5 and R-6 US helicopters   See **R-4/R-5/R-6**

Howa

Japanese automatic rifle. The Japanese government originally equipped its self-defence forces with a version of the US M1 rifle, but at the same time the Howa Machinery Company was commissioned to develop a Japanese assault rifle design. The result was the Type 64, a gas-operated selective-fire rifle of more or less conventional design and manufacture. It was originally intended to be used with a reduced-power NATO round, which the Japanese find more suited to their smaller stature, but there are indications now that it may be rechambered altogether for the 5.56-mm (0.219-in) ammunition.

The rifle is quite light in weight and has a low rate of fire. The gas vent can be adjusted to allow the use of muzzle-launched grenades. By changing the gas-regulator setting the rifle can be used with the normal NATO rounds, although the light weight of the weapon gives a greater recoil than most other NATO weapons. A bipod is fitted as standard, as is a top strap on the butt which keeps the rifle in the shoulder. The bolt locks in the same way as the Simonov by tipping into a recess in the body. Reliability is considered good and performance appears to be adequate.

Weight: 4.3 kg (9 lb 8 oz) *Calibre:* 7.62-mm (0.30-in) NATO reduced-power round *Length:* 99 cm (39 in) *Barrel length:* 45 cm (18 in) *Magazine:* 20-round box *Rate of fire:* 500 rds/min *Muzzle velocity:* 716 m/sec (2350 ft/sec)

Howe

British battleship. The last battleship of the *King George V* Class to be completed, *Howe* was ordered from the Fairfield Shipbuilding Company under the 1937 Programme and laid down at Govan on June 1, 1937. She was originally to have been named *Beatty*, after the famous Admiral of the First World War, but was renamed *Howe* shortly before her launch on April 9, 1940. In the following month her construction was suspended while shipbuilding resources were concentrated on more urgent requirements, and work on her did not recommence for six months. Shor-

tages of men and materials, and alterations to the ship resulting from war experience delayed her completion still further and she did not commission until June 1942. Her displacement was 39 150 tons (standard) and 44 510 tons (full load) which was about 3000 tons above the designed displacement. The increase resulted mainly from additions to the ship's structure (principally an increase in the depth of the underwater protection system), the difficulty of exercising strict control of material weights in wartime, the provision of additional AA guns, and the fitting of air-warning, sea-warning and gunnery radar equipment. Officially she was completed on August 29, 1942, her armament at this time being ten 14-in (356-mm) (2×4, 1×2), 16 5.25-in (133-mm) DP (8×2), 48 40-mm (1.57-in) AA (6×8) and 18 20-mm (0.79-in) AA (18×1); within a few months the 20-mm (0.79-in) armament was increased to 40 guns (40×1).

She joined the Home Fleet at Scapa Flow on August 27, 1942, and spent the following two months carrying out trials and working up. For the first few months of 1943 she was employed on patrol duties and covered the passage of several Russian convoys. In May she was transferred to the Mediterranean to cover Operation Husky (the invasion of Sicily) and joined Force H at Algiers on June 1. On the night of July 11/12, in company with *King George V* she bombarded airfields at the western end of Sicily. In September she was assigned to cover the landings at Salerno, and after the surrender of Italy formed part of the occupation force at Taranto. Shortly after this she escorted the surrendered Italian Battle Fleet from Malta to Alexandria prior to returning to Home Waters. Between November 1943 and May 1944 she was refitted at Devonport prior to being transferred to the Eastern Fleet. Alterations included the removal of her aircraft equipment, the addition of 16 2-pdr (2×8), 8 40-mm (1.57-in) (2×4), and 8 20-mm (0.79-in) (4×2) AA guns, and the removal of 6 20-mm (0.79-in) (6×1) AA guns.

She joined the Eastern Fleet at Trincomalee on August 8, 1944, and on September 8 covered air strikes against installations on Sumatra. On December 2, she became flagship of the newly-formed British

Pacific Fleet and in February 1945 arrived in her new theatre of war. During March-May 1945 she covered the US landings at Okinawa and carried out several bombardments of islands in the Sakishima Gunto group. In June she was taken in hand for refit at Durban, the principal object being to increase the strength of the AA armament to counter the kamikaze threat. All her single 20-mm (0.79-in) guns were removed and 24 2-pdr (6×4) and 18 40-mm (1.57-in) (18×1) AA guns added. While she was being refitted the war ended, and when the work on her was completed in September 1945 she was attached to the East Indies station. She returned home at the end of the year and arrived at Portsmouth in January 1946 where she was refitted for service as a training ship. She served in this role at Portland until 1951 when she was placed in reserve. She was sold for scrap in 1958.

See also *King George V*.

Displacement: 39 150 tons (standard) *Length:* 227.07 m (745 ft) oa; 213.36 m (700 ft) pp *Beam:* 31.39 m (103 ft) *Draught:* 8.46 m (27 ft 9 in) *Machinery:* 4-shaft geared turbines, 110 000 shp=29 knots *Protection:* 114-380 mm (4½-15 in) main belt; 25-152 mm (1-6 in) decks; 230-406 mm (9-16 in) turrets, 406 mm (16 in) director control tower *Armament:* 10 14-in (355.6-mm) (2×4, 1×2); 16 5.25-in (133-mm) DP (8×2); 48 40-mm (1.57-in) AA (6×8); 18 20-mm (0.79-in) AA (18×1) *Aircraft:* 4 *Crew:* 1553-1558

Howell

US torpedo. The Howell, which was introduced around 1875, differed from the Whitehead torpedo in being driven by a heavy flywheel. It was launched by tube from a surface ship. Prior to discharge, the flywheel was spun by an adjacent steam winch.

The Howell torpedo had three advantages over the compressed-air-driven Whitehead: there was no track left by exhausted air; it did not vary its trim; and the gyroscopic action of the flywheel helped it to run straight. However the noise made by the flywheel gave away its position, and effectively deprived the weapon of the element of surprise.

Later versions of the Howell had a 59 kg (130 lb) flywheel rotating at 12 000 rpm, which gave a range of up to 730 m (2400 ft) at a speed of 30 knots. This made it competitive with the contemporary Whitehead, and since the Howell was simple to manufacture and maintain, it succeeded in keeping the Whitehead out of US Navy service for nearly 20 years.

(1893 model) *Length:* 3.4 m (11 ft 2 in) *Diameter:* 36 cm (14.2 in) *Weight:* 235 kg (518 lb) *Warhead:* 45 kg (100 lb) *Range:* 550 m (600 yards)

HS, Curtiss

US antisubmarine patrol flying-boat. Basically a scaled-down version of the earlier twin-engined H-4/12/16 series, the three-seat HS-1 appeared early in 1917. It was fitted with a 200-hp Curtiss V-X-X water-cooled V-8 engine driving a pusher propeller. This prototype was also used on October 21, 1917, for the first flight of the new 375-hp 12-cylinder Liberty engine. (In some later forms the Liberty could produce 420-hp, but it was

usually classified as a 400-hp powerplant.)

The US Navy ordered 664 aircraft designated HS-1L (for Liberty), armed with one flexible 0.30-in (7.62-mm) Lewis gun and able to carry two 81.6-kg (180-lb) underwing bombs. Construction under licence was divided between several companies: Standard (200); Lowe, Willard and Fowler (150); Gallaudet (60); Boeing (25) and Loughead (2)—the remainder being built by Curtiss. Boeing-built aircraft were distinguishable by having ailerons on the upper wings only.

After some service experience it was found that the bombload was not sufficient for antisubmarine warfare and a new version was developed, the HS-2L, with a 3.66-m (12-ft) increase in wing span, so that two 104-kg (230-lb) underwing bombs could be carried. Aircraft still on order or under construction as HS-1Ls were also thus modified. Approximately 182 HS-1Ls and -2Ls were the first US-built aircraft to be used by the US naval forces in France during the First World War. The HS-2L continued as a basic US Navy patrol and training aircraft for some eight years after the war and some were bought for use as passenger transports or survey aircraft. Just prior to the Armistice, a small number of HS-3s were produced with a modified hull. Curtiss built five and the Naval Aircraft Factory two.

(HS-2L) *Span:* 22.57 m (74 ft) *Length:* 11.89 m (39 ft 1 in) *Gross weight:* 2917 kg (6430 lb) *Maximum speed:* 132.8 km/h (82.5 mph)

Hs 117, Henschel

German surface-to-air missile. The Hs 117 Schmetterling (butterfly), originally designated Hs 297, was designed by a Dr Henrici in 1941 and developed by Henschel in Berlin under the general direction of the firm's chief designer, Professor Wagner. The Reichsluftfahrt-ministerium (air ministry) initially rejected Wagner's overtures on the grounds that the proposed missile was a defensive weapon, but by late 1942 Allied bombers were having an increasing effect on German industrial production and General Walter von Axthelm, Inspector-General of Antiaircraft Defences, reexamined the Hs 117 in his search for a counter to the raids.

Henschel received a development contract in August 1943, and the first test flights of unpowered missiles took place at Peenemünde the following May. The weapon was fired from a modified 37-mm (1.46-in) gun mounting, initial acceleration being provided by two Schmidding 109-553 solid-propellant rocket motors, one above the fuselage and the other below. Each produced 1750 kg (3860 lb) of thrust for four seconds, accelerating the missile to 1100 km/h (685 mph) before falling away. Cruise propulsion was then assumed by a bifuel rocket sustainer motor. The first contracts were placed with BMW for the 109-558, which produced 375 kg (827 lb) of thrust for 33 seconds and then 60 kg (132 lb) for a further 24 seconds. The BMW motor was used in all flight trials but was not entirely satisfactory, and Wagner was working on the 109-729 as an alternative when the war ended. The sustainer was fitted with an automatic control system which maintained the cruise speed at Mach 0.77 (950 km/h [590 mph] at sea level) in order to

aid visual guidance. The larger part of the double-pointed nose housed the warhead, which in early production models comprised 25 kg (55 lb) of uncased Trialen explosive. The normal method of control was by the Parsival system, which used optical tracking of target and missile with a Kehl/Colmar radio-control loop. A separate frequency was available for command detonation of the warhead until suitable proximity fuzes were developed; proposals for the latter included acoustic and Doppler types. Radar guidance systems were also under development when the war ended.

Some 140 test missiles were fired, but only 25 of the 59 fully representative rounds were successful. Production was planned to begin in February 1945, reaching 3000 a month by October, but steady bombing of the Henschel works resulted in the production line being transferred to the Harz mountains in February, and the move was still incomplete by VE Day. The Hs 117 never saw operational service and the Hs 117H air-launched development, intended to arm bombers such as the Do 217, did not proceed beyond the trials stage.

Length: 3.81 m (12 ft 6 in) *Span:* 2.21 m (7 ft 3 in) *Weight:* 454 kg (1000 lb) *Ceiling:* 10 000 m (33 000 ft) *Range:* at least 16 km (10 miles), perhaps double this figure

Hs 123, Henschel

German close-support aircraft. When the previously clandestine Reichsluftfahrtministerium (air ministry) was openly announced on May 15, 1933, one of the chief military-aircraft procurement programmes envisaged was for a dive-bomber. In fact, such a weapon was judged so important that, while a definitive aircraft was designed (which turned out to be the Ju 87 Stuka), a *Sofortprogram* (immediate programme) was quickly put in hand for an interim machine. This *Sofort* aircraft was to be an all-metal biplane, strong enough to withstand any diving attack with bombload, and without any radical features that might delay development.

Submissions were received from Fieseler and the new Henschel Flugzeugwerke at Johannisthal, and three prototypes of each were ordered. The Hs 123 did away with bracing wires, had single faired interplane struts and cantilever main landing gears attached to the small lower wings, and from the start the modern-looking Henschel was favoured over the traditional Fi 98. Only the first Fi 98 was built, and despite vague reports of the Hs 123 having a superior performance the two were strictly comparable. Fieseler were told not to complete the second and third aircraft, and this may have been a mistake because when the second and third Henschels went to the test airfield at Rechlin they both suffered fatal structural failure in dive-bombing simulations. But by that time the die was cast in favour of the Henschel.

It was certainly an attractive machine, with clean lines and excellent manoeuvrability. The original engine was the 650-hp BMW 132A-3, derived from the Pratt & Whitney Hornet, driving a two-blade variable-pitch propeller in all but the first prototype (made by VDM under American Hamilton licence).

Hs 123, Henschel

Above: **Henschel Hs 123 close-support aircraft with prewar splinter camouflage and national markings.** *Below:* **An Hs 123 at the Henschel Flugzeugwerke. The Hs 123 saw action throughout the Second World War equipping satellite air forces on the Eastern Front in 1944**

All the early testing was done between May and August 1935, and the first production Hs 123A-1 flew at the end of the year, deliveries beginning in the summer of 1936 to StGr I/162. Production rate was quite high, because by this time Henschel had occupied their big new plant at Schönefeld, and the formation of further Stukagruppen was rapid.

The engine of the production machine was the more powerful 880-hp BMW 132Dc with direct fuel injection. Two 7.92-mm (0.312-in) MG 17 machine-guns were fitted above the nose, and racks under the lower wing could carry four SC50 50-kg (110-lb) bombs or various other loads. The centreline rack could carry an SC250 250-kg (550-lb) bomb, instead of the underwing load, but the usual belly load was an extra fuel tank which was disposable in emergency.

In 1936 Oberst (later Generalfeldmarschall) Wolfram von Richthofen, chief of staff of the Legion Kondor sent to Spain, urgently requested that some of the first deliveries should be sent to that theatre to see how they performed in action. Even at this early date the Hs 123 was generally regarded as puny and outmoded, and orders were terminated in that year so that the last example came off the line in mid-1938 with the total well short of

1000 aircraft. All were similar and designated Hs 123A-1, though there were numerous modifications and an armoured headrest and rear fairing were made standard. But by 1937 the 123 was generally regarded as obsolete.

Five early production aircraft reached the Legion at Seville in December 1936, and from the start they demonstrated what was to characterize the entire career of this aircraft, one of the smallest to participate in the warfare in Spain or the Second World War: amazing utility, close-support effectiveness, and ability to survive direct hits by bullets and shells. The work of the five Henschels deeply impressed the Spanish, and they promptly ordered 16, putting them into front-line use, and calling them Angelito. But the Luftwaffe refused to believe that the Hs 123 could be so useful, and at the invasion of Poland the Schlachtgeschwader (close-support wings) had been disbanded, and only one Gruppe, II (Schlacht)/LG2, still used the biplane. But this single unit achieved such amazing results with guns, bombs and the staccato gunfire-like noise of its engine at selected rpm, that its planned reequipment was postponed.

The story was the same in the Low Countries and France in May 1940. This Gruppe was normally the Luftwaffe's most forward-based unit and was continually mentioned by name by General Guderian, leader of the Panzers. The message was at last penetrating the closed minds of the Luftwaffe high command, and the Gruppe still existed at the Operation Barbarossa invasion of the Soviet Union in May 1941. By this time the little Henschel had been grossly modified. Its wheel spats had disappeared, the exterior sprouted various extra equipment items and some even had extra machine-guns or cannon under the lower wings. Aircraft were gathered from training schools and even derelict dumps all over Germany and thrown into new front-line Schlachtgeschwader, operating right over the heads of Soviet troops. In January 1943 von Richthofen (by this time a general) suggested reopening production but discovered that the tooling had been scrapped in 1940. So these remarkably useful aircraft were gradually whittled down in violent front-line combat until the last disappeared in mid-1944.

Span: 10.50 m (34 ft 5½ in) *Length:* 8.33 m (27 ft 4 in) *Gross weight:* (normal) 2217 kg (4888 lb) *Maximum speed:* 345 km/h (214 mph)

Hs 126, Henschel

German army cooperation aircraft. The first new design for the Luftwaffe Aufklärung (reconnaissance) and army cooperation units, replacing the old pre-Nazi He 46, was the Hs 122. It was a trim parasol monoplane, designed by a team under Friedrich Nicolaus, and began flight testing in early 1935. It was obviously an excellent machine, but was lacking in power and offered little performance improvement over the He 46. The answer was a different engine, and in the autumn of 1936 the fourth Hs 122B-0 emerged largely rebuilt as the first Hs 126, the numerous changes including a canopy over the front two-thirds of the tandem cockpits. The Jumo 210 engine was temporary, the

British troops examine a captured Hs 126 army cooperation aircraft at Klagenfurt in 1945. The Hs 126 was used in front line and antipartisan operations as well as night attacks

chosen production unit being the 830-hp Bramo Fafnir 323A-1 driving a three-blade VDM propeller.

An all-metal stressed-skin machine, the 126A-1 went into production in December 1937, rate of delivery building up sharply as the Hs 123 tapered off (six years too early, as it was later realized). Armament normally comprised a fixed MG 17 machine-gun on the right side of the top decking and an MG 15 aimed by the observer whose cockpit was sheltered by the front cockpit's canopy with hinged airstream deflectors. A rack on the lower left side of the fuselage could carry an SC50 50-kg (110-lb) bomb, and in place of the usual cameras the bay immediately aft of the rear cockpit could carry two boxes each containing five 10 kg (22 lb) bombs nose-up. The main topographic camera was fixed vertically in the floor of the rear cockpit, the observer also having a hand camera attached by links to the left side.

Total production of the Hs 126 amounted to about 802 aircraft, the last being delivered in January 1941. All versions were very similar, the main difference being a switch to the 880-hp BMW 132Dc engine in the 126A-1, and the 900-hp Bramo 323A-2 or Q-2 in the 126B-1.

Like the smaller Hs 123, the 126 proved exceedingly tough; yet front-line attrition was such that the actual force in the inventory never exceeded 290, and numbers dwindled from the opening of the Russian campaign. In the Polish campaign Luftflotte 1 and 4 deployed some 190 Henschels, which were able to reconnoitre, bomb and even strafe with little opposition. Things were tougher in the Low Countries and France, and in the winter of 1940-41 most Hs 126 units were glad to fly south to the Balkans, Greece and North Africa.

In 1942-45 surviving Henschels operated in various duties, most with wheel spats removed, and about half equipped with glider tow hooks. Many served as close-support

aircraft with specific army divisions, especially Panzers, though there was severe attrition in this role on the Eastern Front. As Allied air and ground defences became ever more formidable, the Hs 126 was forced increasingly into stealthy night operations in Nachtschlachtgruppen (night close-support groups, NSGr) which also included low-powered biplane primary trainers such as the Ar 66 and Go 145, and the equally dated He 45 and 46. A few NSGr served in direct action against the Soviet armies, but most were used in rear areas trying to pin down and exterminate partisan groups.

Span: 14.50 m (47 ft 7 in) *Length:* 10.85 m (35 ft 7 in) *Gross weight:* 3270 kg (7209 lb) *Maximum speed:* 355 km/h (220 mph)

Hs 129, Henschel

German close-support and antitank aircraft. The story of specialized antiarmour aircraft is instructive in many ways. Like today's A-10, the Hs 129 was designed as a relatively low-performance twin, with a very powerful gun on the centreline, heavy armour, retracted landing gears whose tyres projected to facilitate wheels-up landings, a single seat in the nose, and concentration on lethality and survivability rather than speed. A further odd fact is that for long periods such aircraft have been ignored, despite their obvious vital importance in any conceivable land battle. Certainly there was little interest in the tank-killing aeroplane between 1918 and the Spanish Civil War in 1936. But brutal experience in armoured battles reinforced the lessons that tanks can be a menace, and that aircraft can exert a decisive influence in land warfare (contrary to the general belief of the Luftwaffe high command). By April 1937 the concept of a specialized close-support and antitank aircraft (*Schlachtflugzeug*) had emerged, and a preliminary specification was drawn up. Had the Second World War been

Hs 130, Henschel

foreseen, or even the basic importance of close-support aircraft appreciated, the resulting Hs 129 might have entered service at the start of the war, when it could have made a major difference to Germany's fortunes.

Submissions for the *Schlachtflugzeug* were made on October 1, 1937, and eventually Nicolaus's Hs 129 design was judged best, the runner-up being a special version of the twin-boom Fw-189 with a crew of two in a cramped armoured central nacelle. In contrast the Hs 129 was of conventional configuration, and also scored in being a single-seater. Minimum frontal area had been called for, and the triangular-section fuselage was the smallest capable of housing the pilot, heavy armour and forward-firing armament of two 20-mm (0.79-in) MG FF cannon and two MG 17 machine-guns. Two 465-hp Argus As 410B aircooled inverted-V-12 engines gave rather poor performance. The cramped cockpit forced the engine and oil instruments to be located on the inner sides of the nacelles, and the very short control column made even gentle manoeuvres hard work. From first flight in the spring of 1939 pilot view was criticized, and in 1940 the Hs 129A was flatly rejected. A partial answer lay in substituting the 700-hp Gnome-Rhône 14M radial, available from France, and this eventually led to the 129B which first flew in December 1941. By this time the failure to subdue quickly the Soviet Union, and the fierce battle in North Africa, had led to belated recognition of the importance of the 129, and plans for mass production were hastened. By September 1944, when production was terminated, 859 had been built of many Hs 129B sub-types, and despite poor performance, deficient pilot view and a generally indifferent reputation, they made their mark on Allied armour.

Battle was joined in earnest by the 129B-1/R2 in January 1943. This was the first aircraft in action with the hard-hitting MK 101 high-velocity 30-mm (1.18-in) gun, slung under the fuselage with 30 rounds. Even this was unable to pierce the frontal armour of a T-34 or KV-1 and various B-2 versions with R (*Rüstsätze*) kits carried the even harder-hitting MK 103 and many other weapons including the BK 3,7. The heaviest gun used in action was the monster 75-mm (2.95-in) PaK 40L, though this was really too much for the airframe and made the aircraft even more unwieldy and vulnerable. Four rounds could be fired in one long (500-m/550-yards) pass, any of which could knock out the heaviest tank. Other weapons included the WfrGr 21 and 28 (210-mm [8.27-in] and 280-mm [11-in]) rockets, various smaller but faster Panzer-blitz rockets and, most novel of all, the Rheinmetall SG 113A in which six 77-mm (3.03-in) rocket projector tubes were mounted in the fuselage, firing down and slightly to the rear, usually at 100°. All six were triggered by the magnetic-field variation caused by flying over a tank. Each had a 45-mm (1.77-in) AP core, and could easily pierce the thin roof armour, but the basic weapon never became accurate or reliable enough to do much damage.

Though many 129s operated in Tunisia, most saw action with the Luftwaffe and with the satellite air forces of Hungary and Romania on the Eastern Front. On occasions they proved lethal to large Soviet tank formations, but the deficiencies of the aircraft unfortunately greatly reduced its effectiveness, and it was always vulnerable to attacks by fighters.

Span: 14.2 m (46 ft 7 in) *Length:* 9.75 m (32 ft)
Gross weight: (basic 129B-2) 5110 kg (11 266 lb)
Maximum speed: 408 km/h (253 mph)

Hs 130, Henschel

German multirole aircraft series. Few aircraft have ever been the subject of such far-reaching and large-scale development programmes and then been as completely forgotten as the Hs 130. The 130 was not just one aircraft but a whole family of successive new designs differing greatly in size, power and even in mission. The one linking factor was that all were pressurized high-fliers.

The work began in 1938 when Dr Seewald of the DVL (German Flight Research Establishment) invited Henschel to build an ultra-high-altitude testbed aircraft for DVL turbo-compressors and pressure cabins. The resulting Hs 128 prototypes completed a vast amount of research into pressure cabins, pressurization systems and several designs of turbo-supercharger for Jumo 210, DB 601, 603 and 605 engines, as well as the main German power-boost systems (GM-1 nitrous oxide, and MW-50 methanol-water). These impressive aircraft seemed to Theo Rowehl of the Luftwaffe high command just what was needed for photo-reconnaissance over enemy territory. Soon the Hs 130A strategic-reconnaissance aircraft was under contract, three prototypes and seven production machines being ordered. These had 1475-hp DB 605B engines driving large four-blade propellers, the Hs 128 pressure cabin seating two side by side, progressively greater wing span (rising from 22 to 29 m [72 to 95 ft]) and operational ceiling in excess of 15 500 m (50 850 ft).

In early 1941 Henschel proposed the Hs 130B bomber, but this was overtaken by the Hs 130C, a totally new aircraft with a much larger fuselage, 1850-hp DB 603A engines and a crew of four. Normal bombload was 4000 kg (8820 lb), and defensive armament comprised two remote-control barbettes, each with two 13-mm (0.51-in) MG 131 guns, plus a remote-control MG 15 in the tail. Three prototypes flew in the winter of 1942-43, powered by turbocharged BMW 801J, DB 603 and conventional BMW 801A engines. This promising machine was slipped in as a fifth contender in the bomber B programme: when all the other designs became bogged down there was a chance that over 100 Hs 130C bombers would be produced, but the whole bomber programme was abandoned in late 1943, and the Hs 130C with it.

Via the complex and abortive Hs 130D the final type was the Hs 130E, probably the most advanced high-flying aircraft of the Second World War. This was built around the

The Henschel 129B antitank aircraft. The Mk 101 301-mm (1.18-in) cannon was lethally effective against the top armour of Soviet tanks

The Henschel Hs 293 had a rocket motor which assisted control and gave the glide bomb greater velocity when it hit the target. After some initial successes against British and Canadian warships German glide bombs were neutralized by US Navy ECM measures. At Anzio in 1944 the US Navy deployed three ships equipped with jamming equipment to counteract the bombs' radio guidance systems

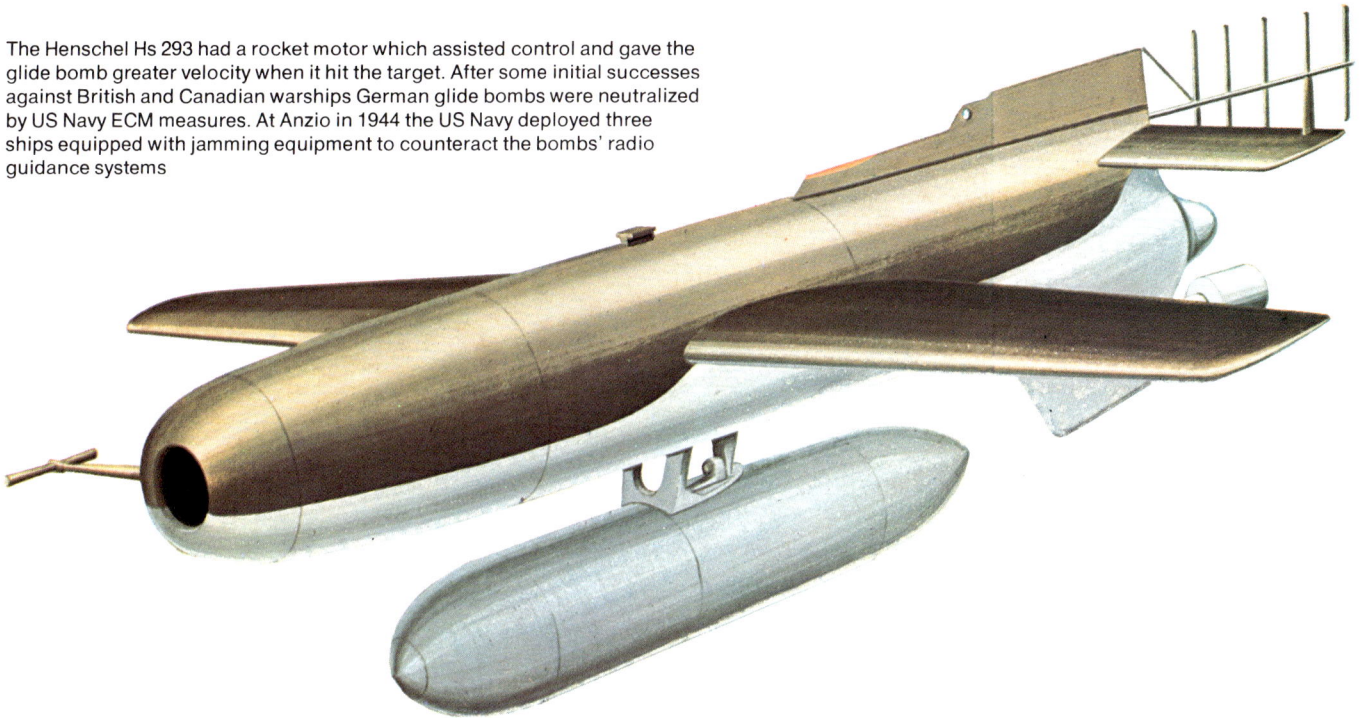

Höhen Zentrale Anlage (high-altitude power-station system) comprising two 1750-hp DB 603B engines, driving extremely large four-blade propellers, supercharged by ducting fed by a *Zentrale* (power station) in the fuselage. The *Zentrale* compressor, the largest ever flown at that time, was driven by a 1500-hp DB 605T in the fuselage just aft of the wings, with very large belly radiators and main engine inlets. Three prototypes of these monster three-seat reconnaissance aircraft flew to around 15 000 m (49 200 ft) throughout 1943. Six E-0 preproduction aircraft were built, and there were more schemes for bomber or 'destroyer' versions. The four-engined 130F was not built. Data are for the 130E-O.

Span: 33 m (108 ft 3 in) *Length:* 22 m (72 ft 2 in) *Gross weight:* 18 100 kg (39 900 lb) *Maximum speed:* 610 km/h (379 mph)

Hs 293, Henschel

German rocket-powered glide-bomb series. The field of guided bombs is one of the many in which Germany was sufficiently advanced early in the Second World War to have gained a possibly decisive advantage if the weapons had entered operational service while the tide was still running in her favour. The Hs 293, for example, was successfully tested before the end of 1940, yet it was not used in action until the autumn of 1943 and even then the He 177 Greif heavy bomber was not available in sufficient numbers to take full advantage of effective but cumber-some glide-bombs.

The Legion Kondor's experience in the Spanish Civil War soon led the Luftwaffe to appreciate the difficulties of attacking moving ships. Henschel was awarded a development contract covering work on small guided bombs soon after the invasion of Poland in September 1939, and in January of the fol-lowing year Dr Herbert Wagner left Junkers to head the guided-weapons team. He studied

the various proposals and submitted the design of a radio-controlled glide-bomb; authorization was forthcoming, and the designation Hs 293 was applied.

The weapon was to be based on the stan-dard SC 500 high-explosive bomb, but aerodynamic testing showed that the design would not be sufficiently fast to penetrate more than lightly armoured targets. To over-come this problem, and to increase maximum range so that the launch aircraft was less vulnerable to the target's defences, the de-sign was modified to accommodate a rocket motor. The forward part of the fuselage carried the warhead and its arming device, with the radio receiver, controls and batteries at the rear. On early models, aerodynamic

control was by conventional ailerons and elevators, but these were later replaced by spoilers. The missile was gyro-stabilized in roll; directional changes were achieved by banking, as no rudder was fitted.

The Hs 293 was carried aloft under the wing of a bomber, the propellants for the bomb's rocket motor being kept warm during transit by hot air fed through hoses from the engines of the launch aircraft. The weapon was normally released at a height of 1000 m (3300 ft), from which altitude it had a maxi-mum range of 11 km (6.8 miles); this increased to 16 km (10 miles) at 6000 m (19 700 ft). The bifuel Walter 109-557 rocket was slung beneath the weapon's fuselage so that the thrust line ran as nearly as possible

An RAF officer examines an Hs 293 glide bomb captured intact packed for transport in 1944

Hs 293, Henschel

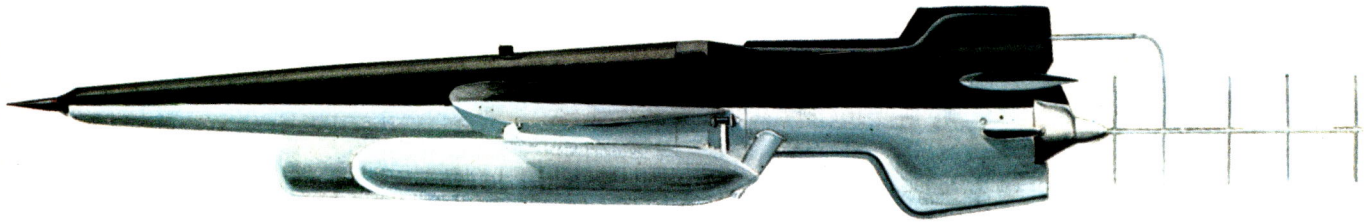

The Hs 294 was derived from the Hs 293 but with a carefully-designed fuselage it could be used as a torpedo since it had a predictable underwater trajectory

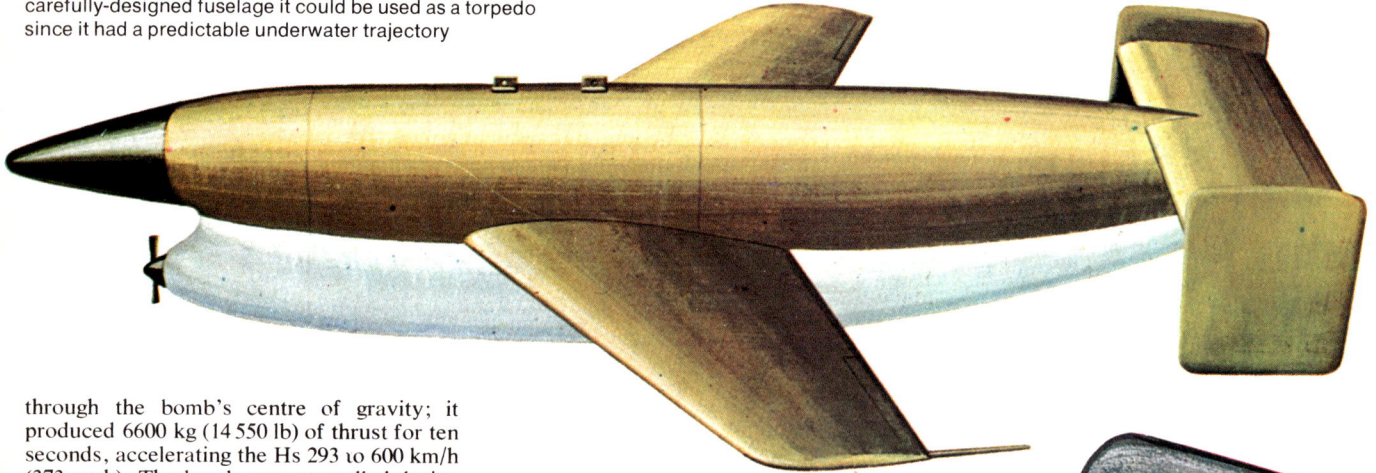

The Hs 298, the first true air-to-air missile. It was the smallest to be designed by Henschel and carried a 48-kg (106-lb) warhead powered by a solid-fuel rocket

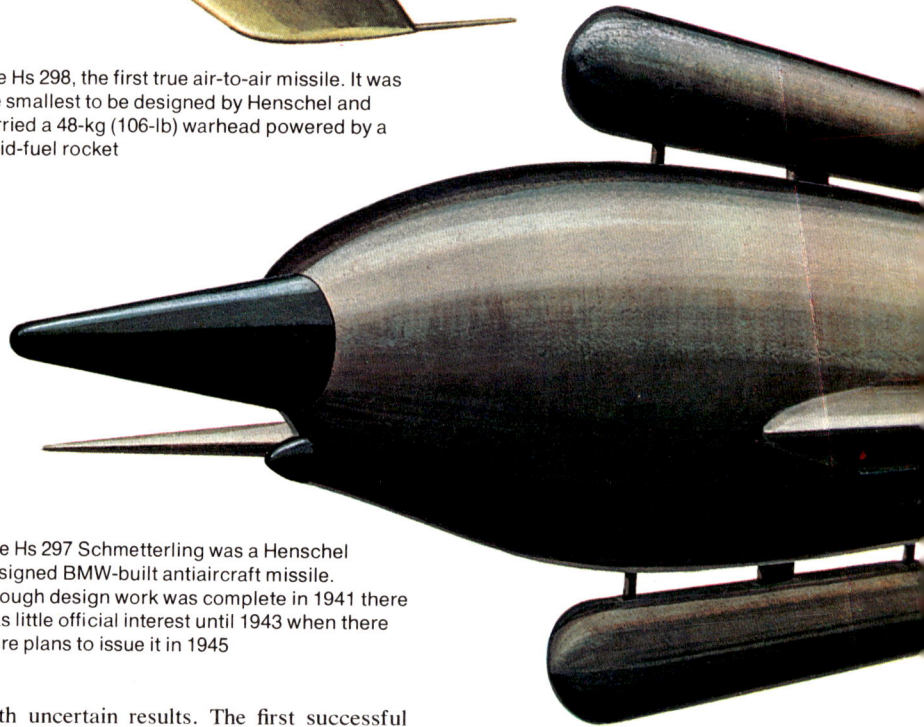

The Hs 297 Schmetterling was a Henschel designed BMW-built antiaircraft missile. Though design work was complete in 1941 there was little official interest until 1943 when there were plans to issue it in 1945

through the bomb's centre of gravity; it produced 6600 kg (14 550 lb) of thrust for ten seconds, accelerating the Hs 293 to 600 km/h (373 mph). The bomb was controlled during flight by an operator in the launch aircraft, using the Kehl-Strassburg radio link to transmit steering commands to the weapon's aerodynamic surfaces; after initial trials showed that the Hs 293 was difficult to follow in bad visibility, a flare was added to the rear of the bomb to aid visual tracking.

The warhead contained approximately 270 kg (600 lb) of Trialen 105 explosive, which was resistant to premature detonation by rough handling or antiaircraft gunfire, though explosive power was sacrificed in achieving these advantages. A delayed-action impact fuze was fitted.

The first test flight, on December 16, 1940, was a complete failure—not surprisingly, since the left and right steering commands to the control surfaces were reversed. The second attempt, two days later, was successful. Bad weather prevented all but a few high-altitude trials taking place that winter, and initial testing was not completed until the summer of 1941. A production contract was awarded that November and mass assembly began in January 1942. Many minor setbacks followed, and it was not until August 25, 1943, that the weapon became operational.

The original plan, conceived by General Werner Baumbach, was to use glide-bombs against North Sea convoys, the Soviet Black Sea fleet and Soviet vessels at Kronstadt and Leningrad. Hitler vetoed this idea, however, and demanded that the weapons should be used to attack North Atlantic convoys. The long-range Heinkel He 177 Greif was not available in any numbers—it had a distressing habit of blowing up in flight—so a compromise was reached: Dornier Do 217s and a handful of He 177s would use Hs 293s to take the pressure off Dönitz's U-Boats, which were being harried by the Allies as they crossed the Bay of Biscay. KG 100 had been training with the weapon since March 1943, and on August 25 it attacked a destroyer force in the Bay of Biscay in bad weather,

with uncertain results. The first successful sortie was made two days later, when 18 aircraft of II/KG 100 attacked the First British Support Group on an antisubmarine sweep south of Cape Finisterre. The escort sloop HMS Egret was sunk and the destroyer HMCS Athabaskan was badly damaged. The Admiralty ordered all warships in the Bay of Biscay to remain at 320 km (200 miles) from the French coast until a countermeasure could be found—round one to the Luftwaffe.

A second Gruppe, II/KG 40, was allocated the task of attacking Mediterranean convoys; Hs 293s were to sink the escorts, allowing the merchantmen to be destroyed by torpedo-armed Ju 88s. Only one of the four attacks made in October and November 1943 was successful, however, and 20% of II/KG 40's

aircraft were lost. Further setbacks were suffered in the Atlantic during December, and by the time of the Anzio landings in January 1944 the US Navy had three warships equipped with jamming gear to counteract the Hs 293s' guidance systems. The Luftwaffe achieved several more successes, including sinking the light cruiser HMS Spartan, but the combination of jamming, smoke screens, antiaircraft fire and fighter attacks proved too much. Hs 293 sorties were discontinued on March 4, and both KG 40 and KG 100 were disbanded in August in the face of heavy losses and the need to conserve fuel for fighters.

Many derivatives of the basic Hs 293 reached various stages of development. The control system was being constantly modified, and steel construction was tried in place of aluminium. The Hs 293B incorporated Dortmund-Duisberg wire guidance instead of radio control in an attempt to overcome jamming, and the Hs 293C combined the body of the 293 with the warhead of the Hs 294 (see below). The Hs 293D, tested in 1942, used a Tonne television camera to relay signals back to a display in the launch aircraft.

The Hs 294 was a substantial redesign which was intended to enter the water and act as a torpedo, while the Hs 295 was an air-to-surface weapon with two rocket motors. The Hs 296 also had two rockets and was to incorporate the Tonne-Seedorf television system as developed for the Hs 293D. None of these variants entered service.

(Hs 293) *Length:* 318 cm (10 ft 5 in) *Span:* 312 cm (10 ft 3 in) *Weight:* 785 kg (1730 lb) *Speed:* 600 km/h (373 mph) *Maximum range:* 16 km (10 miles)

Hs 298, Henschel

German air-to-air missile. The Hs 298 missile, designed by Professor Wagner of the Henschel company for use against bombers, was the smallest designed and produced by Henschel. It has the distinction of being the first missile ever developed specifically as an AAM. The Hs 298 was a mid-wing monoplane with tapered, swept-back wings and a single horizontal stabilizer carrying twin endplate fins. It was designed to be aerodynamically stable in pitch and yaw, with gyrostabilization in roll. The powerplant was a solid-propellant rocket motor designed by Henschel and built by Schmidding as the 109-543; the first stage boosted the weapon to 935 km/h (580 mph) so that it cleared the parent aircraft rapidly and could be acquired visually by the operator, propulsion then being assumed by a sustainer stage of lower thrust but better fuel consumption.

The Hs 298 was intended to be carried by the Do 217 (five missiles) and Fw 190 (two). It was steered by means of a joystick in the launch aircraft, commands being transmitted over the Kehl-Strassburg radio link; a propeller-driven generator provided power for the receiver and the electrically-operated control strips on the trailing edges of the wings and stabilizer. The Do 217 was to have carried two operators: one would keep his reflector sight on the target while the other, using a second sight linked to the first by servos, steered the missile throughout its flight. The warhead, designed for maximum blast effect, was detonated by a Fox or Kranich proximity fuze with an effective radius of action of some 10 m (33 ft).

The Hs 298 was designed in early 1944 and immediately given high priority. Mass production was planned to begin in January 1945, but the only known test firings took place from a Ju 88G on December 22, 1944, with discouraging results: one round exploded prematurely, a second nose-dived into the ground and the third stuck on the launch rail. Work on the Hs 298 was abandoned on the following February 6 in favour of the Ruhrstahl X-4.

Length: 205 cm (6 ft 9 in) *Span:* 125 cm (4 ft 1 in) *Diameter:* 40 cm (1 ft 4 in) *Weight:* 120 kg (264 lb) *Range:* 1.6 km (1 mile) at 680 km/h (423 mph) *Warhead:* 48 kg (106 lb) high explosive

---

HU-16, Grumman US general-purpose amphibious aircraft See **Albatross**

Hudson, Lockheed A-28, A-29

US coastal-reconnaissance/light bomber aircraft. In April 1938 a British Purchasing Commission in the US visited the Lockheed Aircraft Corporation factory at Burbank, California. They were actually looking for a twin-engined aircrew trainer for Anson navigators, but Lockheed's latest 11-passenger Model 14 Super Electra seemed ideal for conversion for use as a land-based maritime patrol aircraft/light bomber, to replace the RAF's Avro Anson Mk Is in that role.

Within days a mock-up was supplied as the Model 214 and an 'off the drawing-board' order for 200 as Hudson Mk Is was issued by the British government. Of mid-wing monoplane construction, the Mk I was powered by two 1100-hp Wright R-1820-G102A Cyclone single-row radials driving three-blade propellers, and flew for the first time at Burbank on December 10, 1938. The armament was to include a power-operated dorsal turret for

An RAF-crewed Lockheed Hudson III. The Hudson served throughout the war in all theatres

Hudson, Lockheed A-28, A-29

The Hudson was the first RAF aircraft to attack a Luftwaffe intruder, and gave sterling service during the withdrawal from Dunkerque in 1940

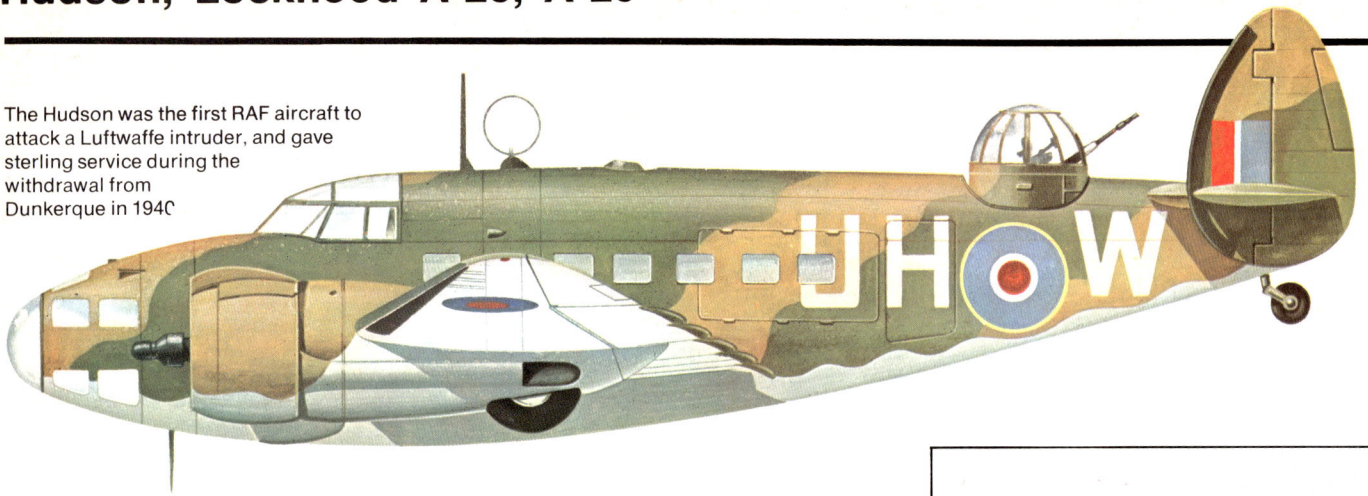

two 0.303-in (7.7-mm) Browning machine-guns, to be built and installed by Boulton Paul Aircraft Ltd when the aircraft arrived in the UK. The first Hudson was delivered in February 1939, and was allocated to Boulton Paul for turret tests. The second, delivered in March 1939, went directly to the Aeroplane and Armament Experimental Establishment at Boscombe Down, where it was retained as a test machine. Initial delivery was somewhat slow, although during 1938 a Lockheed subsidiary company (British Reassembly Division, LAC Ltd) was set up at Speke Airport, Liverpool, to assemble and test the Hudsons which were delivered by sea to the port. In May 1939 the first Hudson Mk I arrived for service with RAF Coastal Command (No 244 Squadron) and the order was increased by a further 50 aircraft. The Royal Australian Air Force also ordered 100 Hudsons (50 Mk I and 50 Mk II) in late 1938; these were Lockheed Model 414s, to be powered by 1050-hp Pratt & Whitney R-1830-SC3G Twin Wasp two-row radials; their first aircraft was delivered on February 9, 1940.

The Hudson was operated by a four-man crew, and in addition to the dorsal gun turret a further, non-retractable 0.303-in (7.7-mm) gun could be fitted in the lower rear fuselage; forward of this, the internal weapons bay could accommodate a bombload of 726 kg (1600 lb).

On the second day of the Second World War, it was announced by the British Air Ministry that the first Luftwaffe aircraft—a Dornier Do 18D maritime patrol and reconnaissance flying-boat from one of the North Sea Küstenfliegergruppen—had been attacked by a Hudson of No 224 Squadron. On November 10, another Do 18D became Coastal Command's first victim, falling to the guns of a Hudson of No 220 Squadron. The Hudson had proved itself, and a further RAF order for 100 Mk Is was issued, together with one for 20 Mk IIs (Lockheed Model 314), which had a strengthened airframe, constant-speed (instead of variable pitch) propellers, and a five-man crew.

By 1940, Hudsons were being used in a variety of roles, including attacks on enemy minesweepers and merchant shipping; bombing raids over enemy-held airfields and other military establishments in Denmark and Norway. They also took part in the evacuation of Dunkerque, giving covering fire where necessary. Some were also used, in suitable camouflage, for low-level photo-reconnaissance missions.

The improved Hudson Mk III was next to

be developed, with uprated 1200-hp R-1820-G205A Cyclone engines and a retractable ventral gun. The last 241 (of 428 built) were further equipped with extra wing internal fuel tanks for the long-range role.

Somewhat confusingly, the Mk III and all subsequent Hudson variants were called Model 414s by Lockheed. To the RAF, the Australian Mks I and II were known as Mks IV and V respectively, the RAF then ordering similar aircraft for itself under the same designations: 30 Hudson Mk IVs (with 1050-hp Twin Wasps and no ventral gun) and 409 short- and long-range Mk Vs (1200-hp Twin Wasps and retractable ventral gun). On March 11, 1941, when the Lend-Lease Bill was instituted, 200 Mk III and 52 Mk IV Hudsons still undelivered at that time were supplied as Lend-Lease items and not direct purchases.

All subsequent deliveries were made as Lend-Lease allocations, and accordingly received US service designations as well as their British and Commonwealth designations, which were Mk IIIA (USAAF A-29 and A-29A), Mk IVA (USAAF A-28), and Mk VI (USAAF A-28A). Of 800 Mk IIIAs built under Lend-Lease funding, the RAF received 320; others were diverted to the RAAF (106), RNZAF (37), RCAF (137), Chinese Nationalist air force (26), USAAF (153) and US Navy (20). All 52 Mk IVAs built were allocated directly to the RAAF.

RAF Hudsons continued their antisubmarine patrols over the North Sea and Western defence areas during 1941-42. Operating from Gibraltar in late 1942 and during 1943, they were used in the Mediterranean theatre not only against U-Boats but against Axis aircraft. Some of these Hudsons were equipped with an additional fixed 0.50-in (12.7-mm) Browning machine-gun in the nose and others with underwing rocket projectiles. Squadrons of Hudsons also served in the Far East, India and Burma, and during the latter campaign they covered the British retreat and continued in the area on supply-dropping missions. They began phasing out of RAF service in 1943-44, but remained on second-line duties as troop transports and air/sea-rescue aircraft. In all, they served with nearly 40 RAF squadrons and other units. From mid-1942 many carried ASV radar, and to VE-Day Hudsons were the chief sea-reconnaissance aircraft in Italy.

Hudsons were also used extensively by the RAAF (12 squadrons) and RNZAF (seven squadrons) in the Far East and South Pacific theatres, both for evacuating islands and for

The prototype of the Bell AH-1 HueyCobra gunship. The Cobra proved highly effective in Vietnam particularly supporting troop carrying helicopters under attack in defended landing zones

attacking shipping and aircraft. They also served as night-fighter escorts, dropping flares for US bombers based at Guadalcanal.

Although the US forces in general did not employ Hudsons to any great extent, 20 Mk IIIAs were diverted to the US Navy in October 1941 and, designated PBO-1, went to VP-82 Squadron at Argentia in Newfoundland. These were armed with four 147-kg (325-lb) depth charges and powered by 1200-hp Wright R-1820-87 engines. The first German U-Boat was sunk by fire from one of these aircraft on March 1, 1942, but by the end of that year they had been phased out in favour of the long-range Liberators and Flying Fortresses. The A-29A version for the USAAF was fitted with troop-carrying benches; 24 A-29s were equipped for photo-reconnaissance and redesignated A-29B; and, beside the Lend-Lease allocations, 300 more Lockheed Model 414s were built for the USAAF as AT-18 (217) and AT-18A (83) advanced trainers, the latter minus the dorsal turret. Total production reached 2940.

(Mk IIIA/A-29) *Span:* 19.96 m (65 ft 6 in) *Length:* 13.51 m (44 ft 4 in) *Gross weight:* 9300 kg (20 500 lb) *Max speed:* 407 km/h (253 mph)

'Huey' Nickname for Bell UH-1 helicopter
See **Iroquois**

HueyCobra, Bell AH-1

US helicopter for land warfare. In 1964 experience in Vietnam had demonstrated the need for a purpose-designed gunship helicopter, to improve on existing general-purpose types being used in that role. The US Army formulated the AAFSS (advanced aerial fire-support system) requirement calling for a powerful and lavishly-equipped two-seater which could support both ground and air

Humber

A Bell SeaCobra—the US Marine Corps version of the HueyCobra—has a 1970-shp T400 Twin-Pac engine and 2050 HueyTug transmission

operations in a land battle. A major need was for a heavily armed escort for vulnerable troop-carrying helicopters operating at low level over hostile armies. Capability was also required in a number of other roles including antitank missile launching, armed reconnaissance, and the support of day or night missions into enemy territory (for example, to rescue downed aircrew). The winner of the AAFSS competition was the Lockheed AH-56A Cheyenne, but as an interim measure Bell proposed a redesigned UH Huey utility helicopter.

The Cheyenne proved problem-ridden and extremely costly, and the project was terminated in the spring of 1960. The interim Bell proposal had by that time become a major production programme, and the AH-1 remained for a decade the world's chief battlefield gunship helicopter, being continually updated to meet new demands.

Bell's company-funded HueyCobra prototype flew on September 7, 1965, and quickly produced a US Army order for two prototypes and a production batch designated AH-1G. Within two years, numbers were in action in Vietnam, and 838 were on order. The original HueyCobra, popularly called the Cobra or Snake, combined the dynamic parts (including the flat-rated 1100-shp Lycoming T53-13 engine and broad 'door-hinge' main rotor) with a completely new fuselage of minimum frontal area seating the pilot on the centreline, immediately ahead of the rotor gearbox, with a gunner or weapon-system officer at a lower level in the nose.

Emerson Electric supplied the TAT (tactical aircraft turret) Type 102b, housing the GAU-2B/A Minigun with an 8000-round drum. This was soon replaced by the XM28 subsystems of two Miniguns, each with 4000 rounds; or two XM129 launchers for 40-mm (1.57-in) grenades; or one Minigun and one launcher. Four 19-round XM159 rocket packs can be carried under the wings; alternatively a number of other loads including the XM35

kit for a GE six-barrel 20-mm (0.79-in) cannon with 1000 rounds can be carried. Carefully interlinked sighting systems enable the gunner to aim and fire the guns or launchers in the turrets, while the pilot controls the fixed stores. When the gunner's grip on the aimed weapons is released they automatically point straight ahead, and come under the control of the pilot.

In 1968 the US Marine Corps ordered the AH-1J SeaCobra, in which twin-engine safety is conferred by a Pratt & Whitney Canada T400 Twin-Pac engine of two 900-shp power sections. Other dynamic parts are the same as in the earlier version, but the tailfin has been strengthened and the tail-rotor blades made wider to absorb greater power of 1250 shp. Among many new detail features is a General Electric turret system housing the long-barrel XM197 20-mm gun (a lightweight version of the M61 Vulcan) with 750 rounds.

In 1973 the AH-1Q TowCobra was produced as a conversion of -1G Cobras. Each pylon carries two two-round launchers for the Hughes Tow antitank missile, both crew-members have a Sperry Rand (Univac) helmet sight subsystem which enables either to use the ×2/×13-magnification Tow sight for the missiles or turreted weapons, or to cue the latter directly. Deliveries began in June 1975, but by this time the AH-1S TowCobra offered greater capabilities and was supplanting the -1Q in conversions (about 400), with a further 305 of the -1S also ordered from new production. The -1S has a 1825-shp T53-703 engine and upgraded dynamic parts for even greater flight performance and manoeuvrability. All 1-Ss have flat glass canopy panels giving better protection and reduced glint; other advances include a better cockpit for nap-of-the-Earth flight, turreted cannon, improved fire-control and stores management, and improved details for reliability. The AH-1R has the -703 engine and upgraded transmission, but no Tow missile system.

In 1978 the latest production HueyCobra

variant was the Marines' AH-1T SeaCobra (officially named Improved SeaCobra) with the dynamic system of the Model 214 originally developed for the proposed Model 309 KingCobra. This has the 1970-shp T400 Twin-Pac engine, and the 2050-shp transmission of the HueyTug, permitting violent manoeuvres at maximum weight. Even broader main-rotor blades with swept tips improve performance further.

Export customers include the Imperial Iranian Army, which uses the -1J SeaCobra, and the Spanish navy which uses the -1G (designated Z-16) in the antishipping role. The Iranian machines number no fewer than 202, with a comprehensive weapon-equipment kit, XM197 cannon and, later, a Tow system.

Rotor diameter: 13.41 m (44 ft), (AH-1T) 14.63 m (48 ft 1½ in) *Fuselage length:* 13.59 m (44 ft 7 in), (AH-1T) 14.68 m (48 ft 2 in) *Gross weight:* (AH-1G) 4310 kg (9500 lb), (AH-1S) 4540 kg (10 000 lb), (AH-1T) 6350 kg (14 000 lb) *Maximum speed:* (in manoeuvres) 352 km/h (219 mph), (with Tow missile system) 315 km/h (196 mph)

Huff-Daland US aircraft   See **Keystone**

Hughes US helicopters
                              See **AAH, Cayuse, Osage**

Hughes US missiles See **Falcon, Maverick, Phoenix, Roland, Tow, Walleye**

Humber

British monitor class. Shortly after the outbreak of the First World War the Admiralty purchased three river monitors, nearing completion at Vickers yard in Barrow. They had originally been laid down for Brazil and were launched in 1913 with the names *Javary*, *Madeira* and *Solimoes* but for service in the Royal Navy were renamed *Humber*, *Mersey*

HMS *Humber*, a river monitor launched in 1913, with steam up in Mudros harbour in 1916. She was sold in 1920 and became a crane lighter

and *Severn* respectively.

As they were intended for river service they had a very shallow hull with only 1.5 m (5 ft) draught and 1.2 (4 ft) freeboard, but nevertheless they proved more seaworthy in coastal operations than might be expected, and undertook long ocean voyages during the war without mishap. They were heavily armed with a twin 6-in (152-mm) gun turret forward, a single 4.7-in (120-mm) howitzer on each side aft and two 3-pdr singles on each side of the superstructure amidships. The hull was protected over its full length by 50-mm (2-in) thick side armour covered by a protective deck. During the war the 4.7-in guns were replaced by a single 6-in gun on the quarterdeck and a 3-pdr AA gun was added on the superstructure.

Initially the three ships served at Dover and were employed in bombardments of the Belgium coast until the end of 1914 when they transferred to the Mediterranean. In June 1915 *Mersey* and *Severn* sailed from Malta for an operation that was to make them famous. Since December 1914 the German cruiser *Königsberg* had been blocked in the delta of the Rufiji river in German East Africa and, having worked her way well into the delta, she was virtually invulnerable to the blockading vessels. *Mersey* and *Severn* possessed the ideal combination of small size and shallow draught for navigating the waterways of the delta, and a heavy armament for attacking the enemy cruiser. They made their first excursion into the Rufiji delta on July 6 and closed to within 10 000 m (11 000 yards) of *Königsberg* for a bombardment which lasted for a large part of the day. However, the enemy vessel was not seriously damaged. The monitors returned on July 11, *Mersey* anchoring in the same position occupied on July 6, while *Severn* moved a mile closer to the *Königsberg*. *Severn* was the first to open fire and, after approximately 30 minutes, a large explosion signalled the detonation of one of the cruiser's magazines. *Mersey* then joined in and under the battering fire of the

A Bell AH-1G HueyCobra armed with rockets and a 7.62-mm (.30-in) Minigun in the chin position. The US Army had a long battle with the US Air Force over who should fly the HueyCobra

Hummel

The British monitor *Humber*, as she appeared in 1913. In 1915 her armament was altered to include a further 6-in (152-mm) gun and a 3-pdr AA gun was added on the superstructure

two ships *Königsberg* was reduced to a blazing wreck.

Mersey and *Severn* continued to operate off the East Coast of Africa until 1918 when they rejoined *Humber*. In 1920 *Humber* was sold into merchant service as a crane lighter while her two sisters were sold for scrap in 1921.

Displacement: 1260 tons (load) *Length:* 81.3 m (266 ft 9 in) oa *Beam:* 14.9 m (48 ft 10½ in) *Draught:* 1.5 m (5 ft) *Machinery:* 2-shaft triple-expansion steam engines, 1450 ihp=12 knots *Protection:* 50 mm (2 in) side *Armament:* 2 6-in (152-mm) (1×2); 2 4.7-in (120-mm) howitzers (2×1); 4 3-pdr (4×1) *Crew:* 100

Hummel

German self-propelled howitzer. This vehicle was developed by the Alkett company in a similar manner to the Hornisse, by taking a chassis derived from units of the PzKpfw III and IV tanks and moving the engine forward to a position alongside the driver, so as to leave a roomy fighting compartment at the rear. This compartment was open-topped, and into it went a 150-mm (5.9-in) schwere Feld-Haubitze 18, the standard medium field howitzer. This was an extremely good gun,

The Hawker Hunter 6, armed with four Aden cannon and a variety of underwing loads. *Above:* The prototype Hunter, the Hawker P 1067 on its test flight in November 1952. The Hunter has been widely exported and remains probably the finest subsonic jet fighter ever built

firing a 43-kg (95-lb) shell to a range of 13 km (8 miles), but on this mounting the maximum range was curtailed by the restricted elevation available. However, maximum range was not a vital factor, since Hummel (bumble bee) was issued to Panzer Division tank battalions as a close-support weapon, and it was almost always used in a direct-fire role as an assault gun. Development began in October 1942, and 666 were built, most of which were used on the Eastern Front.

Weight: 23.13 tons *Length:* 5.79 m (19 ft) *Width:* 2.92 m (9 ft 7 in) *Height:* 2.82 m (9 ft 3 in) *Armour thickness:* 20 mm (0.79 in) *Armament:* 150-mm (5.9-in) sFH 18 howitzer *Powerplant:* Maybach V-12 gasoline, 300 bhp at 3000 rpm *Speed:* 40 km/h (25 mph) *Range:* 200 km (125 miles) *Crew:* 6

Hunter, Hawker

British fighter, attack aircraft and trainer. Beyond doubt the most successful British warplane of the post-1945 era, and possibly the best combat aircraft of its generation, the Hunter was a winner from the start. Always beautiful in appearance and handling, it was shortsightedly allowed to fade in the late 1950s; only later was it realized that nothing like enough had been built to satisfy world demand, and that subsonic multirole fighter-bombers were not at all obsolete.

Owing to lack of government pressure Hawker Aircraft progressed towards swept-wing jet fighters in slow stages. The 1946 project for a fighter powered by the Rolls-Royce AJ.65 axial-compressor engine, later named Avon, did not have any sweep-back. In November 1947 came the P.1062 with swept wing and tail, resembling the Nene-powered P.1081. Finally came a completely fresh start, to Specification F.3/48. Designated P.1067, it had a long cylindrical fuselage with straight-through flow from a nose inlet. The wing and vertical tail were acutely swept, but the horizontal tail was unswept and mounted on top of the fin. Armament was to be two 30-mm (1.18-in) Aden cannon. This proposal of May 1948 was modified over the next two months, resulting in a design having a pointed nose with wing-root inlets, a lower tailplane mounted not far above the fuselage, and a radical new gun pack with four Aden guns and ammunition, which could be installed by hand winches as a single rearmed unit beneath the pressurized cockpit. In view of the Korean War and the RAF's total lack of any modern fighter, a large order was placed for the Hunter F.1 off the drawing board, with the 3400-kg (7500-lb) Avon RA.7 (later Mk 109); this was soon augmented by the F.2, ordered from Armstrong Whitworth with the 3765-kg (8300-lb) Armstrong Siddeley Sapphire 101. The first prototype, then unnamed and designated by the P.1067 type-number, flew in the hands of Neville Duke at Boscombe Down on July 20, 1951. On a previous high-speed run the brakes had burned out, but from the start the flight programme went well. Buffet at the tail was cured by adding a fairing at the junction of the fin/elevator trailing edge, and in June 1952 supersonic speed was achieved in a shallow dive. The powered flight controls, the first on a British fighter, were outstanding, being almost too responsive. The combined landing flaps and airbrakes worked powerfully and were cleared to over 600 knots, but within a certain range of indicated speeds they caused a trim change. Reluc-

tantly the system was abandoned and replaced by an extra airbrake added under the rear fuselage, and to avoid delaying production this was added as an unsightly external excrescence; 30-mm (1.18-in) cases hitting this airbrake caused dents, and large collector bulges were added under all four guns.

In 1953 the devastating armament was fired satisfactorily in a Sapphire F.2. Later, just as the first Avon-engined F.1 Hunters were going to 43 Squadron it was found that under some conditions the guns caused violent engine surging. This resulted, at a politically fraught moment, in a highly public prohibition on high-altitude firing. A fuel-dipping system, briefly reducing fuel flow to the Avon as the guns were fired, soon removed the problem; the Sapphire, with fixed inlet vanes, was not susceptible to this fault. Also in 1953, the first prototype was fitted with an after-burning Avon, rated at 4355 kg (9600 lb), and with extra rear-fuselage airbrakes, new windscreen and pointed nose, was flown by Duke to a world speed record of 1171 km/h (728 mph).

The high priority given to production overcame some of the desperate shortages then prevalent in Britain, and got the F.1 to Nos 43, 54 and 222 Squadrons and the F.2 to Nos 257 and 263 before the end of 1954. They were instantly popular, and could outperform any other fighter of the era, but were still primitive short-range fighters tailored to myopic Air Staff thinking. In late 1954 the first F.4 introduced additional internal fuel capacity, and wing hardpoints for drop tanks and two 454-kg (1000-lb) bombs. In addition to 365 made at Kingston, and Blackpool (Squire's Gate), a further 112 were made by Fairey/SABCA in Belgium and 96 by Fokker/Aviolanda in the Netherlands, most of these being funded by US Off-Shore Procurement. The Dutch aircraft were later additionally armed with two Sidewinder AAMs without affecting the four main pylons. Armstrong Whitworth made 105 of the F.5 version, the similar update of the F.2. These Sapphire aircraft had vents for the synthetic turbine oil which continually erased squadron markings. The Avon-Hunters were the main fighter-bomber of the 2nd ATAF of RAF Germany and the Benelux countries, while the F.5 served in Cyprus, and saw action at Suez in November 1956.

Technical Director Sir Sydney Camm did not pursue his P.1083 with 50° thin wings, nor the delta P.1091 or six-seat P.1128 business jet conversion. He disagreed with afterburning, and the Air Staff went along with his suggestion that an Avon of the much improved 200-series was a better answer. The first Hunter F.6, with the 4536-kg (10000-lb) thrust Avon 203, flew in January 1954 and led to a whole family of much more capable aircraft. Armstrong Whitworth built 119 of the 416 F.6 Hunters, all delivered in 1956-57. Apart from bigger inlet ducts and jetpipe, the F.6 had a dogtooth leading edge introduced late in production, together with an all-flying tailplane which not only gave improved manoeuvrability but solved the perennial problem of flight-control jack-stalling which had led to several ejections. Both changes were made standard and fitted retroactively on all F.6 Hunters, and at least the dogtooth wing was fitted to some F.4s.

Hunter, Hawker

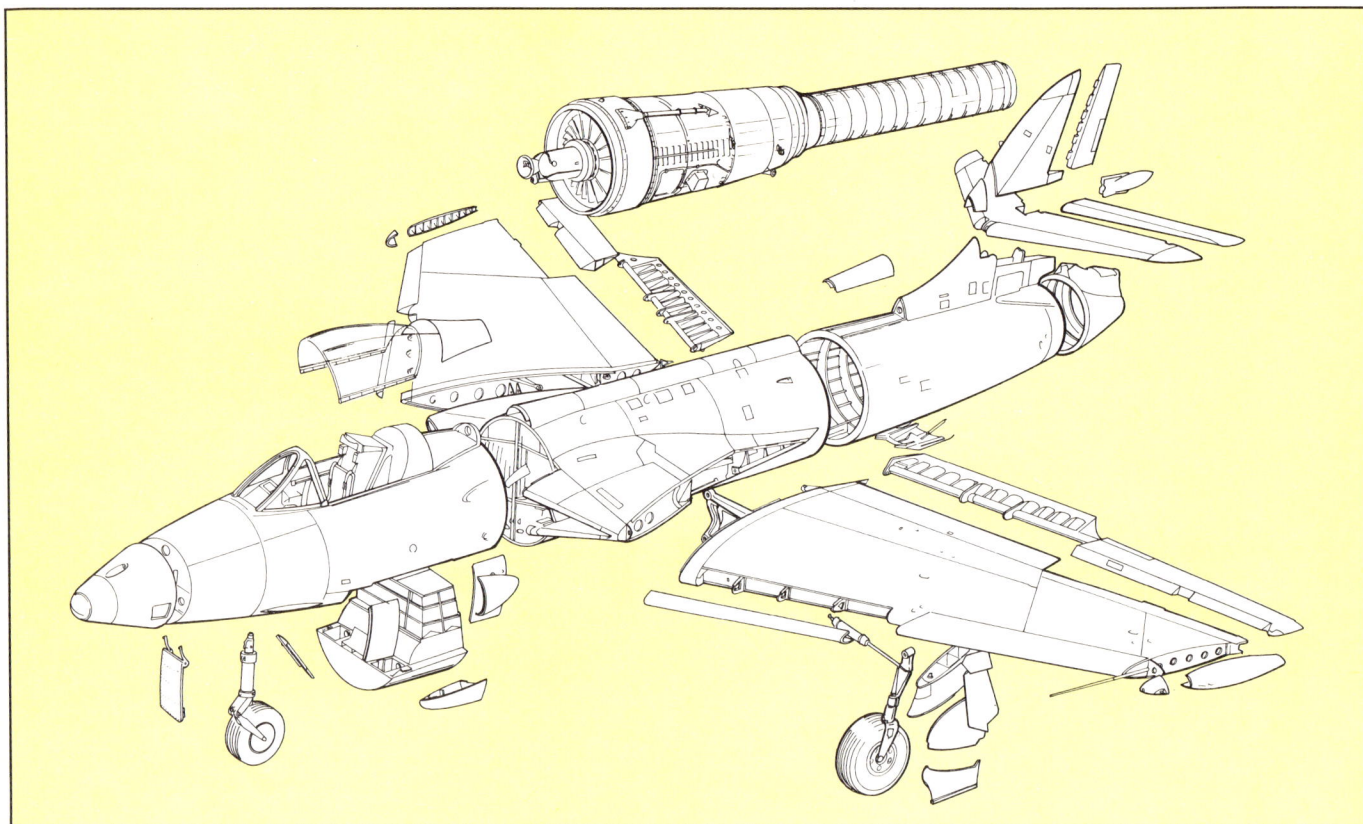

Test-pilot Duke argued for a tandem trainer but was overruled by the Air Staff who ordered the side-by-side T.7 to Specification T.157D; 45 were delivered in 1957-58. These were nearly all armed with a single Aden gun (not in a pack) under the right side, and even this was removed by the mid-1970s in the final T.7D version. The Royal Navy T.8, of which 20 were built, served in many roles, with the final T.8C often fitted with the Harley tracking light for practice interceptions and radar calibration. Nearly all had airfield arrester gear.

In 1958 an improved Hunter, the FGA.9 (fighter, ground attack), was adopted as replacement for the Venom in tropical service; it soon became by far the most important mark in the RAF. Powered by the 4605-kg (10 150-lb) Avon 207, the Mk 9 was produced by Hawker by converting the F.6, main changes being structural stiffening, adding a braking parachute above the jetpipe, extra pylons for a wide variety of loads of bombs, rocket pods or tanks, increased-capacity tires and brakes, and an improved air-to-surface weapon-aiming system. Another F.6 conversion was the FR.10, generally similar to the Mk 9 but housing one forward-facing and two oblique cameras in the nose. The last basic British mark was the Royal Navy's GA.11, a converted F.4 without guns but with airfield arrester gear and special avionics and ground-attack weapons including Tacan. Further conversions resulted in the camera-equipped PR.11.

Production of new Hunters was lifted to a total of 1972 by important export sales, of which the largest were 120 F.50s for Sweden, 112 F.56s for India, and 88 F.58s for Switzerland. The Swedish aircraft were small-bore Hunters, equivalent to the F.4, but the Indians had the Avon 203 and for a while

The Hunter airframe has proved very robust and in the mid-1960s Hawker Siddeley started rebuilding and refurbishing aircraft that had been exported or become surplus to RAF needs. This enabled customers to buy an excellent aircraft armed and equipped for their needs at about one quarter the price of a new aircraft. Hunters have seen action with the RAF in most of the postwar brush fire actions, and export customers have used them in India, Jordan, the Lebanon, Singapore and Rhodesia

received better-equipped aircraft than the RAF F.6s. Many of the exported Hunters have seen extensive combat duty, especially those of India, Jordan, the Lebanon, Singapore and Rhodesia.

By the mid-1960s, when many ex-RAF Hunters had been scrapped, it was belatedly realized that this great aircraft was still competitive, still capable of much improvement and still highly saleable. During 1965-78 Hawker Siddeley continually explored the possibility of putting new aircraft back into production, meanwhile selling well over 600 completely remanufactured Hunters and ultimately, by 1973, refining a process that could turn any mark of Hunter into any other mark—even an old small-bore F.4 into a high-power side-by-side trainer with any desired degree of systems sophistication and weaponry. Rebuilt Hunters offered virtually fatigue-free operation for at least 3000 hours for a price roughly one-quarter that of a new aircraft. The list of customers is very long, and it took Hunter mark numbers up to at least 81. Many of the customers for rebuilds had been purchasers of new Hunters, among them India (which added 48 converted ex-RAF, plus 52 refurbished) and Switzerland (adding 12 ex-RAF, plus 60 refurbished).

In addition to regular squadron aircraft there have been many special test and research Hunters. One of the most promising was an F.6 rebuilt as a single-seat night fighter, with AI.20 radar in an enlarged nose, and Firestreak AAMs. The radar was terrible, though a decent set could have been installed (such as the AI.23 of the Lightning), but the nose actually made this the fastest of all regular Hunters. It could have been a valuable aircraft but fell foul of the unsupported belief of the Air Staff that night fighters had to have two men aboard. Another Hunter had a radar-ranging and beam-riding nose for two Fireflash AAMs,

and a third became the Royal Aircraft Establishment's T.12 research hack.

Span: 10.26 m (33 ft 8 in) *Length:* (most singleseaters) 13.98 m (45 ft 10½ in), (two-seaters) 14.90 m (48 ft 10½ in) *Gross weight:* (F.1) 7348 kg (16 200 lb), (FGA.9) 10 886 kg (24 000 lb) *Maximum speed:* (typical) 1143 km/h (710 mph)

Hunting British aircraft   See **Jet Provost, Provost, Prentice**

Huot

Canadian machine-gun. In 1916 the Canadian Ross rifle was finally phased out of use. At the same time the Canadian Expeditionary Force was critically short of light machine-guns to use in the trenches. The Dominion Rifle Factory in Quebec undertook to build a light machine-gun out of the redundant rifles, and the result was the Huot, named after one of the designers.

The Ross was a straight-pull rifle, which eased the conversion: a simple gas cylinder was screwed on to the muzzle, and a piston run underneath the barrel to work the bolt; a buffer was put behind the bolt to absorb any excess energy, and the whole workings covered with a sheet-steel casing. The feed was from a drum magazine. All this helped to detract from the overall aesthetic effect, but ugly or not the Huot was far cheaper than a Lewis, and therefore attractive. It was subjected to prolonged trials and came through with very few comments (one of them being the rather obvious one that long bursts overheated the barrel) but by the time it was cleared for use the war had ended and the idea was dropped. This was a pity, for had the testing been shorter the gun might have got into service with front-line defences in the latter part of the war.

Weight: 9.07 kg (20 lb) *Calibre:* 0.303-in (7.7-mm) SAA (small-arms ammunition) *Length:* 1.19 m (47 in) *Barrel length:* 63.5 cm (25 in) *Magazine:* 25-round drum *Rate of fire:* 475 rds/min *Muzzle velocity:* 731 m/sec (2400 ft/sec)

HUP US helicopter series   See **Retriever**

Hurricane, Hawker

British multirole fighter. The first monoplane, eight-gun fighter in first-line service with any of the world's air services, the Hawker Hurricane was also the Royal Air Force's first fighter capable of exceeding 480 km/h (300 mph) in level flight with a full operational warload, and the RAF's first fighter to incorporate a retractable undercarriage. The huge contribution of Hurricanes to the aerial defence of Great Britain during the 1940 Battle of Britain alone ensures the design a place in the annals of military aviation history; while their subsequent service in virtually every theatre of war during 1939-45 made the Hurricane a legend in its own era.

Genesis of the Hurricane can be traced to August 1933, when Hawker's chief designer Sydney Camm (later knighted) completed plans for a four-gun biplane fighter to Air Ministry Specification F.7/30. Privately convinced that the age of the biplane was already past, Camm started in October that year to design a Fury Monoplane fighter. This was an unofficial project and it was not until September 1934 that plans of a larger project with PV.12 (Merlin) engine and retractable landing gear were submitted to the Air Ministry. Camm and his design team began construction of the first machine without waiting for officialdom's reaction, but in February 1935 Hawker's were given a contract to

The Hawker Hurricane was the first monoplane eight-gun fighter in first line service in the world in 1937. It was part of the team of Hurricane and Spitfire that defended Britain during the Luftwaffe attacks in 1940

Hurricane, Hawker

construct a 'high-speed monoplane' serialled K5083, to meet the requirements of AM Specification F.36/34. Based on Camm's existing plans and powered by a 1030-hp Rolls-Royce Merlin II, the prototype form first flew on November 6, 1935. K5083 was delivered to the RAF for service evaluation in February 1936, and received highly favourable reports from its test pilots. Accordingly Hawker immediately started work to bring the design up to production standards, and on June 3, 1938, received an initial production contract for 600 machines. On June 27 the Air Ministry approved the name Hurricane for the new fighter, and with mounting anxiety about the possibility of a European war, production was given high priority. The first aircraft, L1547, made its first flight on October 12, 1937.

Re-equipment of the RAF's front-line units began in December 1937, when No 111 Squadron received four Hurricanes, and by the end of February 1938 had exchanged all its Gloster Gauntlets for the new fighters. Within six weeks No 3 Squadron, based at Kenley, began replacing its Gladiator biplanes with Hurricanes, and by September 1938, the month of the Munich crisis, three more squadrons were equipped or were in the process of reequipping with Hurricanes. The year's respite offered by the Munich 'peace in our time' agreement saw a rapid increase in Hurricane production, sufficient to give the RAF a total of 18 Hurricane-equipped squadrons at the outbreak of war on September 3, 1939. Small orders were also received from Belgium, Jugoslavia, Romania, South Africa, Canada, Persia and Turkey.

Four of the British squadrons (Nos 1, 73, 85 and 87) were despatched to France in September 1939 as fighter cover for the British forces, and on October 30 a Hurricane L1842 of No 1 Squadron, piloted by Pilot Officer P W O Mould, claimed the RAF's first aerial victory in France, a Dornier bomber. Between then and early May 1940 the Hurricane units in France were seldom engaged in combat, but after the German Blitzkrieg invasion of the Low Countries commenced on May 10 every RAF pilot was in constant action against numerically superior opposition. The French campaign lasted barely five weeks, during which time Hurricanes claimed a very high proportion of the 1300 Luftwaffe aircraft lost. They suffered grievous losses themselves: 75 Hurricanes were shot down or destroyed by enemy action, and a further 120 were abandoned on French airfields as unserviceable, lacking fuel, or simply burned in situ. A similar fate befell the Hurricanes hastily despatched to Norway in May-June 1940.

From July to November 1940 the German Luftwaffe attempted to destroy RAF Fighter Command in Britain as a prelude to a projected seaborne invasion of the United Kingdom. The famous aerial struggle, now known as the Battle of Britain, is amply recorded elsewhere, but the part played by the Hurricanes in achieving ultimate victory is seldom fully appreciated.

During the battle an overall total of 1715 Hurricanes were flown in combat—more than the total of *all* other RAF aircraft involved—and these claimed almost 80% of the RAF's aerial victories during that fateful summer. At the peak of the battle in early

September, a total of 30 Hurricane squadrons and units were complemented by 18 Spitfire squadrons and ten 'other fighters' units.

The dismal saga of Allied defeats during 1940-41 in Greece, Crete, and the other Middle East zones of operations included numerous examples of Hurricanes fighting vainly against the numerically superior German forces. Despite ultimate defeat in these campaigns, Hurricanes never failed to impose heavy casualties upon their opponents. All were fought by the Hurricane Mk 1s, which were modified versions of their initial 1939 production form. By 1940, however, Hawker's design team was already studying and experimenting with ways of improving armament, endurance and performance, and this resulted in the Mark IIa version, which commenced delivery to the RAF in September 1940. Powered by a Rolls-Royce Merlin XX engine, the Mk II was faster, heavier, and armed with 12 0.303-in (7.7-mm) Browning machine-guns (after the first 120 machines had been delivered with only eight guns). Production 12-gun Hurricanes began leaving the factory in late 1940, designated Mk IIB, and these incorporated attachments for 200-litre (44-Imp gal) external fuel tanks for extended range, and underwing racks for (initially) two 113-kg (250-lb) bombs. Both marks were issued to both day- and night-fighter squadrons during 1941-42, and played a significant part in the UK air defence by night, while mounting daylight offensives across enemy-occupied Europe.

A significant progressive improvement to the Hurricane's operational potential was the introduction of the Mk IIC version, armed with four 20-mm (0.79-in) Hispano cannons in its wings, of which variant 4711 were eventually constructed. The need for more powerful guns for fighters had been appreciated by Hawker's designers as far back as 1936, but the Mk IIC first appeared

A Hawker Hurricane Mk I with constant-speed airscrew. Hurricanes took on the German bombers while the Spitfires tangled with the escorting fighters during the Battle of Britain. After the Hurricane had become too slow for interception work it became an excellent ground-attack fighter armed with two 40-mm (1.57-in) cannon. This aircraft, the IID, 'tank buster' or 'tin opener' could knock out Axis tanks using special tungsten-cored ammunition. Other versions were armed with bombs or rockets and were deployed in the Far East where they hit Japanese transport and communications. Prior to the introduction of escort carriers catapult launched Hurricanes were carried on converted merchantmen for protection against Luftwaffe attacks on Allied convoys

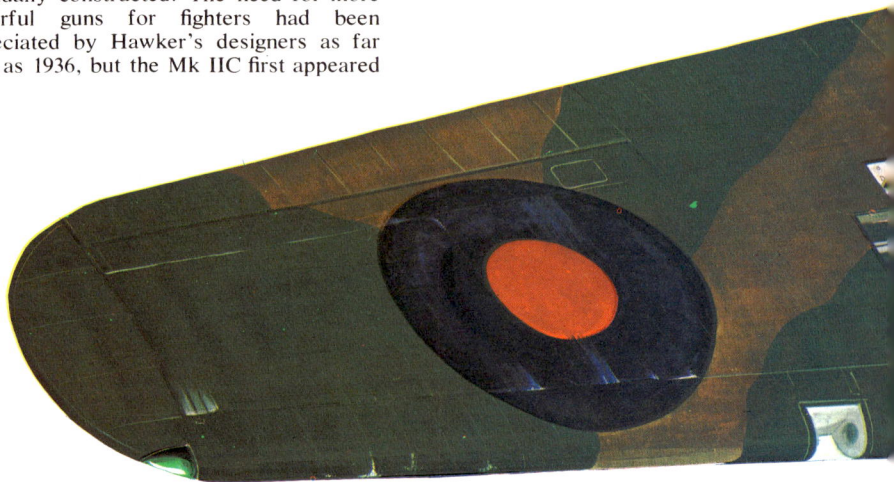

and flew (prototype V2461) on February 6, 1941. Further heavily-armed variants were the Mk IID, which carried two 40-mm (1.57-in) antitank guns in underwing pods; and Mk IIs fitted with underwing rails for 76-mm (3-in) rocket projectiles (maximum of four under each wing). The 'tank-buster' IIDs proved highly effective in the North African land campaigns, exemplified by the exploits of No 6 Squadron RAF. More powerfully engined and armoured variants, designated Mk IV and Mk V, were later produced mainly for the low-level ground-attack role, and

these amply justified their existence in the Middle and Far East campaigns of 1943-45.

The early war years saw an alarming increase in shipping losses, both RN and mercantile, and in late 1940 Hawker investigated the possibilities of adapting the Hurricane as a catapulted fighter for protection aboard merchant ships, and at the same time modified a Hurricane for deck operations aboard aircraft carriers. Achieving modest successes in 1941, the catapult Hurricanes (colloquially known as Hurricats) had only a brief operational life; but the carrier-borne

A Hurricane Mk I with wooden two-blade propeller during the Battle of Britain

Sea Hurricanes, designated Mk IB and IC, were used extensively by the Fleet Air Arm from early 1942 until mid-1944. Another little-publicized facet of the Hurricane story is the large quantity—almost 20% of all Hurricanes ever built—which was supplied to the Soviet air force from 1941. No 151 Wing RAF comprised of Nos 81 and 134 Squadrons, was formed in August 1941 and moved by sea to the Murmansk area. Here the Hurricanes divided their time between operations against the Luftwaffe and training Soviet pilots, and at the end of November 1941 the aircraft

Hurricane, Hawker

A Hawker Hurricane IIC PZ865, the last Hurricane to be built with an appropriate slogan by the cockpit. The IIC was used for ground attack armed with bombs, other Hurricanes used rockets or cannon. They were particularly effective against armour-hitting tanks on their thinly protected hull top surfaces. Earlier in the war Hurricanes had been the partner to Supermarine Spitfires during the Battle of Britain—while the Spitfires tangled with escorting Bf 109s, the Hurricanes bore down on the German bombers. Armed with eight .303-in (7.62-mm) machine-guns they carried a massive fire-power by the standards of 1940

British Aerospace

Hurricane, Hawker

The last production Hurricane, a IIC bomber, flown by chief test pilot P W S Bulman. The aircraft was later registered as G-AMAU

were handed over to the Soviets and the British pilots returned home. Subsequently over 2900 Hurricanes were supplied via Iran.

In the Far East theatre of operations the Hurricane played a leading and vital part, from the early debacles of Singapore and Sumatra, until the final victory in Burma in August 1945. When Japanese forces invaded Singapore 51 Hurricanes, mostly crated, were the only RAF fighters immediately available, and they were quickly outnumbered and destroyed. As the Allies gathered strength in 1942-43 for the reconquest of Burma, supplies of Hurricanes to the Far East steadily increased, and by June 1943 a total of 23 Hurricane squadrons (nearly 700 aircraft) were ready for the projected land offensive. These were mainly Mk IIs, though

by then a few Mk IVs had reached Ceylon. By 1944 a further 14 squadrons were operating Hurricanes, including the Indian Air Force. The Hurricane's superb stability, robust construction, and outstanding versatility proved ideal for the primitive conditions of the 'Forgotten War' zone, and provided close support and tactical reconnaissance for the jungle troops during 1943-45. By late 1944 many Hurricanes had been replaced by Thunderbolt fighters, yet on VJ Day (August 15, 1945) three RAF squadrons (Nos 17, 20 and 28), and eight Indian squadrons were still flying Hurricanes on first-line operations.

Throughout the war, in all theatres of operations, Hurricanes were prominent in virtually every second-line role open to a single-seat high-performance monoplane. By

the close of 1943 the RAF still retained over 3500 Hurricanes on charge, two-thirds of which were in store awaiting issue. They were to extend the design's reputation for versatility by being employed successfully on meteorological, photo-survey, communications, radar, gun-calibration, air-sea search and rescue, operational training, and many other unpublicized duties. Several small batches were also supplied to neutral countries including Eire and Turkey.

The last RAF squadron to operate Hurricanes was No 6, which continued to fly its Mk IVs in Palestine until late 1946. At the end of the war 50 Hurricanes were sold to Portugal, where several were still in service in 1951, and 16 machines were sent to Persia. In all, a total of 14 231 Hurricanes were built, 1451 of these in Canada. Single examples are preserved in many countries as memorials to one of the classic fighters of all time.

A Hurricane IIC 'Hurribomber' which was armed with four 20-mm (0.79-in) cannon and shackles for 113-kg (250-lb) bombs. Some 2952 Hurricane IIs were supplied to the Soviet Union to make up losses on the Eastern Front

(Mk I) *Span:* 12.19 m (40 ft) *Length:* 9.55 m (31 ft 4 in) *Gross weight:* 2990 kg (6600 lb) *Maximum speed:* 508 km/h (316 mph) at 5300 m (17 500 ft)

(Mk II) *Span:* 12.19 m (40 ft) *Length:* 9.81 m (32 ft 2¼ in) *Gross weight:* 3650 kg (8050 lb) *Maximum speed:* 546 km/h (339 mph) at 6700 m (22 000 ft)

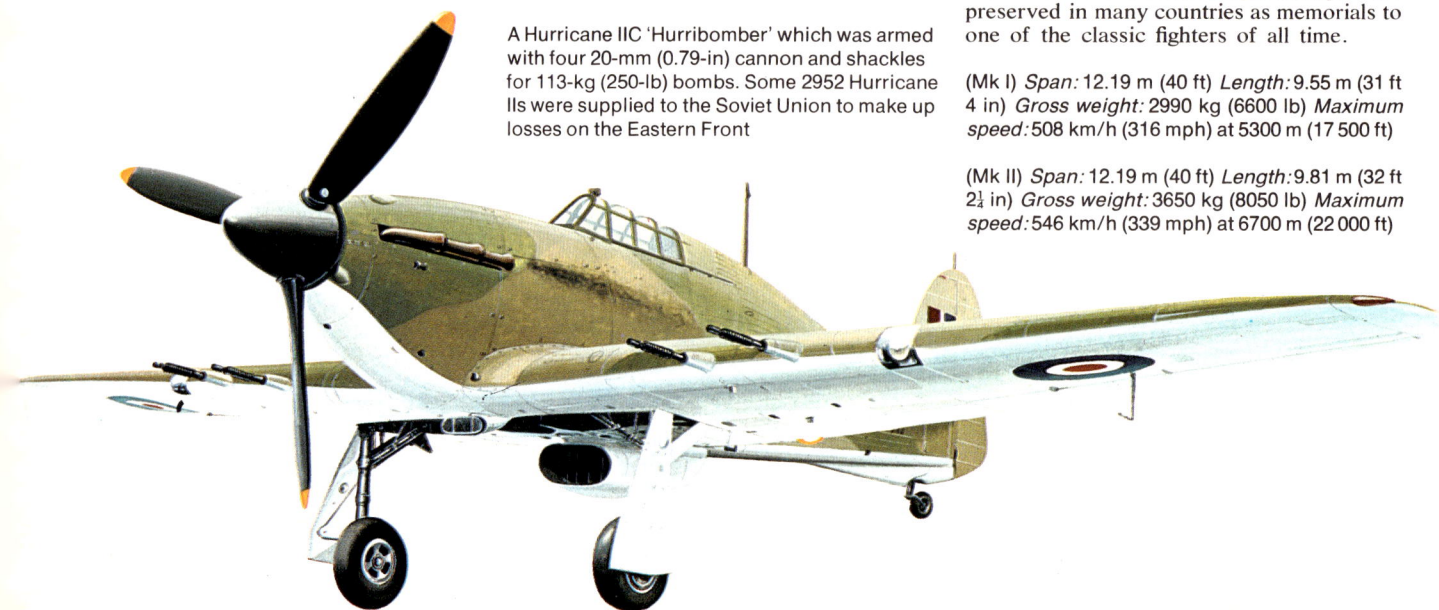

Kaman Aircraft Corp.

A Kaman H-43A Huskie helicopter hovers over a simulated air crash during a training exercise. Fire fighting equipment is slung from its cargo hook and a rescue crew of five is carried. The H-43A, popularly known as Pedro, saw action in Vietnam

Huskie, Kaman H-43

US rescue and utility helicopter. Kaman Aircraft Corporation was founded in 1945 and developed helicopters using intermeshing rotors having blades fitted with a servoflap control system. The HOK-1, powered by a 600-hp Pratt & Whitney R-1340 Wasp piston engine, served with the US Navy and Marine Corps from the early 1950s. It seated up to five passengers or could be used for photography or, with two stretchers, for rescue work.

The H-43A was developed for the USAF from the HOK-1 and the HUK-1 utility variant. It was powered by an R-1340-43 engine, and carried special equipment for firefighting at airfields and major depots. Other new features included a new four-finned tail, a redesigned interior, and four-leg landing gear with ski/wheels. Officially named Huskie, the H-43A was in service by 1960, though it was of less importance than the later variants powered by the Avco Lycoming T53 turboshaft engine. The first of these was the HH-43B, with a 720-shp T53-L-1A engine discharging through a long exhaust stack extending back from the engine over the tail. This was followed by the HH-43F, with the 825-shp T53-L-11A engine and new equipment for specialized duties.

In their normal firefighting role, where they were popularly known as Pedro, Huskies of

Husqvarna

The HH-43B, second production version of the Huskie, with the distinctive exhaust stack discharging over the tail

all variants usually carried a 454-kg (1000-lb) sphere filled with firefighting chemicals and pumping gear, slung on a cable from the belly attachment. In operation, the sphere was lowered close on to a fire, the box-like fuselage and engine inlets of the helicopter being protected from the effects of a fire only a few feet away. The crew had asbestos suits and special equipment for freeing occupants from crashed aircraft.

Between the late 1950s and 1974 the USAF had more than 200 Huskies of various versions on readiness at major operational airfields. Small batches were supplied under the Mutual Assistance Program to Burma, Colombia, Morocco, Iran, Pakistan and Thailand. At least one was used by the US Navy as a QH-43G remotely piloted drone.

(H-43B and F) *Rotor diameter:* 14.33 m (47 ft) *Length:* 7.67 m (25 ft 2 in) fuselage and tail boom *Gross weight:* 3084 kg (6800 lb) *Maximum speed:* 193 km/h (120 mph)

Husqvarna

Swedish submachine-guns and pistols. Husqvarna Våpenfabrik AB of Huskvarna, Sweden, was a commercial gunmaking firm, which for many years made sporting rifles and shotguns. In 1938 the company began making a submachine-gun, the M37-39, which was basically the Finnish Suomi built under licence. In the M37-39 version the barrel was about 114 mm (4.5 in) shorter, the trigger and guard were enlarged so as to be usable by a gloved hand, and the slope of the butt was slightly altered. This weapon was sold widely abroad; at the same time, an unchanged copy of the Suomi M31 was made in small numbers for the Swedish army, designated M37-39F.

In 1945 the Swedish army requested a submachine-gun, and Husqvarna produced their Hovea M45 in competition with the Carl Gustav M45. There being little to choose between them, it was the Carl Gustav which, not unnaturally, was chosen since it came from the government arsenal. Husqvarna then offered the Hovea to the Danish army, who accepted it for service; a licence was negotiated, and it was subsequently manufactured in Denmark at the government arsenal. The Hovea M45 closely resembles the Carl Gustav; the only obvious differences are that the air holes in the barrel jacket are smaller and there is no magazine housing. The magazine is held in place in the feedway by two sloped ramps, one in front and one behind, with ribs on the magazine engaging grooves in these ramps. Originally designed to use the Suomi box magazine, the Hovea will also accept the later model of Carl Gustav magazine.

The Convair (GD) B-58 Hustler supersonic bomber served only briefly with the USAF because of its high cost and limited capability. It was phased out of service with Strategic Air Command from 1970, only 86 having been built

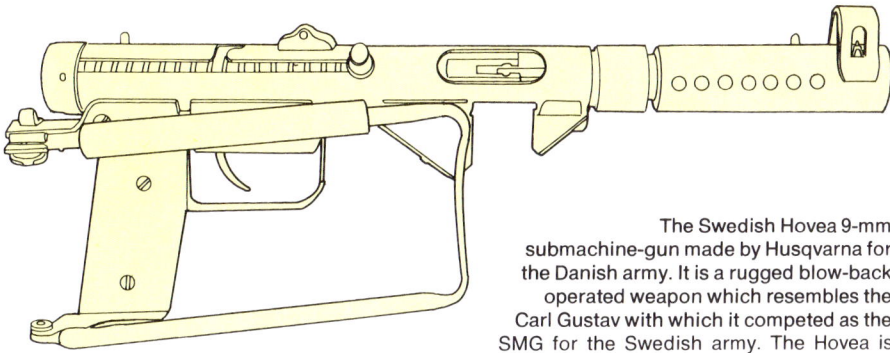

The Swedish Hovea 9-mm submachine-gun made by Husqvarna for the Danish army. It is a rugged blow-back operated weapon which resembles the Carl Gustav with which it competed as the SMG for the Swedish army. The Hovea is licence-built in Denmark

The Husqvarna factory also manufactured the 9-mm (0.35-in) Lahti automatic pistol under licence from Finland between 1942 and 1946. These were put into use by the Swedish army as their M40, remaining in use into the late 1970s.

The Husqvarna company went out of business in the late 1960s.

See also Carl Gustav.

(Hovea) *Weight:* 3.35 kg (7 lb 6 oz) *Calibre:* 9 mm (0.35 in) Parabellum *Length:* 80.8 cm (2 ft 8 in) *Barrel length:* 21.5 cm (8.5 in) *Magazine:* 36-round box *Rate of fire:* 600 rds/min *Muzzle velocity:* 365 m/sec (1200 ft/sec)

(Lahti) *Weight:* 1.12 kg (2 lb 8 oz) *Calibre:* 9 mm (0.35 in) Parabellum *Length:* 27.2 cm (10.7 in) *Barrel length:* 14 cm (5.5 in) *Magazine:* 8-round detachable box *Muzzle velocity:* 387 m/sec (1270 ft/sec) approx

Hustler, Convair (GD) B-58

US supersonic bomber and crew trainer. Though it served in the US Air Force for only a limited period, and because of extremely high cost and limited strategic capability may not have been entirely cost-effective, the B-58 Hustler probably resulted in more new aviation technology than any other aircraft in history. Certainly at the outset the very notion of a supersonic bomber was wholly incapable of being realized at all. In March 1949 the GEBO-II (Generalized Bomber II) study for a supersonic delivery system seemed pure science fiction.

Convair's Fort Worth division became one of the industrial contenders for the FZP-110 (later styled MX-1626) project that was launched in 1951. After years of research on parasiting (carrying small, faster aircraft over strategic distances beneath large but slow bombers, such as the B-36) the Fort Worth project team decided the supersonic aircraft had to fly by itself. Without parasiting there was no way to meet the range required by the USAF, so it was decided to cheat a little by putting the payload outside, allowing the aircraft to be significantly smaller than if it itself housed the payload. The nuclear weapon, and a great deal of fuel, were put inside an extremely large pod slung under a very slim fuselage which housed just the radar-bombing system and crew of three in tandem: pilot, navigator-bombardier and defence-systems operator (DSO). A further big step forward in 1951 was General Electric's go-ahead on the X-24A, an extremely advanced afterburning supersonic turbojet with a variable-stator compressor of radical conception. By 1954 the complete engine was on test as the J79, and in the 1970s GE claimed it had 'more time at Mach 2 'than all other engines combined'. This was mainly due to the Mach-2 cruise performance of the Hustler.

In every way the B-58, as the aircraft was designated in 1952, broke new ground. The aerodynamics were based on Convair's Lippisch-inspired delta used for the F-102, but with totally new control systems of immense power, advanced conical camber, and a new structure made of light but stiff honeycomb sandwich of light alloy, glass-fibre and stainless steel. The four separate engine nacelles were the first to have axially powered double-shock centrebodies, large secondary airflows and complex primary/secondary variable nozzles. Navigation was handled by what was probably the most advanced avionic system then attempted, the ASQ-42V, managed by Sperry Rand. It had an inertial subsystem, large mapping and doppler radars, astro-tracker and various weapon-delivery subsystems interlinked by a pre-digital, pre-solid-state computer. Further avionics handled Elint (electronic intelligence) and ECM (electronic countermeasures), and these multiplied in number and capability throughout the life of the aircraft.

Although there were numerous deep studies into special-reconnaissance, long-range-intercepter, Tactical Air Command, and even transport versions, only the basic type of Hustler was built: the B-58A for SAC, with the stepped-cockpit TB-58A crew trainer. The prototype flew at Fort Worth on November 11, 1956, and went supersonic in December. Deliveries to SAC began on December 1, 1959, and ultimately Convair (by then General Dynamics, Fort Worth) built 86, plus 30 development aircraft most of which were rebuilt for inventory service. The main users were the 43rd Bomb Wing, at Carswell and later at Little Rock AFB, and

Huszar

the 305th at Bunker Hill, later renamed Grissom, AFB. In the course of its meteoric career this incredible tight-packed machine set numerous world records, including almost all the closed-circuit-with-payload records. One pilot won the Blériot Trophy, offered in 1930 to whoever first averaged 2000 km/h (1243 mph) for 30 minutes—an unbelievable achievement at that time. Several transatlantic flights were made at averages higher than 1600 km/h (1000 mph); US round trips were flown at over 1930 km/h (1200 mph); Tokyo-London was flown at average TAS (true airspeed) well over 1600 km/h (1000 mph); and one crew took a 5000-kg (11 020-lb) payload to over 26 000 m (the precise figure was 85 360.84 ft).

Though the basic mission remained a high-altitude one, with Mach numbers up to 2.09, the Hustler was exceptionally good at low-level penetrations at a steady Mach 0.93. In a hair-raising and action-packed development flight one B-58 flew over 2250 km (1400 miles) from Fort Worth to Edwards at full throttle at 150 m (500 ft) or less above the ground, remaining under the radar while crossing four large states. Payloads included several bomb, bomb/fuel, photo/ECM/fuel, and other pods, as well as two-component pods (TCP) dropped at different times, and an MWC (multi-weapons capability) retrofit that added four underwing pylons for any of five types of small nuclear weapon or other payload. In the tail was a 20-mm (0.79-in) T-171 Gatling, remotely sighted by radar monitored by the DSO. There were many schemes for Hustler-launched missiles, including ballistic and cruise types.

Despite its outstanding range the B-58 was unable to fly the longest SAC missions and this, combined with its very high costs, gradually made it appear less cost-effective than the projected B-1. Though SAC commander Tom Power called it 'one of the finest weapon systems in the world today', and wanted it restored to production, in 1969 the Department of Defense announced phase-out of service with effect from January 1970.

Span: 17.32 m (56 ft 10 in) *Length:* 29.49 m (96 ft 9 in) *Gross weight:* (after air refuelling) 80 340 kg (177 120 lb) *Maximum speed:* 2205 km/h (1370 mph) *Range:* 8290 km (5150 miles) on internal fuel without air refuelling

Huszar

Austro-Hungarian destroyer class. A 400-ton destroyer, similar to the British 30-knotter type, was laid down by Yarrow on the Clyde in September 1904. This vessel, *Huszar,* ran her trials in September 1905, and in the same month the first of five sisters was laid down at Stabilimento Tecnico, Trieste: *Ulan, Streiter, Wildfang, Scharfschütze* and *Uskoke.* The first of these was ready a year later, and in 1907-08 a further six were laid down at the Ganz & Danubius yard, Fiume: *Turul, Pandur, Csikos, Reka, Dinara* and *Velebit.* The earlier vessels were built with short funnels, but to improve draught to the furnaces they were later given taller funnels. They were distinguished by funnel-bands, and until the early months of the war were painted dark grey, reverting thereafter to a lighter colour scheme.

On December 3, 1908, *Huszar* ran aground off Trastein in stormy weather. The hull was beyond repair but during 1909-10 her machinery and armament were recovered and a new hull was built at Pola arsenal. The ships were organized in four flotillas of three each, the 3rd, 4th, 5th and 6th Torpedobootgruppen. On June 4, 1917, *Wildfang* was mined and sunk west of Peneda in the Northern Adriatic. On April 16, 1918, *Streiter* sank off Fiume after a collision with the SS *Petka,* one of the ships in a convoy she was escorting. *Ulan* was ceded to Greece under the peace treaty and became the *Smyrni,* being discarded in 1932. The remaining nine went to Italy and France as reparation and were scrapped.

Displacement: 386 tons (normal), 400 tons (full load) *Length:* 68.3 m (224 ft 1 in) wl *Beam:* 6.25 m (20 ft 6 in) *Draught:* 1.8 m (5 ft 11 in) max *Machinery:* 2-shaft triple-expansion, 6000

ihp=28 knots *Armament:* 1 66-mm (2.6-in)/45-cal; 7 47-mm (1.85-in)/44-cal (replaced by 5 66-mm (2.6-in)/30-cal before 1914); 2 45-cm (17.7-in) torpedo tubes (2×1) *Crew:* 65

Hvalrossen

Danish torpedo boat class. Three were built at the Royal Dockyard, Copenhagen; *Hvalrossen* (Walrus), *Delfinen* (Dolphin) and *Svaerdfisken* (Swordfish). They were more like small destroyers than previous Danish torpedo boats, and struck a modern note in having their torpedo tubes in two twin deck-mountings. The short funnels were raised during the First World War to improve draught in the boilers.

The Royal Danish Navy was fully occupied in preserving the country's territorial waters from incursions by both British and German warships. On December 14, 1918, *Svaerdfisken* had her stern blown off by a mine in Danish waters, and three men were killed and eight wounded.

In 1922-23 they were given pendant numbers *E.1-3,* changed to *P.1-3* in 1929. *Delfinen* and *Svaerdfisken* were stricken in 1932; *Hvalrossen (P.1)* was still in existence in 1940, having undergone modernization, but she was scuttled in 1943 with other units.

Displacement: 187 tons (normal) *Length:* 45.19 m (148 ft 3 in) oa *Beam:* 5.18 m (17 ft) *Draught:* 2.13 m (7 ft) *Machinery:* 2-shaft 3500 ihp=26 knots *Armament:* 1 76-mm (3-in) QF; 1 8-mm (0.315-in) AA machine-gun; 4 45-cm (17.7-in) torpedo tubes (2×2) *Crew:* 33

Hvidbjørnen

Danish frigate class. In 1960 four frigates were authorized, *Hvidbjørnen* (F.348), *Vaederren* (F.349), *Ingolf* (F.350) and *Fylla* (F.351). They are diesel-driven, with a relatively light armament but have a helicopter and a comprehensive radar outfit to enable them to patrol the fishing grounds in the North Sea, Faroes and Greenland.

The Danish frigate *Beskytteren* (F.340), a modified version of the *Hvidbjørnen* Class built in the 1960s for patrol of fishing grounds

The Marlin submachine-gun, supplied to resistance workers in Crete during the war

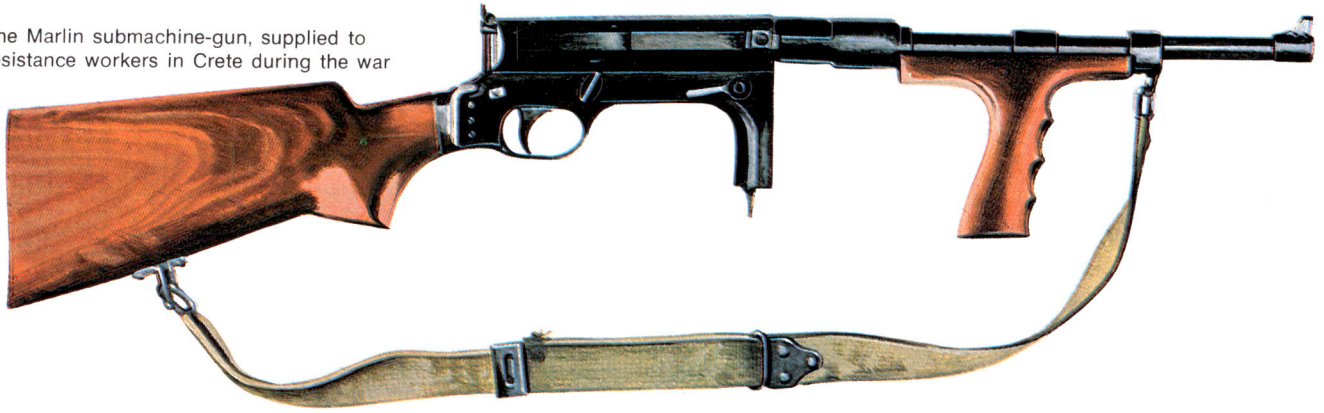

Unlike most frigates they have an extensive rescue capability with transportable pumps, fire-fighting gear and a fully-equipped sick bay. Their high freeboard and squat profile underlines the fact that they are designed to operate in some of the roughest seas in the world. They are strengthened for operating in icy conditions, and the margin of stability allows for 225 tons of ice on the upperworks.

The armament comprises a single 76-mm (3-in) of an elderly OTO-Melara design. The surveillance radar is a Plessey AWS-5 modified with a Selenia antenna, and includes helicopter control. The sonar is a Plessey PMS-26.

In 1974-75 a slightly modified version was built at Aalborg Vaerft, which had built *Fylla* and *Vaederren*. She is the *Beskytteren* (F.340), and she has a slightly larger hull, reduced crew and improved helicopter facilities.

Displacement: 1345 tons (standard), 1650 tons (full load) *Length:* 72.6 m (238 ft 2 in) oa *Beam:* 11.6 m (38 ft) *Draught:* 4.9 m (16 ft) *Machinery:* 1-shaft diesel, 6400 bhp=18 knots *Armament:* 1 76-mm (3-in); 1 Alouette III helicopter *Crew:* 75

Hyde

US submachine-guns. George J Hyde was a German-born American firearms designer. After working on weapons design in Germany during the First World War, he went to the US in 1926 and worked as a gunsmith there. In the 1930s he became interested in submachine-guns and in 1935 produced the Hyde Model 35. This appears to have been influenced by the Thompson, having a finned barrel, two pistol grips, a wooden stock and a box magazine. Though it performed well on trials, the US Army turned it down on account of some objectionable mechanical features, notably the rear-mounted cocking knob which flew back and forth with the action of the bolt and came back to within half an inch of the firer's eye at each shot.

Hyde then developed the Atmed submachine-gun for the Atmed Corporation; this was no more than a slightly modified Model 35, having a rectangular receiver instead of a tubular one. It was offered to the US Army and performed well on tests, but since it appeared to offer no advantages over the existing Thompson it was not accepted for service.

In 1942 Hyde collaborated with the Inland Division of General Motors to produce the Hyde-Inland submachine-gun. This used the basic blowback mechanism of the Model 35, but with a side-mounted cocking lever and a wooden stock and fore-end. After some small modification, it was standardized as the US Army's Submachine-gun M2 in May 1942. Arrangements were then made for the manufacture of 164450 guns by the Marlin Firearms Corporation, but due to difficulty with subcontractors they were unable to produce any weapons until early in 1943, by which time the M3 submachine-gun had been standardized. As a result, the approval of the M2 was rescinded, no more than about 400 guns having been made.

Desperate for a cheap, easily-made and reliable submachine-gun, the US Army Ordnance Department began its own development project early in 1941, and George Hyde was brought in as the design expert. At the same time the Ordnance Department called in Frederick W Sampson of the Inland Division of General Motors to advise on those aspects of design which affected mass production, and a close study was made of the British Sten gun in order to reap the benefits of British experience. The resulting weapon used a cylindrical receiver and short barrel, a sliding butt and box magazine, and was approved as the M3 submachine-gun in December 1942.

Hyde produced no more major firearms designs, and died in 1964.

(Model 35) *Weight:* 4.31 kg (9 lb 8 oz) *Calibre:* 0.45 in (11.43 mm) *Length:* 89 cm (2 ft 11 in) *Barrel length:* 28.6 cm (11.25 in) *Magazine:* 20-round box *Rate of fire:* 725 rds/min *Muzzle velocity:* 293 m/sec (960 ft/sec)

(M2, Hyde-Inland) *Weight:* 4.20 kg (9 lb 4 oz) *Calibre:* 0.45 in (11.43 mm) *Length:* 81.5 cm (2 ft 8 in) *Barrel length:* 30.7 cm (12 in) *Magazine:* 20- or 30-round box *Rate of fire:* 500 rds/min *Muzzle velocity:* 293 m/sec (960 ft/sec)

Hyderabad, Handley Page

British heavy night bomber. Produced to meet a 1922 Air Ministry specification for a twin-engined medium-range night bomber, the Handley Page Hyderabad was the last twin-engined bomber of wooden construction, apart from the de Havilland Mosquito, to serve with the RAF. A fabric-covered equal-span biplane with a four-wheel main

The Handley Page Hyderabad four-seat night bomber, an adaptation of the W.8 civil airliner powered by twin 450-hp Lion engines

undercarriage mounted in two two-wheel units, it was developed from Handley Page's W.8 civil airliner of 1919, and powered by two 450-hp Napier Lion water-cooled W-type engines driving four-blade wooden propellers.

The main changes from the earlier commercial machine involved structural strengthening of the airframe to accommodate the bombload of 500 kg (1100 lb) carried under the fuselage and lower wings. The pilot's cockpit was moved up and back, and single Lewis machine-guns were mounted in a low-set cockpit in the extreme nose, in a mid-upper fuselage cockpit and in a ventral position, sited to fire downwards and to the rear. The prototype made its first flight in October 1923, and an eventual total of 45 were ordered, though the last six were completed as the improved Hinaidi of metal construction.

The new bomber replaced 99 Squadron's Aldershots in December 1925, but its performance was no more of an improvement over that of its predecessors of 1918 than was its general appearance, and the only other regular RAF squadron to use Hyderabads, No 10, was not formed until January 1928. The Hyderabad was replaced in front-line service by its successor, the Hinaidi, in 1930, though it did manage to remain in service with two Auxiliary Air Service squadrons until 1933.

Span: 22.86 m (75 ft) *Length:* 18.03 m (59 ft 2 in) *Gross weight:* 6164 kg (13 590 lb) *Maximum speed:* 175 km/h (109 mph)

Hydra

Dutch torpedo boat class. *Hydra* and *Scylla*, the two boats of the class, were built by Yarrow & Co of Poplar, on the Thames, and were similar to their standard British 38-m (125-ft) British design. Launched in 1900, they both survived the First World War and were scrapped in the 1920s. They served as the basis for a further series of torpedo boats built in Dutch shipyards.

On trials in May 1900, *Hydra* reached 24.37 knots on a displacement of 84.5 tons,

and her sister's trials were also satisfactory. Both vessels spent their lives in the East Indies fleet.

Displacement: 77 tons (normal), 90 tons (full load) *Length:* 39.62 m (130 ft) *Beam:* 4.11 m (13 ft 6 in) *Draught:* 1.83 m (6 ft) *Machinery:* 1-shaft triple-expansion, 1200 ihp = 21 knots *Armament:* 2 37-mm (1.46-in)/40-cal (2 × 1); 3 45-cm (17.7-in) torpedo tubes (3 × 1) *Crew:* 18

Hyuga

Japanese battleship/carrier. Much of Japanese naval strategy during the Second World War was based on the fast-carrier task force concept. The vast distances over which the war was waged dictated to a large measure Japanese naval strategy. Even before the outbreak of war Japanese naval officers had realized the need for, and value of, the carrier as an integral part of the battle group, and naval doctrine and operational training had been directed to this end. Consequently the loss of four large fleet carriers at the Battle of Midway in June 1942 was a disaster of the first magnitude. Admittedly work had begun on constructing a large new class of fast fleet carriers, but they would not be ready for service for at least another two to three years. In the meantime the Japanese navy was urgently in need of carriers, or some other means of operating naval aircraft in support of the fleet far from land bases. Consequently plans were hurriedly prepared to convert a number of vessels to aircraft carriers. Among those so selected was the hull of the battleship *Shinano*, still under construction, the merchant liner *Scharnhorst* (renamed *Shinyo*), and the seaplane carriers *Chitose* and *Chiyoda*.

It was realized that even with this conversion programme these vessels would not be ready for service as carriers before the end of 1943 at the very earliest, and the Japanese decided to embark on a policy of semiconversion in an effort to provide the fleet with some sort of air support. The idea was to use the after part of some of the larger warships for a small flight deck for aircraft operations, accepting a certain loss in firepower as a

consequence. The vessels selected for conversion to these 'hybrid' carriers were the battleships *Hyuga* and *Ise* and the cruiser *Mogami*. The 'hybrid' carrier was not an entirely new concept, for the British *Furious* had set the precedent in 1917 when a flying-off deck was built over the forward part of the ship, and the Swedish cruiser *Gotland* had an aircraft operating area aft.

Work on converting *Hyuga* and her sister ship *Ise* began early in 1943 and the ships re-entered service in the autumn of that year. The conversion entailed removing the two after turrets and surmounting the whole area behind the after superstructure with a large hangar (which raised the deck by two levels) topped by a small flight deck. An elevator was situated in the centre of the flight deck around which ran two sets of rails for manoeuvring the aircraft forward to the two 25-m (82-ft) catapults, sited to port and starboard on tall supports immediately forward of the flight deck. Catapults were essential for launching the aircraft, for the aft position of the small flight deck precluded any possibility of aircraft carrying out an unassisted take-

The converted Japanese battleship/carrier *Hyuga* under attack by US Navy aircraft during the Battle of Cape Engano, October 25, 1944

US Navy

Hyuga on December 4, 1940, prior to her conversion from a battleship to battleship/carrier. In the latter role she had her two after turrets removed and replaced by a short flight deck with catapults sited to port and starboard. An elevator was situated in the centre of the flight deck

off. Similarly there was insufficient space for aircraft to land on; although it was originally intended that the ship would carry 22 Judy D44 dive-bombers, it was eventually provided with 22 Paul E16A seaplanes. These were to be catapult-launched at the rate of one every two minutes, and on completion of a mission were to land on the water alongside. To lift the seaplanes back on to the deck a large crane was sited to port on the after part of the flight deck.

During the conversion the secondary casemate 140-mm (5.5-in) guns were removed and an extra eight 127-mm (5-in) AA added. The light AA was also increased and a total of 57 25-mm (1-in) AA carried.

Following the Philippine Sea battle in June 1944 the light AA was further increased to 108 25-mm (1-in) (31×3, 15×1), while in September 1944 a total of 180 127-mm (5-in) rocket launchers mounted in racks of 30 were sited at the after end of the flight deck to port and starboard. The launchers fired phosphorous rockets which trailed long wires designed to catch in the wings and propellers of attacking aircraft.

Owing to a lack of aircraft and pilots following the disastrous battles during the summer of 1944, the two battleship/carriers sailed with the decoy force for the Battle of Leyte Gulf in October 1944 without any aircraft on board. This was their one and only action in their hybrid role. Following Leyte Gulf the two ships reverted to their battleship role and the two catapults were removed to improve the arc of fire of C and D turrets. Both ships were eventually sunk in Kure harbour in July 1945 during air raids carried out by American naval aircraft of the Third Fleet.

Displacement: 35 200 tons (*Ise* 35 350 tons) *Length:* 219.61 m (720 ft 6 in) *Beam:* 33.83 m (111 ft) *Draught:* 8.99 m (29 ft 6 in) *Machinery:* 4-shaft geared turbines, 80 825 shp=25.3 knots *Protection:* 102-305 mm (4-12 in) main belt, 32-170 mm (1.26-6.7 in) deck, 203-305 mm (8-12 in) turrets, 305 mm (12 in) barbettes, 152 mm (6 in) casemates, 152-305 mm (6-12 in) conning tower *Armament:* 8 14-in (356-mm) (4×2); 16 5-in (127-mm) AA (8×2); 57 25-mm (1-in) AA (19×3); 22 seaplanes *Crew:* 1463

Name	conversion yard	conversion commenced	conversion completed
Hyuga	Sasebo navy yard	1/7/43	30/11/43
Ise	Kure navy yard	15/3/43	8/10/43

The forward turrets of *Hyuga* awash after her sinking by US Navy bombers at Kure in 1945

I1

Japanese submarine class, built 1923-29. The design of the four submarines comprising this class was derived from the German *U 139* (a large 'U-Cruiser' allotted to France as part of post-First World War reparations) and Japan's own prize, the slightly smaller *U 125*. *I1-I4*, classified as Type J1 from *Junyo Sensuikan* (submarine cruiser), represented a new departure for the Japanese navy. They were intended for long-range penetration and the requirements called for a radius of action of 38600 km (24000 miles), to allow cruising far out into the Pacific and Indian Oceans.

Three submarines, Nos *74-76*, were initially ordered from the Kobe yard of Kawasaki under the 1923-38 Fleet Law, but before they were completed the fourth boat was ordered under the same law. As they were intended for long-range raiding operations the boats were fitted with light armour to the hull and the conning tower. During construction the whole system of Japanese submarines was changed. Originally each had been known by a simple number, but in the summer of 1924 all existing boats and those building were given a new series of numbers prefixed by 'I' for fleet boats, 'RO' for medium-sized boats and 'Ha' for coastal boats. Thus Nos *74-76* became *I1-I3* and as *I4* was laid down in 1926 she conformed to the new system from the start. To test the endurance of the class *I1*, the first to be completed, undertook a trial cruise during which she covered a distance of 25000 nautical miles and dived to a depth of 80 m (260 ft), deeper than any previous Japanese submarine. Sufficient stores were carried for a 60-day patrol.

The boats were modernized in 1939-41, and the torpedo tubes were updated to fire the new oxygen-driven Type 95 torpedo. The class was again modified in 1943 after the Japanese had been forced on to the defensive following the failure of the Midway operation and the long-drawn-out battles around the Solomon Islands, cutting off the garrisons of outlying islands. The only safe way of supplying them was by submarines converted to transports, with armament replaced by stores. *I1* and *I2* were the first boats to be altered for this role with the removal of the 140-mm (5.5-in) guns and reduction of the number of torpedoes. As transports they could carry not only supplies but also a 14-metre (46-ft) Daihatsu landing craft on deck (later an amphibious tank or midget submarine).

Though they sank seven Allied ships totalling 34521 tons, and damaged two more, none of the class survived the war. *I3* was sunk in December 1942, and *I4* two weeks later, both by American PT-boats while on supply runs in the Solomons. *I1* was rammed and driven ashore on January 29, 1943, by New Zealand corvettes *Kiwi* and *Moa*. *I2* was sunk in April 1944 by the destroyer USS *Saufley*.

Displacement: 2170/2791 tons (surfaced/submerged) *Length:* 97.5 m (320 ft) oa *Beam:* 9.2 m (30 ft 3 in) *Draught:* 5.71 m (18 ft 9 in) max *Machinery:* 2-shaft diesel/electric, 6000 bhp/2600 shp=18/8 knots (surfaced/submerged) *Armament:* 6 53-cm (21-in) torpedo tubes (4 bow, 2 stern), 20 torpedoes; 2 140-mm (5.5-in) (2×1) *Crew:* 68

I-1, Polikarpov

Soviet fighter aircraft. A product of the design team led by Nikolai Nikolaevitch Polikarpov, the I-1 (*Istrebitel*, fighter) was a single-seat, low-wing cantilever monoplane and the first Soviet-designed fighter to enter series production. The prototype, IL-400b, was powered by a 400-hp M-5 engine (based on the US Liberty powerplant) driving a twin-blade wooden propeller. The aircraft flew for the first time on August 23, 1923, stalled shortly after takeoff and crashed from a height of approximately 14 m (46 ft). Further trials showed the centre of gravity to be incorrect, but stability was eventually achieved on production models with a revised engine mounting which moved the centre of gravity further forward. Armament consisted of two 7.62-mm (0.30-in) machine-guns mounted above the engine.

Additional flight tests and service experience with production aircraft (designated I-1) still indicated a tendency to stall when coming out of tight turns, when entering or coming out of steep climbs, and pulling out of a spin. The I-1 thus appeared unsuited to its intended role, but the attempts to solve its

Japanese submarine *I1*. She was rammed and driven ashore by New Zealand corvettes in 1943

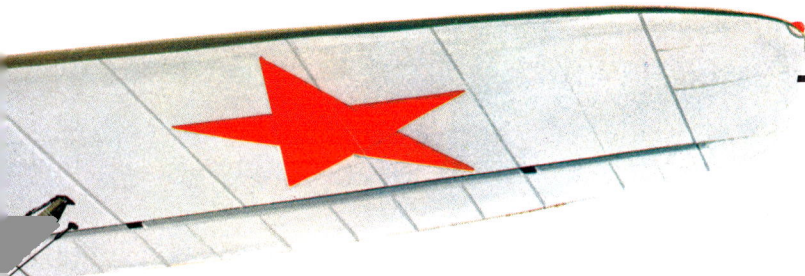

The Tupolev I-4, an all-metal single-seat sesquiplane fighter designed in 1926-27 by a team headed by A N Tupolev. It was powered by a Gnome-Rhône 420-hp M-22 radial, a licence-built version of the Bristol Jupiter. A tough and reliable aircraft, the I-4 was used by the Soviet air force between 1928 and 1934

type struts. The wheeled undercarriage was made of metal and incorporated rubber shock absorbers. The standard armament consisted of two synchronized 7.62-mm (0.30-in) PV-1 machine-guns mounted in the engine cowling. The powerplant was a 600/650-hp M-17 V-type engine (a licensed version of the German BMW VI) and drove a two-bladed propeller. This gave a maximum speed of 278 km/h (173 mph), but the weight hampered the I-3's manoeuvrability. The type was maintained in production until 1934, and approximately 400 were built for use by Soviet air force fighter squadrons.

The I-3 prototype was modified in the spring of 1929 as a two-seat fighter variant. It had an increased wing span, and a lengthened fuselage to house a rear cockpit which was to be equipped with twin machine-guns. Designated DI-2, this version did not enter series production.

Span: 11 m (36 ft 1 in) *Length:* 8.01 m (26 ft 3 in) *Gross weight:* 1846 kg (4070 lb) *Maximum speed:* 278 km/h (173 mph)

I-4, Tupolev

Soviet fighter aircraft. In spring 1926 the design bureau headed by A N Tupolev was given a brief for the design of an all-metal, single-seat sesquiplane fighter, to be powered by a Gnome-Rhône 420-hp M-22 radial engine—a licence-built version of the Bristol Jupiter. Pavel Osipavich Sukhoi led the design team, and the prototype of the ANT-5 (the bureau designation of the I-4) was completed by mid-1927. The wings and tailplane were of characteristically angular design, and during the early stages of development the lower wings were cut back to little more than stubs which were braced to the upper wing panels by Y-shaped struts. In test flights during the summer of 1927 the aircraft was declared to be highly manoeuvrable and to have good handling characteristics. It was therefore put into production for the Soviet air force as the I-4, and deliveries began in 1928. Standard armament comprised two forward-firing synchronized 7.62-mm (0.30-in) PV-1 machine-guns mounted in front of the pilot. The I-4 was found to be tough and reliable in service, remaining in use for six years. During that time a total of 370 aircraft were produced.

I-4s were often used for experimental purposes. In 1931, two I-4s were mounted on the upper wing surfaces of a TB-1 twin-engined bomber and then air-launched. Some were also used during the same period as testbeds for the new 76-mm (3-in) recoilless cannon. The first Soviet aircraft to be equipped with leading-edge wing slats was also a modified I-4.

Span: 11.40 m (37 ft 5 in) *Length:* 7.28 m (23 ft 11 in) *Gross weight:* 1430 kg (3153 lb) *Maximum speed:* 231 km/h (144 mph)

problems furthered to some extent the development of the low-wing monoplane as a fighter type. Only 33 I-1s were built.

Span: 10.80 m (35 ft 5 in) *Length:* 7.31 m (24 ft) *Gross weight:* 1530 kg (3375 lb) *Maximum speed:* 230 km/h (143 mph)

I-2, Grigorovich

Soviet fighter aircraft. Design work began on this single-seat fighter under the direction of Dimitri Pavlovich Grigorovich in the summer of 1924. The prototype flew for the first time in September the same year, powered by a 400-hp M-5 water-cooled engine, driving a two-blade propeller. The I-2 was a biplane with heavy I-type interplane struts and bracing wires, and a simple plywood semimonocoque fuselage. Certain deficiencies became obvious during trials: the cockpit was too small, with a limited field of view for the pilot; the machine-guns were badly positioned; and difficulties were encountered when pulling out of a spin.

A new version was produced, designated the I-2*bis*, with improved aerodynamic characteristics. The tail surfaces were modified to a more angular shape, giving better handling qualities, and a larger cockpit was fitted to give a better view from the pilot's

seat. The I-2*bis* was equipped with two fixed forward-firing synchronized 7.62-mm (0.30-in) machine-guns in the engine cowling. The I-2 and I-2*bis* were the first home-designed fighters to be built in any quantity by Soviet factories. The undercarriages of both versions could be fitted with either skis or wheels. A total of 211 aircraft was produced between 1926-29.

(I-2*bis*) *Span:* 10.8 m (35 ft 5 in) *Length:* 7.3 m (24 ft) *Gross weight:* 1575 kg (3475 lb) *Maximum speed:* 235 km/h (146 mph)

I-3, Polikarpov

Soviet fighter aircraft. In May 1927 the prototype of the I-3 single-seat biplane fighter, designed by a team headed by Nikolai Polikarpov, flew for the first time. The new type incorporated features from a previous Polikarpov design, the 2I-N1 powered by a 450-hp Napier Lion engine which was the first Soviet two-seat fighter—first flown in 1926, the 2I-N1 was never developed beyond the prototype stage.

The I-3 was mostly constructed of wood. It had an oval-section semimonocoque fuselage, and the equal-span forward-staggered wings were fabric-covered on a wooded framework. Bracing comprised wires and N-

I5

Japanese submarine, built 1929-32. *I5* was ordered under the 1927-31 naval programme, and built at the Kawasaki yard, Kobe. She was classified as a Type J1M, and represented a modified version of *I1*. To increase her scouting capability she was

The *I2*, converted for cargo carrying when Japan began to suffer losses in her surface fleet

Antony J Watts

equipped to carry a floatplane, and was the first Japanese submarine to have this facility (though the British *M2* had been fitted with a floatplane hangar and catapult in 1925).

The *I5*'s aircraft had to be dismantled for stowage in a pair of retractable tubular hangars located aft of the conning tower to port and starboard. Reassembly was carried out on deck, and the floatplane was lowered into the water by crane. It was found that the operation took too long (by contrast, *M2*'s aircraft was stowed complete), making the Japanese boat very vulnerable to attack while surfaced. However, trials and experiments conducted with *I5* did provide valuable information which helped in the design of subsequent classes of Japanese aircraft-carrying submarines. In 1940, the seaplane and hangars were removed and, with the installation of a 140-mm (5.5-in) gun, *I5* became an attack submarine. On July 19, 1944, she was sunk east of Guam by the US destroyer escort *Wyman*. During her wartime career, the submarine inflicted no damage on Allied shipping, which perhaps indicates that the policy of using submarines with the fleet to attack enemy warships was a failure.

Displacement: 2243/2921 tons (surfaced/submerged) *Length:* 97.5 m (320 ft) oa *Beam:* 9.2 m (30 ft 3 in) *Draught:* 5 m (16 ft 6 in) *Machinery:* 2-shaft diesels/2 electric motors, 6000 shp/2600 hp=18/8 knots (surfaced/submerged) *Armament:* 6 53-cm (21-in) torpedo tubes, 20 torpedoes: 1 140-mm (5.5-in) (from 1940, 2 140-mm); 1 seaplane (abandoned 1940) *Crew:* 68

I6

Japanese submarine built 1932-35. *I6* (Type J2) was ordered under the 1931 First Replenishment Law and was a further development of the *I1* Class, like *I5*, equipped with aircraft-carrying facilities. Dimensions were slightly increased over those of the *I1* Class and more powerful diesels were fitted to increase the surfaced speed by 2 knots. Higher fuel consumption, however, led to a reduction in the radius of action from 24 000 nautical miles to 20 000 nautical miles. Armament was also modified, only a single 5-in (127-mm) gun being mounted in front of the conning tower. The floatplane carried was similar to the type carried by *I4*. The gun planned for mounting aft of the conning tower was omitted since it was believed that its siting would interfere with the assembly of the floatplane. One improvement to the design, however, was the fitting of a catapult on the after deck casing.

I6 was laid down on October 14, 1932, launched on March 31, 1934, and completed on May 15, 1935. She is credited with sinking two Allied merchant ships totalling 11 321 tons and damaging an aircraft carrier during the Second World War. She is believed to have been sunk near Saipan in the Mariana Islands near the end of June 1944.

Displacement: 2243/3061 tons (surfaced/submerged) *Length:* 98.45 m (323 ft) oa *Beam:* 9.07 m (29 ft 9 in) *Draught:* 5.33 m (17 ft 6 in) *Machinery:* 2-shaft diesels/2 electric motors, 8000 shp/2600 hp=20/7.5 knots (surfaced/submerged) *Armament:* 6 53-cm (21-in) torpedo tubes, 17 torpedoes; 1 127-mm (5-in); 1 13-mm (0.51-in); 1 seaplane (later removed) *Crew:* 68

The Japanese submarine *I5* during her trials on July 31, 1932. She was sunk in July 1944

I7

Japanese submarine class, built 1934-38. The 1934 Second Replenishment Law was instrumental in increasing the number of long-range ocean-going submarines available to the Japanese navy. Classified Type J3, *I7* and *I8* were the final development of the Type J which originated with *I1* and, like their forerunners, were designed for long-range penetration missions with a scouting role as their main function. The two boats were also fitted out for use as squadron leaders to long-range submarine flotillas. They were larger than the Type J2, displacing an extra 330 tons and 10.7 m (35 ft 1 in) longer. There was provision for a floatplane, and the hangar facilities were similar to those in *I5*. However, the aircraft-handling crane of the earlier craft was replaced by a catapult mounted aft of the conning tower. The power of both diesel and electric motors was raised, giving a surfaced speed of 23 knots and a submerged speed of 8 knots. The hull was strengthened, increasing the maximum safe diving depth to 100 m (328 ft).

During 1943 a twin 25-mm (1-in) AA mount replaced the single 13-mm (0.51-in) in the conning tower. Late in 1944 *I8*'s aircraft facilities and 140-mm (5.5-in) gun were removed and she was equipped to carry four Kaiten suicide submarines, two stowed forward and two aft of the conning tower. *I7* ran aground and was scuttled following an action with the US destroyer *Monaghan* on June 22, 1943. On March 31, 1945, *I8* was sunk by the US destroyers *Morrison* and *Stockton* while engaged on a Kaiten operation off Okinawa.

Displacement: 2525/3583 tons (surfaced/submerged) *Length:* 109.27 m (358 ft 6 in) oa *Beam:* 9.07 m (29 ft 9 in) *Draught:* 5.26 m (17 ft 3 in) *Machinery:* 2-shaft diesels/2 electric motors, 11 200 shp/2800 hp=23/8 knots (surfaced/submerged) *Armament:* 6 53-cm (21-in) torpedo tubes, 20 torpedoes; 1 140-mm (5.5-in); 5 13-mm (0.51-in) (2×2, 1×1); 1 seaplane *Crew:* 80

No	laid down	launched	completed
I7	9/34	7/35	3/37
I8	10/34	7/35	10/38

The submarine *I8*, showing her seaplane on its catapult mounting aft of the conning tower

I8 on April 12, 1939. She was sunk by the US destroyers *Morrison* and *Stockton* in March 1945

I9

Japanese submarine class, built 1938-42. Trials and operational experience with the earlier Type J designs had shown the Japanese that it was not wholly satisfactory to combine scouting, raiding and squadron-leader roles in one design. This led to the development of three different types known as 'A' (squadron leader), 'B' (scouting) and 'C' (attack). The first of the new long-range designs was the 'A', derived from the concepts underlying the *I7* (Type J3) Class.

The *I9* Class (Type A1) were intended as headquarters ships capable of coordinating the attacks of a group of submarines. Unlike the Wolfpack tactical system employed by German U-Boats, each group of Japanese submarines was assigned an area of operations under command from a headquarters boat, within which each boat acted independently except when concentrated for an attack on an enemy fleet. Japanese thinking, in contrast with that of other navies, regarded the submarine as an integral part of the battle fleet. Its primary role was to scout for the fleet to which it was attached and attack units of the enemy fleet. The possibilities of using submarines for mercantile warfare were almost totally ignored. This led to concentration on the construction of large, heavily armed submarines.

For their headquarters role the *I9* Class was fitted with a wide range of sophisticated telecommunications equipment, and its complement included headquarters staff. Endurance was increased from the standard 60 to 90 days and the radius of action raised to 2000 nautical miles surfaced and by 30 nautical miles submerged. The machinery was more powerful, but with increased displacement speeds remained about the same as in the Type J submarines. The *I9*s carried a floatplane, and the hangar (which was partially faired into the hull) and the catapult were sited forward of the conning tower. The single gun was placed aft of the conning tower where its operation would not interfere with the aircraft.

Displacement: 2919/4149 tons (surfaced/submerged) *Length:* 113.61 m (372 ft 9 in) oa *Beam:* 9.55 m (31 ft 4 in) *Draught:* 5.33 m (17 ft 6 in) *Machinery:* 2-shaft diesels/electric motors, 12400 shp/2400 hp=23.5/8 knots (surfaced/submerged) *Armament:* 6 53-cm (21-in) torpedo tubes, 18 torpedoes; 1 140-mm (5.5-in); 4 25-mm (1-in) (2×2); 1 seaplane *Crew:* 100

No	fate
I9	lost 6/43
I10	lost 7/44
I11	lost 1/44
700-710	cancelled 1942

I12

Japanese submarine, built 1942-44. *I12* was ordered under the 1941 Additional Programme and was the only headquarters submarine of Type A2 to be built. At the time of her construction a high-priority programme for diesel-engined escort ships was just about to be implemented, and consequently *I12* was equipped with rather inferior diesels giving her a surface speed of only 17.5 knots, compared with the 23.5 knots of the earlier Type A, B and C boats. This precluded her from operating with major units of the fleet as the Japanese high command had intended. Bunkerage, on the other hand, was increased and her radius of action was 22000 nautical miles, 6000 nautical miles more than that of the Type A1. The basic design of *I12* was the same as that of the *I9* Class, and like them she was fitted with a floatplane hangar and catapult.

She was laid down on November 5, 1942, launched on August 3, 1943, and completed on April 25, 1944. A second vessel was originally laid down to this design, but the plans were recast while she was still under construction and she was completed as *I13* (Type AM). *I12* is credited with the sinking of an Allied merchant ship of 7176 tons, and was herself lost some time after January 1945.

Displacement: 2934/4172 tons (surfaced/submerged) *Length:* 113.5 m (372 ft 4 in) oa *Beam:* 9.55 m (31 ft 4 in) *Draught:* 5.33 m (17 ft 6 in) *Machinery:* 2-shaft diesels/2 electric motors, 4700 shp/1200 hp=17.5/6.25 knots (surfaced/submerged) *Armament:* 6 53-cm (21-in) torpedo tubes, 18 torpedoes; 1 5.5-in (140-mm); 4 25-mm (1-in) (2×2); 1 floatplane (later removed) *Crew:* 100

I13

Japanese submarine class, built 1943-45. *I13* was originally laid down as a second unit of the *I12* Class, but during construction the design was altered to enable an extra floatplane to be carried. The new plans, designated Type AM, called for the fitting of bulges to increase freeboard and improve stability. The hangar arrangement and conning tower and their siting were also changed, the large circular hangar with its massive watertight door being resited slightly to starboard, and the conning tower to port and extending up and over the hangar.

Orders for a further six units of this design were placed at the Kobe yard of Kawasaki, but the advanced Allied antisubmarine capabilities and ease with which US forces were sinking large Japanese submarines led to an admiralty decision to cancel these orders. Three, however, were reinstated at the express wish of Admiral Yamamoto. They were to be employed as advance scouts and pickets for the main fleet, replacing the heavy cruisers in this role.

A further aid to improving the capabilities of these submarines and extending their submerged radius was the fitting of a primitive form of snorkel in the form of two fixed curved pipes in the conning tower, details of which had been supplied by the Germans.

In spite of Admiral Yamamoto's personal order to continue construction of the submarines, work progressed at a very slow pace. Apart from *I13*, only *I14* had been completed by the end of the war, work on *I1* and *I15* ceasing in March 1945 when they were 70% and 90% complete respectively. *I13* was lost on July 16, 1945, and *I1*, *I14* and *I15* were scrapped.

Displacement: 3603/4762 tons (surfaced/submerged) *Length:* 113.61m (372 ft 9 in) oa *Beam:* 11.73 m (38 ft 6 in) *Draught:* 5.89 m (19 ft 4 in) *Machinery:* 2-shaft diesels/2 electric motors, 4400 shp/600 hp=16.75/5.5 knots (surfaced/submerged) *Armament:* 6 53-cm (21-in) torpedo tubes, 12 torpedoes; 1 140-mm (5.5-in); 7 25-mm (1-in) (2×3, 1×1); 2 floatplanes *Crew:* 108

No	laid down	launched	completed
I1	6/43	6/44	—
I13	2/43	11/43	12/44
I14	5/43	3/44	3/45
I15	4/43	4/44	—

I15

Japanese submarine class, launched 1939-42. These submarines, designated Type B, were scouting craft designed to work in conjunction with the Type A headquarters submarines. They were developed from the Type KD6 and construction was carried out parallel with that of the Type A and Type C submarine. For scouting the *I15* Class submarines carried a single floatplane stowed in sections in a small circular hangar extending forward of the conning tower. On the deck casing forward of the hangar there was a catapult reaching almost to the bows.

In order to simplify design and construction and to speed delivery of the boats, as many aspects of the design equipment as possible were made common to all three types. Machinery was thus identical to the Type A *I9* Class, though bunkerage was reduced and the radius of action was thus 2000 nautical miles less. Armament was the same as in *I9* Class, except that only 17 torpedoes were carried.

Initially only six submarines (*I15-I25*) were ordered to this design under the 1937 Programme, but under the 1939 Programme a further 14 vessels were ordered. The boats entered service between September 1940 and April 1943 having been built at Kure navy yard (*I15, I26, I30, I37*), Yokosuka navy yard (*I17, I23, I29, I31, I36*), Mitsubishi-Kobe (*I19, I25, I28, I33, I35*), Kawasaki-Kobe (*I21*), and Sasebo navy yard (*I27, I32, I34, I38, I39*).

During the war a number of units had a 140-mm (5.5-in) gun added in front of the conning tower to enable the boats to act as attack submarines. Towards the end of 1944 *I36* and *I37* were modified to carry four Kaiten suicide submarines.

Displacement: 2584/3654 tons (surfaced/submerged) *Length:* 108.66 m (356 ft 6 in) oa *Beam:* 9.30 m (30 ft 6 in) *Draught:* 5.11 m (16 ft 9 in) *Machinery:* 2-shaft diesels/2 electric motors, 12 400 shp/2000 hp=23.5/8 knots (surfaced/submerged) *Armament:* 6 21-in (53-cm) torpedo tubes, 17 torpedoes; 1 140-mm (5.5-in); 2 25-mm (1-in) (1×2); 1 floatplane *Crew:* 94

No	launched	fate
I15	3/39	war loss 2/11/42
I17	7/39	war loss 19/8/43
I19	9/39	war loss 25/11/43
I21	2/40	war loss 29/11/43
I23	11/39	marine casualty 14/2/42
I25	6/40	war loss 3/9/43
I26	4/40	marine casualty 25/10/44
I27	6/40	war loss 12/2/44
I28	12/40	war loss 17/5/42
I29	9/40	war loss 26/7/44
I30	9/40	war loss 13/10/42
I31	3/41	war loss 12/5/43
I32	12/40	war loss 24/4/44
I33	5/41	marine casualty 13/6/44
I34	9/41	war loss 13/11/43
I35	9/41	war loss 22/11/43
I36	11/41	surrendered and scuttled
I37	10/41	war loss 19/11/44
I38	4/42	war loss 12/11/44
I39	4/42	war loss 26/11/43

I 15 during service as a supply vessel, with two 'Daihatsu' tracked landing boats loaded on her deck. Ships in this class were modified during the war to take four or six Kaiten one-man suicide torpedoes for kamikaze missions against US warships

Shikho Fukui

I-15, I-152, I-153, Polikarpov

Soviet fighter aircraft, first flown 1933. In February 1933 work was begun at the TsKB (central design bureau of the Aviatrust) in Moscow on a new biplane fighter from the prolific designer N N Polikarpov. Designated TsKB-3, this aircraft followed the basic principles of the Polikarpov/Grigorovich I-5 design of 1930. It was a single-bay staggered-wing biplane, the two-spar unequal-span wooden-frame fabric-covered wings supported by I-shaped interplane struts. The welded steel-tube fuselage was also fabric covered, and cantilever mainwheel legs were introduced. It had been intended to use the 480-hp M-22 engine, but this was replaced by an improved Wright SGR-1820-F3 nine-cylinder Cyclone radial. Drag was reduced by simplifying the struts, and by the gull form of the upper wing roots which were faired into the fuselage ahead of the cockpit.

In flight tests which began in October 1933, test pilots enthused over the aircraft's performance and handling characteristics. By early 1934 it had been accepted by the government and went into series production under the designation I-15. Deliveries to service squadrons began later in the year, the aircraft being powered by the 700-hp M-25 engine, a Soviet-built version of the Cyclone. Armament comprised two or four 7.62-mm (0.30-in) Nadashkevich PV-1 machine-guns—evolved from the . Maxim gun—mounted in the forward fuselage and synchronized to fire through the propeller arc. Production I-15s were also equipped with an armoured-steel seat, and a 260-litre (57-Imp gal) fuel tank was installed immediately in front of the cockpit. Early models had a two-blade fixed-pitch wooden propeller but this was later replaced by the variable-pitch AV-1 two-blade metal variety. Bomb racks were fitted beneath the lower wings to carry two 5-kg (11-lb) and two 12-kg (26-lb) bombs.

The I-15s saw most of their combat service in Spain, beginning in October 1936, and by spring 1937 some 200 were being used by the Republican forces, by whom they were given the nickname *Chato* (snub-nosed). These aircraft acquitted themselves well, especially against the He 51s of the Legion Kondor, although they were less successful against the Fiat C.R.32*bis*. However, overall per-

The Polikarpov I-15, designed in 1933, saw its first combat with the Republican air force during the Spanish Civil War. By the time of the Second World War it was virtually obsolete

formance was good, especially during the Battle of Jarama in February 1937. By the time Soviet forces attacked Finland in November 1939 the I-15 was virtually obsolete, but some aircraft fitted with a ski undercarriage were used during this winter campaign. A small number were used in the close-support role against the Luftwaffe in the early weeks of the German invasion. Total production was approximately 733 aircraft.

Polikarpov's design team had begun further development of the basic I-15 as early as 1934. There was some structural strengthening; the wing span and area were increased; and an orthodox wing centre-section, raised parasol-fashion above the fuselage, replaced the upper gull wing in an attempt to give a better field of vision. A long-chord engine cowling was fitted and the main fuel capacity increased to 310 litres (68 Imp gal). The aircraft in this form was designated I-152 (or I-15*bis*). It was powered by an uprated 750-hp M-25V engine, and production had to be delayed for some time until these powerplants were available. Armament was improved to four Shpitalny-designed ShKAS machine-guns with a rate of fire of 1800 rds/min. Two auxiliary fuel tanks could be fitted beneath the lower wings, each holding 100 litres (22 Imp gal). External loads of two 50-kg (110-lb) or four 25-kg (55-lb) bombs could also be carried. Armour protection was again provided for the pilot. The I-152 appeared in small numbers in Spain in

late 1937, but most served to great advantage in the Mongolian-Siberian-Manchurian border areas during conflicts with the Japanese in 1938, albeit against somewhat inferior aircraft. Towards the end of that year, however, when they came into contact with Nakajima Ki-27s, the I-152s found themselves outclassed. Soviet forces attacking Finland in 1939 were still equipped with these aircraft, which were destroyed in some numbers by the Luftwaffe during the early months of the Second World War, but by the end of 1941 they had more or less disappeared from front-line service. One I-152, with two Merkulov ramjets fitted experimentally to the lower wings, flew on January 25, 1940, but did not produce any worthwhile results. Production of the I-152 amounted to about 2400 aircraft, though this figure may not include aircraft which may have been sold to China in the early production period.

After the success of the I-15 in Spain and the I-152 in the Japanese battles, the protagonists of the biplane as a fighter were still able to make their voice heard, and a further development of the I-15 was entrusted to A Y Shcherbakov of the Polikarpov team. He maintained the basic design structure of the I-152, but reduced the overall wing span and gross wing area, reverting also to the gull upper-wing formation. One of his innovations was a retractable main undercarriage: the tripod-legged wheels pivoted through 90° to rest in fuselage centre-section bays. The tail skid was also replaced by a wheel. This

The Polikarpov I-153, nicknamed *Chaika* (gull) because of its upper wing shape, was one of the few fighter biplanes to have a retractable undercarriage

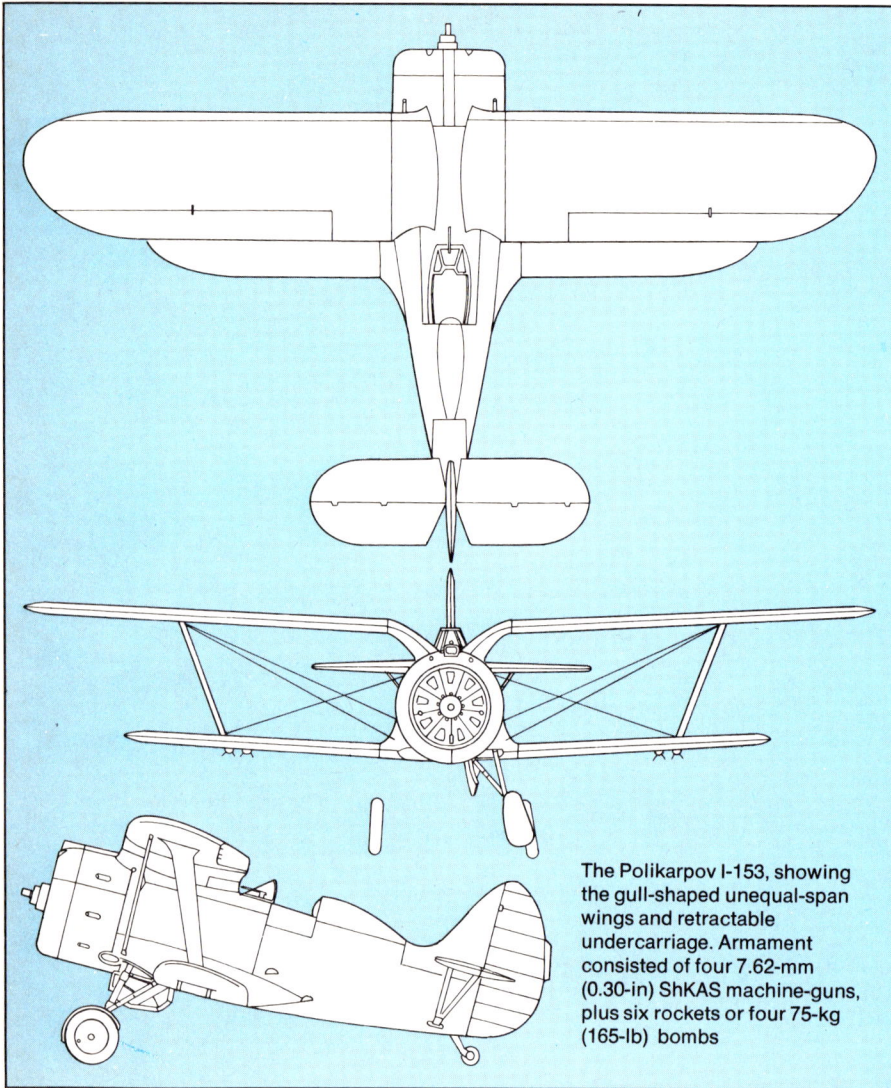

The Polikarpov I-153, showing the gull-shaped unequal-span wings and retractable undercarriage. Armament consisted of four 7.62-mm (0.30-in) ShKAS machine-guns, plus six rockets or four 75-kg (165-lb) bombs

(I-152 with M-25V engine) *Span:* 10.20 m (33 ft 6 in) *Length:* 6.28 m (20 ft 7 in) *Gross weight:* 1730 kg (3814 lb) *Maximum speed:* 346 km/h (215 mph)

(I-153 with M-63 engine) *Span:* 10 m (32 ft 10 in) *Length:* 6.18 m (20 ft 3 in) *Gross weight:* 1900 kg (4189 lb) *Maximum speed:* 443 km/h (275 mph)

I 16

Japanese submarine class, built 1938-41. This was the third type of long-range submarine (Type C) that the Japanese planned. The Type C concentrated on a comprehensive offensive weapons outfit, and the *I 16* Class was designed as an attack submarine to work in conjunction with the Type A and Type B boats. The design was developed from the Type KD6 and was similar in many ways to the *I 15* Class, with the same machinery and performance figures. A single 140-mm (5.5-in) gun was mounted, but the torpedo armament was increased with the mounting of two extra bow tubes, together with three extra torpedoes. The clear space aft of the conning tower was provided with fittings for carrying midget submarines.

aircraft was designated I-153 (or I-15*ter*) and the prototype, powered by an M-25V engine, flew for the first time in late 1938. Production models were urgently needed to cope with Ki-27s on the Mongolian border, and the first of these reached the Khalkhin Gol in July 1939. They had the more powerful 1000-hp M-62R nine-cylinder radial, a Shvetsov development of the Cyclone, and retained the same basic armament as the I-152, though the underwing racks could carry a 150-kg (330-lb) bombload or six RS-82 rocket missiles. Success against the Japanese was almost instantaneous, and further experiments on the I-153 were encouraged by the Soviet authorities. The I-153 BS appeared in 1939 with two Beresin-designed 12.7-mm (0.5-in) BS machine-guns. In the same year the I-153 V and I-153 V GK were tested, with pressurized cockpits and, in the latter, a Shvetsov M-63 engine fitted with a TK-3 turbo-compressor. (There were two high-altitude models of the I-152 also, one with a pressurized cabin and one with a TK-3 compressor.) The main production model was, however, the standard I-153, powered by the 1100-hp M-63 engine (an uprated M-62R) and christened *Chaika* (gull) by the Soviet air force. Estimated total production of the I-153 was 3437, bringing series production of the I-15 family

to about 6580 aircraft. The I-153 was used on front-line service against the Luftwaffe in the early stages of the Second World War, on the Finnish Front and later in the Far East. Many were destroyed or captured by the Germans before they were relegated to the less arduous task of tactical reconnaissance. Some I-153s in German hands were later given over to Finland after her capitulation, and served with the Finnish air arm until 1943. By early 1944 the I-153 had been phased out of service by the USSR altogether.

(I-15 with M-22 engine) *Span:* 9.75 m (32 ft) *Length:* 6.10 m (20 ft) *Gross weight:* 1370 kg (3020 lb) *Maximum speed:* 350 km/h (217 mph)

No	builder	launched	fate
I 16	Mitsubishi (Kobe)	7/38	war loss 19/5/44
I 18	Sasebo navy yard	11/38	war loss 11/2/43
I 20	Mitsubishi (Kobe)	1/39	marine casualty 10/10/43
I 22	Kawasaki (Kobe)	12/38	marine casualty 1/10/42
I 24	Sasebo navy yard	11/39	war loss 11/6/43

The Polikarpov I-16 was the first low-wing monoplane intercepter with retractable undercarriage to enter service anywhere in the world. Although it appeared in 1934, its existence was unknown outside the Soviet Union until it was used by the Republicans during the Spanish Civil War. It continued in first-line service until 1943

A pair of Polikarpov I-16 Type 24 fighters, armed with two machine-guns and two cannon

Five vessels were ordered to the new design and entered service during 1940-41. Towards the end of 1942, *I 16* was converted to a transport submarine with the midget submarine fittings on the after casing adapted to enable the submarine to carry a 14-m (46-ft) landing craft while some of the reload torpedoes were removed and the space used for cargo stowage.

Displacement: 2554/3561 tons (surfaced/submerged) *Length:* 109.27 m (358 ft 6 in) oa *Beam:* 9.14 m (30 ft) *Draught:* 5.33 m (17 ft 6 in) *Machinery:* 2-shaft diesels/2 electric motors, 12 400 shp/2000 hp=23.5/8 knots (surfaced/submerged) *Armament:* 8 53-cm (21-in) torpedo tubes, 20 torpedoes; 1 140-mm (5.5-in); 2 25-mm (1-in) *Crew:* 95

I-16, Polikarpov

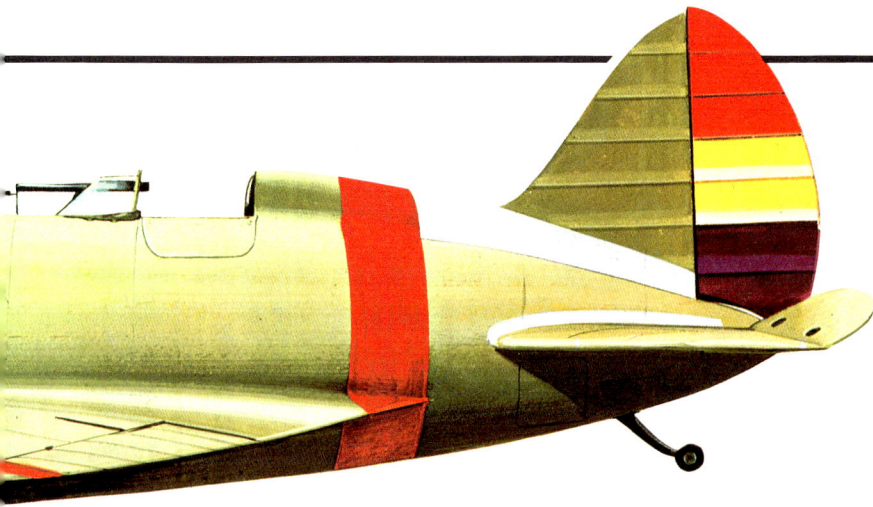

Soviet fighter. Poor communications between the Soviet Union and other countries kept this remarkable fighter virtually unknown in the West until it was used by the Republican forces in the Spanish Civil War, where it was given the nickname *Rata* (rat) by the opposing rebel forces. During the Second World War the I-16 was compared unfavourably with Western fighters. Such comparisons overlooked the fact that its contemporaries were the P-26A, Gauntlet and Fiat C.R.30, and in relation to these aircraft the I-16 was an extremely advanced design. Unlike most other countries, the Soviet Union explored every practical innovation in fighter design and armament from 1928 onward, including cantilever monoplanes, and large-bore guns (chiefly of the recoilless type). The predominance of the monoplane in the Second World War obscures the many criticisms which could have been made of it ten years previously. The monoplane tended to be heavier than the biplane, less robust and less manoeuvrable; and its higher landing speed made it unsuitable for use on small and bumpy airfields. Often the monoplane was slower in the air, and pilots were generally opposed to such innovations as retractable landing gear and cockpit hoods. Yet in 1932 despite the apparent superiority of the traditional configuration, the Soviet Union drew up a specification for a new fighter stipulating a cantilever monoplane wing mounted low on the fuselage, fully retractable landing gear and an enclosed cockpit, a design which placed them ahead of any other country.

Two design bureaux competed. Tupolev's TsAGI produced the ANT-31, with the VVS (air force) designation I-14, designed by a team led by Pavel Sukhoi; N N Polikarpov's Aviatrust TsKB (central construction bureau) produced the TsKB-12, later designated I-16. The I-14 flew first, on October 8, 1933, and the I-16 followed on the last day of that year. The I-14 seemed superior, having a 570-hp Bristol Mercury engine instead of the old 450-hp Bristol Jupiter (licence-built by Aviatrust as the M-22) and a heavy armament of two synchronized machine-guns and two 20-mm (0.79-in) cannon in the wings, instead of only two machine-guns. It was also considerably faster, at about 385 km/h (240 mph) at best height compared with under 320 km/h (200 mph) for the I-16. In any case, the parallel biplane, Polikarpov's TsKB-3 (later I-15) was almost as fast as the I-14 and more

A ski-equipped Polikarpov I-16, as used by the Soviet air force against the Finns during the Winter War of 1939-40

manoeuvrable, and production of the I-15 was authorized within weeks, while both monoplanes were continued.

An impartial observer might have considered the Polikarpov monoplane the least successful of the three rival designs. It was even stubbier and more rotund than its monoplane rival, and the longitudinal stability was poor. On the other hand its manoeuvrability was outstanding and it was almost a 1932 example of modern CCV (control-configured vehicle) philosophy, in which combat manoeuvrability is enhanced by reducing natural stability although, unlike the I-16, today's fighter makes up for this with a powerful computerized flight-control system. To the end of its days the I-16's poor stability, especially when climbing or with power off, made it tricky and potentially dangerous. Several hundred are believed to have been written off in accidents during the 1930s alone.

In early 1934 it was, surprisingly, decided to put the I-16 into production in preference to the larger, but in many ways better, I-14. Factories 1 (Moscow Khimki) and 21 (Gorki) were fully tooled up within two months, and deliveries began in August 1934. A substantial number of the aircraft took part in the 1935 May Day flypast over Red Square.

The Type 1 production version had a 480-hp M-22, driving a propeller with two fixed metal blades and Hucks starter dogs on the front of the shaft. (The Hucks was a powered starter originally used by the Allies in the First World War.) The I-16's engine looked too big for the small wooden monocoque fuselage. The pilot sat well to the rear in an enclosed cockpit. The generous wing had spars of new Kolchug aluminium alloy and steel, Dural ribs and leading edge, and fabric covering elsewhere. Outboard of the large inwards-retracting landing gear, which was raised by 44 turns of a hand crank, were two of the new fast-firing ShKAS 7.62-mm (0.30-in) machine-guns which had no equal elsewhere. Neither did the I-16, for that matter; yet nobody seems to have noticed it despite its use in large numbers in the 1935 manoeuvres held near Kiev, attended by foreign observers.

In February 1934 a new prototype flew, mounting the 700-hp M-25 (licensed Wright Cyclone) engine, with individual ejector exhaust stubs projecting through a new cowling faired into the fuselage. The aircraft reached 455 km/h (283 mph), making it the

fastest fighter in the world. But although Soviet airfields everywhere were being extended, it was not until 1935 that the faster fighter, designated I-16 Type 4, could be accepted. In an unsuccessful attempt to reduce accidents, the inner section of each of the enormous ailerons was made in the form of a split flap, lowered for landing whilst retaining lateral control movements. By 1936 every fourth I-16 was a UTI-4 (later I-16UTI) with tandem open cockpits and fixed landing gear. Later trainers had retractable landing gear, many being rebuilt early-series fighters. The Type 5 introduced armour; the Type 6 the 730-hp M-25A; and the Type 10 the 750-hp M-25V and two extra ShKAS synchronized guns above the fuselage.

In the autumn of 1936 numerous Type 6s reached Spain with Soviet personnel to fight for the Republicans, and for the next three years several hundred I-16s of several series saw constant combat, during which their advantages were negated and drawbacks magnified by the rigid Soviet system of close political control, denying any freedom to the pilots to fight in ways that made the best use of the aircraft. Though named *Mosca* (fly) by the Republicans who flew it the I-16 was known in the West as *Rata*—the name it was given by the Nationalists. Against the Bf 109B, the Type 10 had the advantage in climb, firepower and fractionally in turn radius, though the German aircraft was less tricky and rolled faster, and was capable of a similar speed. Against other opponents the I-16 had a marked advantage if properly flown. After the Civil War Spain used I-16s as fighters at least until 1944, and as advanced trainers until late 1952.

Much larger battles took place from 1937 onwards in China and along the frontier with Mongolia and Manchuria. In countless hard dogfights the I-16 earned great respect among the Japanese, who called it *Abu* (gadfly), despite the superior manoeuvrability of one of the Japanese fighters, the navy A5M. Early in 1940 the Japanese evaluated an I-16 flown by a Mongolian deserter, and found much to criticize.

The I-16 was equipped to launch six RS-82 rockets from underwing racks and further developments of experimental armament were later undertaken. These included 75-mm (2.95-in) APK cannon, a ground-attack installation with various bombloads, and a battery of four ShKAS machine-guns firing obliquely downwards below the cockpit. But

the main advance in 1938 was the I-16 Type 17, in which the wing machine-guns were replaced by 20-mm (0.79-in) ShVAK cannon. Like late-model Type 10s, this aircraft had an open cockpit, and often an improved gunsight. A much greater advance which followed in 1939, after two years of flight testing, was the Type 18, fitted with the 1000-hp M-62 engine (an all-Soviet development of the M-25). This gave better all-round performance despite considerable increases in weight due to the heavier armament and greater armour protection. Weight increase was countered by reducing fuel capacity and reverting to the wing machine-guns, though the cannon were restored in the Type 24. An alternative armament was one or two 12.7-mm (0.50-in) BS guns in the fuselage as well as, or instead of, the wing cannon. Type 24 was the final fighter model, and 4000 were built out of a total of 7100 I-16s of all types.

I-16s of all the main types fought in the war against Finland in 1939-40. They were usually fitted with skis, which were retractable and therefore did not impair performance. When the Germans invaded the Soviet Union in June 1941 the 3000 remaining I-16s were still by far the most important Soviet fighter, and despite the large numbers destroyed on the ground and in air battles they continued in large-scale front-line use into 1943. It was common, especially in the first year of fighting against the Luftwaffe, to use the I-16 to ram German aircraft when all ammunition was spent, and some were fitted with a steel-bladed propeller to inflict damage on the enemy aircraft.

There were many related types, one of them the I-16SPB dive-bomber which, like some of the Type 24s, had the M-63 engine with power generally slightly higher than the -62. The best-known exploit of the SPB came in August 1941 when a force numbering more than 20, each carrying 500 kg (1100 lb) of bombs, were ferried, slung under the wings of TB-3 heavy bombers, to a bridge over the Danube, which they then destroyed.

See also TB-3.

Span: 9 m (29 ft 6 in) *Length:* (to Type 17) 6.07 m (19 ft 11 in), (Types 18, 24 and UTI) 6.13 m (20 ft 1 in) *Gross weight:* (Type 1) 1345 kg (2965 lb), (Type 24) 1912 kg (4215 lb) *Maximum speed:* (Type 1) 360 km/h (224 mph), (Type 24) 525 km/h (326 mph)

I-17, Polikarpov

Soviet fighter/bomber aircraft. An all-metal, low-wing, single-seat monoplane with a retractable undercarriage, the prototype I-17-1 (TsKB-15) flew for the first time on September 1, 1934, powered by an imported 840-hp Hispano-Suiza 12 Y liquid-cooled V-type engine. It was armed with two 20-mm (0.79-in) cannon and two 7.62-mm (0.30-in) ShKAS machine-guns in the wings. It was rapidly followed by the second prototype, the I-17-2 (TsKB-19), using a Klimov 860-hp M-100 engine, a modified Soviet variant of the 12 Y. Armament comprised one 20-mm ShVAK cannon which fired through the propeller boss and four wing-mounted 7.62-mm ShKAS machine-guns. There was also provision for an underwing bombload of 100 kg (220 lb). A third prototype, the I-17-3 (TsKB-33) with slight structural refinements and armament reduced to three machine-guns, was flown in 1936. A year later it was modified as a parasite fighter to be launched from a TB-3 heavy bomber, but the project was abandoned.

Small numbers of the I-17-2 were built between 1937-39 and saw some service with the Soviet air force in the early stages of the Second World War. They were phased out by 1942.

(I-17-2) *Span:* 10.1 m (33 ft 1 in) *Length:* 7.4 m (24 ft 3 in) *Gross weight:* 1915 kg (4225 lb) *Maximum speed:* 490 km/h (305 mph)

I 21

Japanese submarine class, built 1924-28. The *I 21* Class (Type KRS) boats were modelled on the German minelaying submarine *U125* which Japan had acquired as reparation at the end of the First World War. They had a surface radius of action of 10 500 nautical miles at 8 knots, and a rather low submerged radius of 40 nautical miles at 4.5 knots. Sufficient supplies were carried to enable the boats to remain at sea independent of replenishment for 20 days, and the maximum submerged depth attainable was 60 m (195 ft).

The mines were carried in an after compartment and launched from horizontal submerged tubes, as in *U 125.* Four torpedo tubes were sited in the bows, and a gun was mounted forward of the conning tower.

Four vessels were ordered under the 1919 Programme from the Kobe yard of Kawasaki, but financial problems resulted in the last three boats being completed by the Kobe navy yard.

The design was not very successful and lacked longitudinal stability, and as the Japanese naval strategy did not envisage defensive minelaying tactics, these ships remained the only Japanese-designed minelaying submarines.

In 1938 they were renumbered *I 121-I 124* in order to avoid confusion with the *I 15* and *I 16* Classes then under construction.

By 1940 the class was considered obsolete, and with their wide radius of action it was decided to use them as refuelling tankers to supply the overseas seaplane bases Japan was then setting up throughout the Pacific. Late in 1940 fixings were mounted to the deck casing for the attachment of aviation-fuel tanks. Following the loss of *I 123* and *I 124*, the remaining two vessels were used for training in home waters.

I22, a member of the I21 Class, the only Japanese-designed minelaying submarines

Displacement: 1383/1768 tons (surfaced/submerged) *Length:* 85.19 m (279 ft 6 in) oa *Beam:* 7.46 m (24 ft 6 in) *Draught:* 4.42 m (14 ft 6 in) *Machinery:* 2-shaft diesels/2 electric motors 2400 shp/1100 hp=14.5/7 knots (surfaced/submerged) *Armament:* 4 53-cm (21-in) torpedo tubes, 12 torpedoes; 1 140-mm (5.5-in); 42 mines *Crew:* 70

No	launched	fate
I 21	3/26	surrendered and scrapped
I 22	11/26	war loss 6/45
I 23	3/27	war loss 8/42
I 24	12/27	war loss 1/42

I-28, Yatsenko

Soviet fighter aircraft. Few details are available of this neat radial-engined fighter, designed by V P Yatsenko in 1938 and flown in early 1939. Chronologically it followed the Lavochkin (LaGG) I-22, but preceded the Yak I-26 (Yak-1). Like both its rivals it was constructed almost entirely of wood. The fuselage (and probably the wing, which was of inverted-gull form) was skinned with plywood impregnated and bonded with phenol-formaldehyde resin. The engine was a 950-hp Shvetsov M-87A. Armament was four 7.62-mm (0.30-in) ShKAS machine-guns arranged in pairs on each side of the forward fuselage. The I-28 was much lighter than all its rivals, and the reason for its early termination is not known.

Span: about 9.5 m (31 ft) *Length:* not known *Gross weight:* 2665 kg (5875 lb) *Maximum speed:* 545 km/h (340 mph)

I 40

Japanese submarine class, built 1941-43. The six scouting submarines of the *I 40* Class ordered under the 1941 War Emergency Programme were developed from the *I 15* Class. Known as the Type B2 the design was almost identical to the *I 15.* A further eight submarines planned under the 1942 Programme were subsequently cancelled.

Certain units of the *I 40* Class, like some of the *I 15* Class, were modified for use as attack submarines, their aircraft facilities being replaced by an extra 140-mm (5.5-in)

gun. *I 44* was refitted towards the end of 1944 to carry six Kaiten suicide submarines, the hangar, 140-mm gun and catapult being removed.

Displacement: 2624/3700 tons (surface/submerged) *Length:* 108.66 m (356 ft 6 in) oa *Beam:* 9.30 m (30 ft 6 in) *Draught:* 5.18 m (17 ft) *Machinery:* 2-shaft diesels/2 electric motors, 11 000 shp/2000 hp=23.5/8 knots (surfaced/submerged) *Armament:* 6 53-cm (21-in) torpedo tubes, 17 torpedoes; 1 140-mm (5.5-in); 2 25-mm (1-in); 1 floatplane *Crew:* 94

No	builder	completed	war loss
I 40	Kure navy yard	7/43	11/43
I 41	Kure navy yard	9/43	11/44
I 42	Kure navy yard	11/43	3/44
I 43	Sasebo navy yard	11/43	2/44
I 44	Yokosuka navy yard	1/43	4/45
I 45	Sasebo navy yard	12/43	10/44

I 46

Japanese submarine class, built 1943-44. The six submarines comprising the class were ordered from the Sasebo navy yard under the 1941 War Programme. Only three were laid down, the others being cancelled in 1943, and a further four units planned under the 1942 Programme were also cancelled. Known as the Type C2 attack submarines, the design was identical to that of the *I 16* Class, except that they lacked fittings to carry midget submarines.

Towards the end of 1944, *I 47* and *I 48* were altered to carry four Kaiten submarines and *I 47* was later refitted to carry six.

I 46 was sunk by the US destroyer *Helm* on October 28, 1944, and *I 47* by the destroyers *Conklin, Corbesier* and *Raby* on January 23, 1945. *I 47* was surrendered at the end of the war and scuttled by the US Navy.

Displacement: 2557/3564 tons (surfaced/submerged) *Length:* 109.3 m (358 ft 6 in) oa *Beam:* 9.1 m (29 ft 9 in) *Draught:* 5.3 m (17 ft 6 in) *Machinery:* 2-shaft diesels/2 electric motors 12 400 shp/2000 hp=23.5/8 knots (surfaced/submerged) *Armament:* 8 53-cm (21-in) torpedo tubes, 20 torpedoes; 1 140-mm (5.5-in); 2 25-mm (1-in) (2×1) *Crew:* 95

No	launched	completed
I 46	1943	2/44
I 47	1943	7/44
I 48	1944	9/44

I 51

Japanese submarine, built 1921-24. *I 51* was the first of the large cruiser submarines to be built for the Japanese navy. She was laid down at Kure navy yard in April 1921 as *No 44*, launched on November 29, 1921, and completed on June 20, 1924. During that year she received the number *I51*. The ambitious design derived from the large British fleet submarines then in service, and formed the basis of the numerous types of Japanese cruiser submarines. These made up the major part of Japan's submarine fleet and strongly reflected Japanese strategic preoccupations.

Known as the KD1 Type, *I51* was powered by four diesels driving four shafts. The radius of action was 20 000 nautical miles at 10 knots surfaced. The machinery layout did not prove successful and two of the diesels and their shafts were removed soon after completion. The boat was heavily armed, but the 76-mm (3-in) gun mounted aft of the conning tower was also removed early on. She was removed from active service in April 1940.

Displacement: 1500/2430 tons (surfaced/submerged) *Length:* 91.4 m (300 ft) oa *Beam:* 8.8 m (29 ft) *Draught:* 4.6 m (15 ft) *Machinery:* 4-shaft diesels/2 electric motors, 5200 shp/2000 hp=20/10 knots (surfaced/submerged) *Armament:* 8 53-cm (21-in) torpedo tubes (6 bow), 24 torpedoes; 1 120-mm (4.7-in); 1 76-mm (3-in) (later deleted) *Crew:* 60

I 52

Japanese submarine, built 1922-25. *I52* was the second type of cruiser submarine to be built for the Japanese navy, her design being based on that of the German *U 139* type of the First World War. Originally laid down in February 1922 as *No 51*, she was launched in June the same year and was completed as *I52* in 1925.

Five submarines were to have been ordered to this design, but under the terms of the Washington Treaty only *I52* was built. When Japan began to accelerate submarine construction, the designs of *I51* and *I52* provided valuable experience. *I52* was again renumbered *I152* in May 1942, but was scrapped soon afterwards.

Displacement: 1500/2500 tons (surfaced/submerged) *Length:* 100.81 m (330 ft 9 in) oa *Beam:* 7.62 m (25 ft) *Draught:* 5.11 m (16 ft 9 in) *Machinery:* 2-shaft diesels/2 electric motors, 6800 shp/2000 hp=22/10 knots (surfaced/submerged) *Armament:* 8 53-cm (21-in) torpedo tubes (6 bow), 16 torpedoes; 1 120-mm (4.7-in); 1 76-mm (3-in) *Crew:* 60

I 52

Japanese submarine class, built 1942-44. Ordered under the 1941 Additional Programme this class (Type C3) was practically identical with the previous *I46* Class, except for its lower-powered diesels. They were, however, more powerfully armed with a second 140-mm (5.5-in) gun sited abaft the conning tower. Torpedo armament was also modified, only six tubes instead of eight being mounted.

Under the 1941 War Programme five submarines had been planned with another 15 under the 1942 Programme. Only three submarines, *I52*, *I53* and *I55*, were completed. The orders for the remainder were cancelled in 1943.

A further class of 25 submarines to a modified design (Type C4) was planned under the 1942 Modified Programme, but this too was cancelled in 1943. The Type C4 design displaced 2756 tons, an increase of about 190

tons, and with its more powerful diesels would have reached a speed of 20.5 knots. Armament would have been the same as in the *I46* Class.

I53 was modified early in 1945 to carry four Kaiten suicide submarines (subsequently increased to six), and her gun armament was completely removed. *I52* and *I55* were sunk in action with US forces during the summer of 1944. *I53* surrendered at the end of the war and was scuttled by American naval forces.

Displacement: 2564/3644 tons (surfaced/submerged) *Length:* 108.66 m (356 ft 6 in) oa *Beam:* 9.30 m (30 ft 6 in) *Draught:* 5.11 m (16 ft 9 in) *Machinery:* 2-shaft diesels/2 electric motors, 4700 shp/1200 hp=17.75/6.5 knots (surfaced/submerged) *Armament:* 6 53-cm (21-in) torpedo tubes, 19 torpedoes; 2 140-mm (5.5-in); 2 25-mm (1-in) *Crew:* 95

No	launched	completed
I52	1943	12/43
I53	1943	2/44
I55	1943	4/44

I 53

Japanese submarine class, built 1924-29. Known as the Type KD3A and KD3B the nine submarines of this class ordered under the 1923-28 Law combined the finest features of *I51* and *I52* in the design. The class comprised two subgroups with different dimensions. Compared to *I51* and *I52*, dis-

The Type KD2 cruiser submarine *I52*. Launched in 1925 she was the only one of five submarines planned for this class to be completed. She was laid down as *I51*, completed as *I52* and was again renumbered in May 1942 when she became *I152*

The *I53* Class, or Type KD3A, submarine *I55*, later *I155*, on trials in Hiroshima Bay in late 1927, shortly after her completion in the September of that year

placement was increased by about 250 tons. Armament was similar to that of *I52*, but the latter's 76-mm (3-in) gun was omitted in this class.

I63 was sunk in shallow water on February 2, 1939, after collision with *I60*. The wreck was refloated and scrapped the following year. *I60* was herself sunk off Krakatoa Island on January 17, 1942, by the British destroyer *Jupiter*. In May 1942 the surviving units were renumbered within the sequence *I153-I159*, by the addition of 100 to their old numbers. By this time the vessels had become obsolete and were withdrawn from front-line service and retained in home waters to train submarine crews.

I156 and *I159* were reactivated during the spring of 1945. Their 120-mm (4.7-in) guns were removed and they were adapted to carry two Kaiten suicide submarines forward of the conning tower. Apart from *I60* and *I63* the remainder of the class survived the war and were either scrapped or scuttled by the Americans.

(Type KD3A) *Displacement:* 1800/2300 tons (surfaced/submerged) *Length:* 100.6 m (330 ft) oa *Beam:* 7.9 m (26 ft) *Draught:* 4.8 m (15 ft 9 in) *Machinery:* 2-shaft diesels/2 electric motors, 6800 shp/1800 hp=20/8 knots (surfaced/submerged) *Armament:* 8 53-cm (21-in) torpedo tubes (6 bow), 16 torpedoes; 1 120-mm (4.7-in) *Crew:* 61

(Type KD3B) *Displacement:* As KD3A *Length:* 101 m (331 ft 4 in) *Beam:* as KD3A *Draught:* 4.9 m (16 ft) All other details as KD3A

I54

Japanese submarine class, built 1942-44. The *I54* Class (Type B3) was the final development of the scouting submarines to reach operational status. Like the late Types A and C, the Type B3 was almost identical to preceding types except for the lower-powered diesels and increased bunkerage. The radius of action was thus increased from the 14 000 nautical miles of the Type B2 (*I40* Class) to 21 000 nautical miles. A floatplane hangar and catapult were fitted.

Seven vessels were originally ordered and

Type KD3A

No	builder	completed
I53	Kure navy yard	3/27
I54	Sasebo navy yard	12/27
I55	Kure navy yard	9/27
I58	Yokosuka navy yard	5/28

Type KD3B

No	builder	completed
I56	Kure navy yard	3/29
I57	Kure navy yard	12/29
I59	Yokosuka navy yard	3/30
I60	Sasebo navy yard	12/29
I63	Sasebo navy yard	12/28

a further 14 were planned under the 1942 Modified Programme. Only three of these boats were built, the orders and plans for the remainder being cancelled in 1943.

An improved Type B4 Class of 18 vessels was planned under the 1942 Modified Programme. Displacement would have been increased to 2800 tons with a surfaced speed of 22.5 knots from more powerful diesel engines. It was also planned to fit a total of eight 53-cm (21-in) torpedo tubes with 16 torpedoes and, for the first time since the completion of *I22*, the boats planned would have carried eight mines. The planned Type B4 vessels were cancelled in 1943.

Towards the end of the war *I56* and *I58* had their 140-mm (5.5-in) gun, the seaplane hangar and the catapult removed and were adapted to carry four (subsequently six) Kaiten submarines aft of the conning tower. On July 29, 1945, *I58* sank the US cruiser *Indianapolis* which was carrying parts of an atomic bomb to the island of Guam. *I54* and *I56* were both sunk by US naval forces (*I54* on October 23, 1944, during the Battle of Leyte Gulf; *I58* was lost off Okinawa on April 18, 1945), while *I58* was surrendered and subsequently scuttled by the Americans.

Displacement: 2607/3688 tons (surfaced/submerged) *Length:* 108.7 m (356 ft 6 in) oa *Beam:* 9.3 m (30 ft 6 in) *Draught:* 5.2 m (17 ft) *Machinery:* 2-shaft diesels/2 electric motors, 4700 shp/1200 hp=17.75/6.5 knots (surfaced/submerged) *Armament:* 6 53-cm (21-in) torpedo tubes, 19 torpedoes; 1 140-mm (5.5-in); 2 25-mm (1-in) (1×2); 1 floatplane (deleted in some boats) *Crew:* 94

No	builder	completed
I54	Yokosuka navy yard	3/44
I56	Yokosuka navy yard	6/44
I58	Yokosuka navy yard	9/44

I61

Japanese submarine class, built 1926-30. This class of three submarines, known as Type KD4, was developed from the *I53* Class.

I53, later *I153*, the first of the Type KD3A submarines, on trials in the spring of 1927

The Type KD4 *I61* before her accidental sinking following a collision in October 1942

Ordered under the 1923-28 Law, the design was a slightly modified follow-on from the preceding Type KD3. The reduced tonnage was largely accounted for by the omission of two 53-cm (21-in) bow torpedo tubes.

I61 sank after colliding with a gunboat on October 2, 1941, and was scrapped after being refloated the following February. *I64* was torpedoed by the US submarine *Triton* on May 17, 1942. *I62* was renumbered *I162* in May 1942, and in March 1944 she was removed from active service. She returned to active service in the spring of 1945, modified to carry two Kaiten submarines (requiring the removal of her gun) and was surrendered at the end of the war.

Displacement: 1720/2300 tons (surfaced/submerged) *Length:* 97.7 m (320 ft 6 in) oa *Beam:* 7.8 m (25 ft 6 in) *Draught:* 4.8 m (15 ft 9 in) *Machinery:* 2-shaft diesels/2 electric motors, 6000 shp/1800 hp=20/8.5 knots (surfaced/submerged) *Armament:* 6 53-cm (21-in) torpedo tubes, 14 torpedoes; 1 120-mm (4.7-in) *Crew:* 61

No	builder	launched	completed
I61	Mitsubishi, Kobe	11/27	4/29
I62	Mitsubishi, Kobe	11/28	3/30
I64	Kure navy yard	10/29	8/30

I 65

Japanese submarine class, built 1931-32. This design (Type KD5) was developed from the previous *I61* (Type KD4) Class and incorporated a redesigned hull form of much greater strength than the earlier KD Type submarines. This enabled the class to extend its maximum submerged depth from the 60 m (195 ft) of the *I61*s to nearly 76 m (250 ft). A 100-mm (3.9-in) weapon was mounted instead of the 120-mm (4.7-in) on previous designs, and a light AA gun was mounted abaft the conning tower.

I67 was lost during exercises in August 1940. *I65* and *I66* were renumbered *I165* and *I166* respectively on May 20, 1942, and survived to within a few months of the end of the Second World War. *I165* was sunk on June 27, 1945, by US aircraft; *I166* was torpedoed by the British submarine *Telemachus* on July 17, 1944.

No	builder	launched	completed
I65	Kure navy yard	6/31	12/32
I66	Sasebo navy yard	6/31	11/32
I67	Mitsubishi, Kobe	4/31	8/32

I 68

Japanese submarine class, built 1931-38. The *168* Class (Type KD6A and KD6B) was ordered under the 1931 and 1934 Replenishment Laws and laid down between 1931 and 1934, entering service between 1934-38. The design was developed from the KD5 (*165* Class), but displacement and dimensions were slightly increased. The class was divided into two subgroups of slightly different displacement. Larger double-acting two-stroke diesels of a new design were mounted in the *168* Class, and increased the power to 9000 hp from the 6000 hp of the KD5s. This increased the surface speed by 2.5 knots. The strengthened hull design which had proved successful in the KD5s was used in the *168* Class.

168, *169* and *170* were completed with a 100-mm (3.9-in) gun, but the remainder of the class were fitted with a 120-mm (4.7-in) gun. The class was renumbered on May 20, 1942, *168* being designated *I168*, etc. *I171* and *I174* were refitted as transport submarines at the end of 1942, the 120-mm gun being removed and fittings provided on the foredeck casing to enable a 14-m (46-ft) landing craft to be carried.

The submarine *168* (later *I168*), lead ship of her class, the Type KD6, under way in 1943

Displacement: 1705/2330 tons (surfaced/submerged) *Length:* 97.7 m (320 ft 6 in) oa *Beam:* 8.2 m (26 ft 9 in) *Draught:* 4.7 m (15 ft 6 in) *Machinery:* 2-shaft diesels/2 electric motors, 6800 shp/1800 hp=20.5/8.25 knots (surfaced/submerged) *Armament:* 6 53-cm (21-in) torpedo tubes, 14 torpedoes; 1 100-mm (3.9-in); 1 13-mm (0.51-in) *Crew:* 61

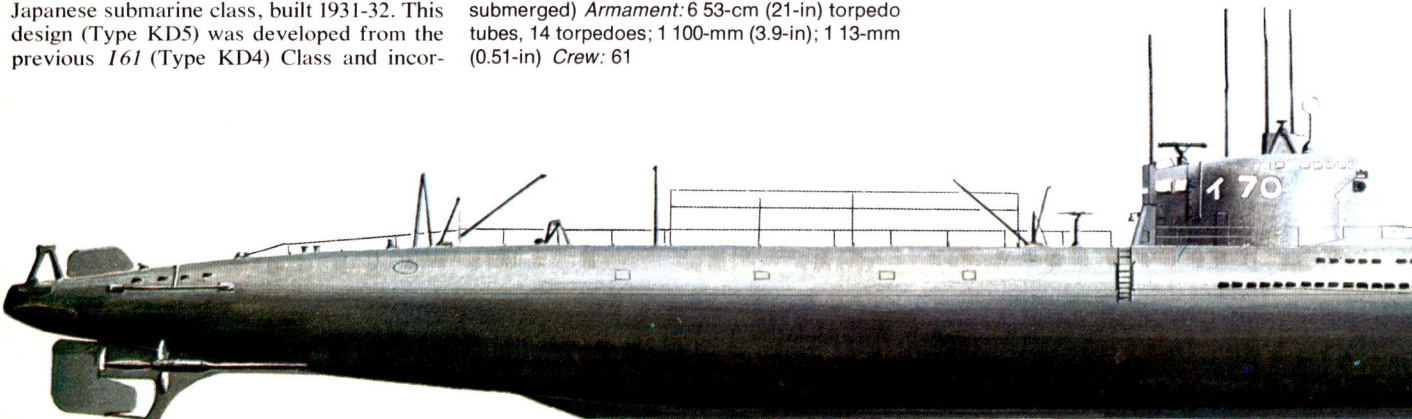

I 72 at anchor in April 1939. Renumbered *I 172* in May 1942, she was sunk by the minesweeper USS *Southard* in the following November

Type KD6A

No	builder	completed	fate
I 68	Kure navy yard	7/34	war loss 27/7/43
I 69	Mitsubishi, Kobe	9/35	war loss 4/4/44
I 70	Sasebo navy yard	11/35	war loss 10/12/41
I 71	Kawasaki, Kobe	12/35	war loss 1/2/44
I 72	Mitsubishi, Kobe	1/37	war loss 11/11/42
I 73	Kawasaki, Kobe	1/37	war loss 26/1/42

Type KD6B

No	builder	completed	fate
I 74	Kawasaki, Kobe	15/8/38	marine casualty 3/4/44
I 75	Mitsubishi, Kobe	18/12/38	war loss 1/2/44

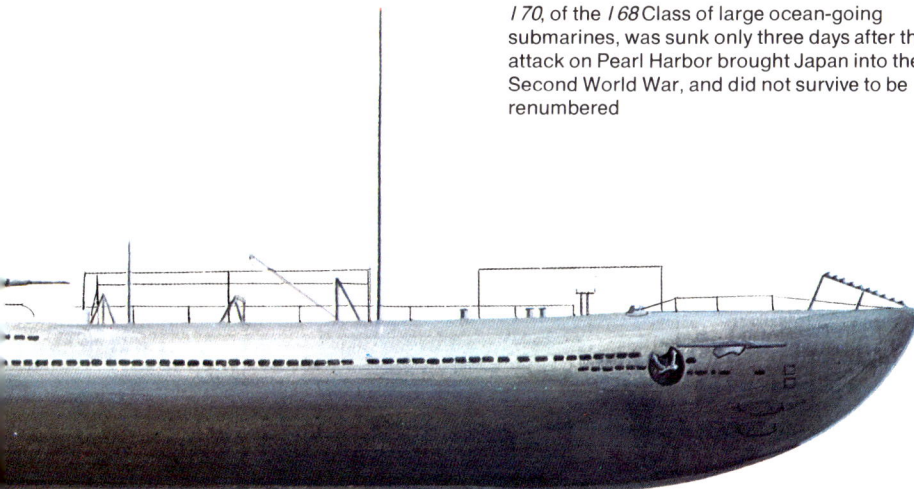

I 70, of the *I 68* Class of large ocean-going submarines, was sunk only three days after the attack on Pearl Harbor brought Japan into the Second World War, and did not survive to be renumbered

(Type KD6A) *Displacement:* 1785/2240 tons (surfaced/submerged) *Length:* 104.7 m (343 ft 6 in) oa *Beam:* 8.2 m (27 ft) *Draught:* 4.6 m (15 ft) *Machinery:* 2-shaft diesels/2 electric motors, 9000/1800 hp=23/8.25 knots (surfaced/submerged) *Armament:* 6 53-cm (21-in) torpedo tubes (4 bow), 14 torpedoes; 1 100-mm (3.9-in) (*I 68-I 70*); 1 120-mm (4.7-in) (*I 71-I 73*) *Crew:* 61

(Type KD6B) *Displacement:* 1810/2564 tons (surfaced/submerged) *Length:* 105 m (344 ft 6 in) oa *Beam:* 8.2 m (27 ft) *Draught:* 4.6 m (15 ft) *Machinery:* As KD6A *Armament:* 6 53-cm (21-in) torpedo tubes (4 bow), 14 torpedoes; 1 120-mm (4.7-in) *Crew:* 61

I 76

Japanese submarine class, built 1940-43. The *I 76* Class (Type KD7) was the final development of the KD Type submarine. Ordered under the 1939 Programme, the ten vessels were laid down in 1940-41 and entered service between 1942-43.

No	fate
I 76	war loss 5/44
I 77	war loss 10/44
I 78	war loss 5/43
I 79	marine casualty 7/43
I 80	war loss 4/44
I 81	war loss 1/44
I 82	war loss 9/43
I 83	war loss 4/44
I 84	war loss 6/44
I 85	war loss 6/44

The basic design was practically identical to the *I 68* Class, but with a slight increase in tonnage and dimensions. In the original design only two twin 25-mm (1-in) AA weapons were specified. During construction, however, it was decided that a heavy deck gun was essential and so a 120-mm (4.7-in) weapon was sited forward of the conning tower, and one of the twin 25-mm (1-in) mounts was omitted.

The class was renumbered on May 20, 1942, the original numbers all being increased by 100.

I 176, *I 177* and *I 181* were converted to transport submarines early in 1943 with the removal of the deck gun and some of the reload torpedoes, to provide space for internal cargo and fittings for a 14-m (46-ft) landing craft to be carried externally.

Displacement: 1833/2602 tons (surfaced/submerged) *Length:* 105.5 m (346 ft) oa *Beam:* 8.2 m (27 ft) *Draught:* 4.6 m (15 ft) *Machinery:* 2-shaft diesels/2 electric motors, 8000 hp/1800 hp=23/8 knots (surfaced/submerged) *Armament:* 6 53-cm (21-in) torpedo tubes, 12 torpedoes; 1 120-mm (4.7-in); 2 25-mm (1-in) AA *Crew:* 86

I-153 and I-154, Polikarpov Soviet fighter aircraft   See **I-15**

I 201

Japanese submarine class. These Type ST submarines were designed after exhaustive tests and trials with the high underwater speed experimental submarine *No 71*. The hull was fully welded and very carefully streamlined; no gun or other deck obstruction was allowed which might impair the underwater performance. Even the 25-mm (1-in) mount retracted into a streamlined housing in the conning tower. The whole design concentrated on underwater performance, and new

electric motors were installed giving the vessels an underwater speed of 19 knots. The high-capacity batteries carried sufficient energy to give the vessels an underwater radius of action of 135 nautical miles at 3 knots. The maximum submerged depth achieved by the submarines was 110 m (360 ft), the greatest depth achieved by a Japanese submarine. In many respects the vessels resembled the German Type XXI and when completed they were the first operational GUPPY type submarine in the world. Specially designed lightweight MAN diesels were used for surface propulsion, to keep displacement low. Only small bunkerage was provided, and the surfaced radius of action was only 5800 nautical miles with an endurance of 25 days.

Construction employed full mass-production techniques, with the submarines assembled in section in factories, the completed sections being welded together on the slip. The whole operation from start to finish

Outboard and inboard profiles of the Japanese *I 76* Class submarine *I 82*. Also known as the Type KD7 and developed from the Type KD6 *I 68* Class, the ten vessels of this class were ordered under the Fourth Replenishment Law of 1939 but were not completed until 1943. During construction one of the planned twin 25-mm AA mountings was replaced by a 4.7-in gun

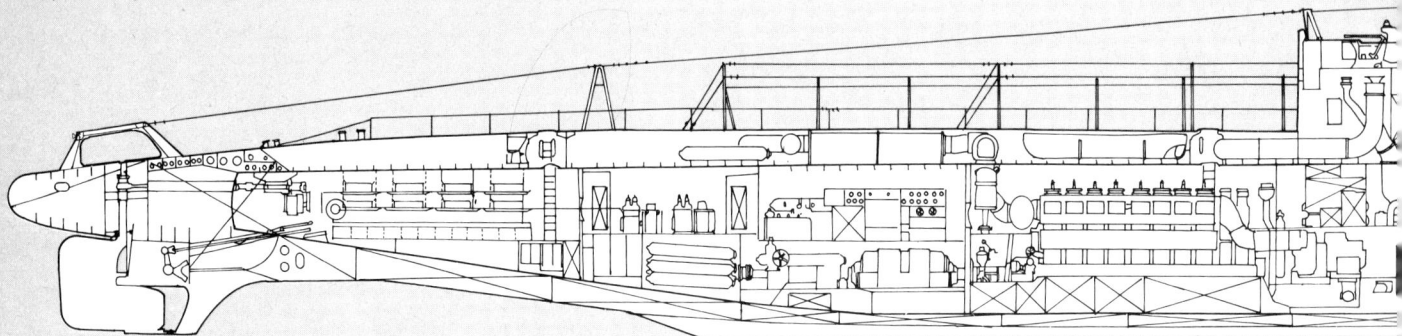

Powered by two-shaft diesel/electric motors, the *I 76* Class had a surface radius of action of only 8000 nautical miles at 16 knots and a submerged radius of 50 nautical miles at 5 knots. Stowage for 12 torpedoes was provided, though after 1942 three of the class, with some spare torpedoes removed, were modified to act as transport submarines

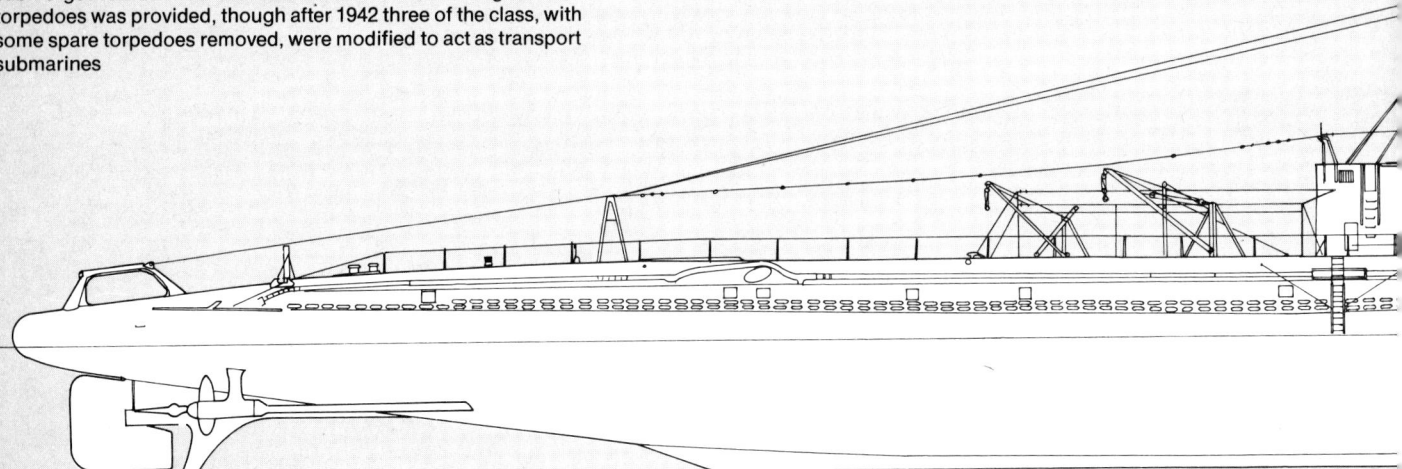

took on average only ten months. A total of 23 units were ordered from the Kure navy yard under the 1943 Programme, construction commencing in March 1944. A further 76 units were projected under the 1944 Programme, but the progress of the war and the decision to concentrate construction on suicide units led to the cancellation of *I 209-I 223* in 1945, and the units in the 1944 Programme were never ordered at all. *I 201* entered service on February 2, 1945, followed on February 12 by *I 202* and on May 29 by *I 203*. *I 204-I 208* were laid down but never completed and all the boats were surrendered at the end of the war.

Displacement: 1291/1450 tons (surfaced/submerged) *Length:* 79 m (259 ft) oa *Beam:* 5.8 m (19 ft) *Draught:* 5.5 m (18 ft) *Machinery:* 2-shaft diesels/2 electric motors, 2750 bhp/5000 hp=15.75/19 knots (surfaced/submerged) *Armament:* 4 53-cm (21-in) torpedo tubes, 10 torpedoes; 2 25-mm (1-in) AA *Crew:* 31

I-250, MiG

Soviet mixed-power intercepter fighter. Early history of Soviet work on ramjets is not documented in the West, but by 1939 several design teams, one of them led by Merkulov, were studying their possible application to fighters and other fast aircraft. Possibly the first aircraft in the world to fly on inbuilt (as distinct from externally-added) ramjet power was the MiG (or Mikoyan) I-250 (though one report claims that its rear engine was a rocket). Mikoyan himself took great interest in the ramjet and certainly had a hand in its design and installation in the rear fuselage of the I-250, which was apparently a completely new design begun in 1943. Powered by a VK-107 of 1600-1700 hp, it had an annular inlet round the spinner for the coolant radiator and carburettor, and a second lower inlet to the ramjet duct which passed above the low-mounted wing. Flight trials began in March 1945, and though the I-250 was possibly the

fastest piston-engined aircraft of its time its performance was not in the same class as a jet's. The aircraft is thought to have been armed with a combination of cannon and machine-guns. Data below are those reported unofficially.

Span: 10 m (32 ft 10 in) *Length:* not known *Gross weight:* 3680 kg (8113 lb) *Maximum speed:* 825 km/h (513 mph)

I-320, MiG

Soviet all-weather intercepter. In 1948 the Soviet government instructed selected design bureaux to build a radar-equipped all-weather intercepter to be powered by two RD-45 (Nene-derived) turbojets, each of 2270-kg (5000-lb) thrust. Mikoyan's submission was the I-320, later given the VVS service designation R-1 (although it is not thought to have seen inventory service). It was similar to an enlarged MiG-15 with the circular nose inlet

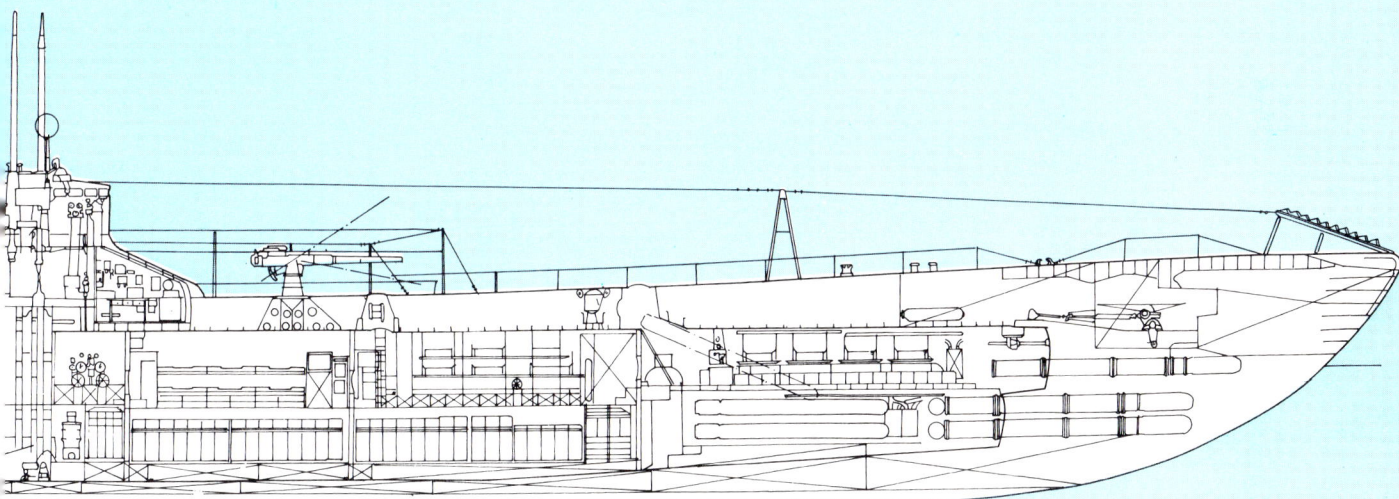

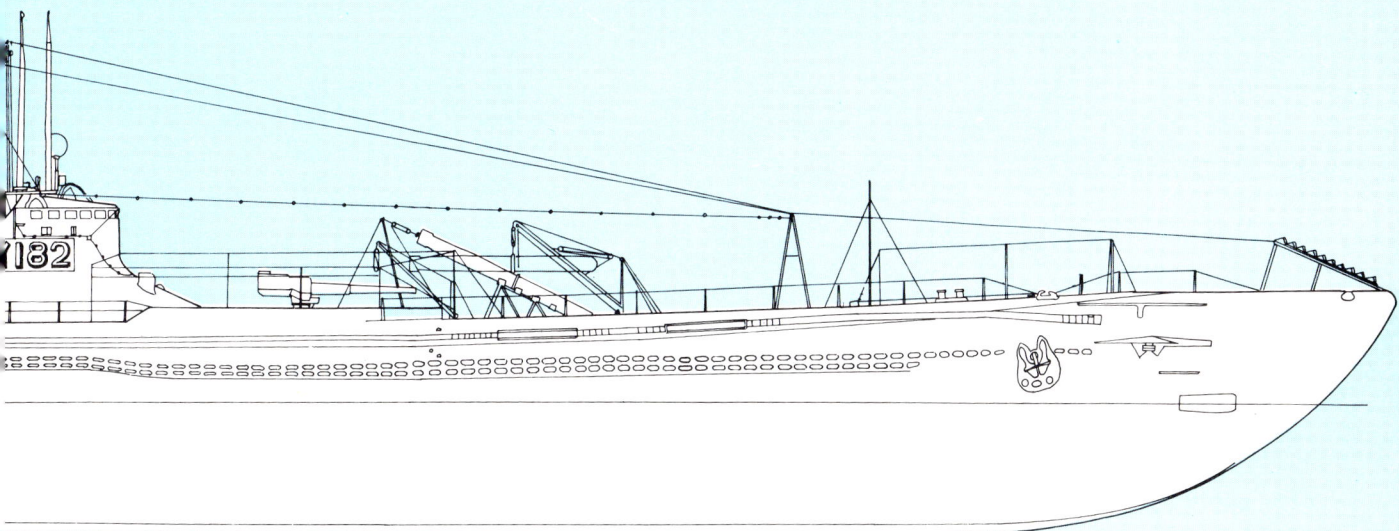

feeding both RD-45F engines, one of which was fitted in the underside of the forward fuselage and exhausted under the wing, while the other was installed in the rear fuselage. Armament comprised three large cannon, two on the right of the lower forward fuselage and one on the left; one report states that these were 37-mm (1.46-in) Nudelmann N-37, each with 40 rounds. The radar occupied a cylindrical pod in the upper part of the nose above the inlet. The I-320 seated the pilot and a radar observer side by side. There are no reliable data.

I351

Japanese submarine class, built 1943-45. The *I351* Class (Type SH) submarines were designed as replenishment vessels for seaplanes and flying boats. The requirement laid emphasis on cargo capacity at the expense of armament, and although the design originally provided for a 140-mm (5.5-in) gun this was subsequently omitted. Speed and a high radius of action were not considered to be essential features, and at 14 knots surfaced the radius was 13 000 nautical miles. The cargo capacity was 390 tons, of which 11 tons was fresh water and 365 tons aviation fuel, while the remaining 14 tons was for aircraft armaments. These included either 60 250-kg (550-lb) bombs or 30 250-kg bombs and 15 torpedoes. Extra accommodation was provided for 13 aircrew.

Three submarines were ordered from the Kure navy yard under the 1941 Programme, with a further three in the 1942 Programme that was subsequently cancelled. The first vessel was laid down in May 1943, but by then the requirement for seaplane replenishment submarines had been superseded, and work on *I351* and *I352* proceeded very slowly. *I353* was cancelled before being laid down and *I351* and *I352* were not launched until 1944. *I351* was finally completed on January 28, 1945, and sunk by the US submarine *Bluefish* on July 14. The uncompleted hull of *I352* was sunk in an air raid on June 22, 1945.

Displacement: 3512/4290 tons (surfaced/submerged) *Length:* 111 m (363 ft 9 in) oa *Beam:* 10.2 m (33 ft 6 in) *Draught:* 6.1 m (20 ft) *Machinery:* 2-shaft diesels/2 electric motors, 3700 shp/1200 hp=15.75/6.33 knots (surfaced/submerged) *Armament:* 4 53-cm (21-in) torpedo tubes (bow), 4 torpedoes; 4 3-in (76-mm) trench mortars (2×2); 7 25-mm (1-in) (2×2, 3×1) *Crew:* 77

I361

Japanese submarine class, built 1943-44. The successful use of old submarines as transports for supplying garrisons on islands cut off by advancing US forces led the Japanese to design a special transport submarine, the Type D1. Armament and speed were of little importance but high endurance and high radius of action were essential. The radius of action was 15 000 nautical miles at 10 knots with 120 nautical miles at 3 knots submerged, and the vessels had an endurance of 60 days.

The design provided for a deck gun and two bow 53-cm (21-in) torpedo tubes. *I361* was completed with the tubes, which were found to produce a wave. The bow tubes

were therefore omitted on all subsequent units, and the bow section on these vessels was streamlined, and 2 m (6 ft 6 in) longer than the original design. The conning tower was also redesigned to a more streamlined shape. Of the 82 tons of cargo, 22 tons were stored in watertight containers between the deck casing and the pressure hull.

Eleven units were ordered under the 1942 Programme, and one slightly modified unit (*I372*) under the 1943 Programme. A further 92 units planned under the 1943 Programme were never ordered. All surviving units were converted at the end of January 1945 to carry five Kaiten suicide submarines, the deck gun being removed and the fittings for the landing craft adapted. Thus modified the submarines carried five Kaiten.

Displacement: 1779/2215 tons (surfaced/submerged) *Length:* 75.60 m (248 ft) oa *Beam:* 8.92 m (29 ft 3 in) *Draught:* 4.72 m (15 ft 6 in) *Machinery:* 2-shaft diesels/2 electric motors, 1350 shp/1200 hp=13/6.5 knots (surfaced/submerged) *Armament:* 2 53-cm (21-in) torpedo tubes (*I361* only); 1 140-mm (5.5-in); 2 25-mm (1-in) *Crew:* 60

No	completed	fate
I361	5/44	war loss 30/5/5
I362	5/44	war loss 18/1/45
I363	7/44	war loss 20/10/45
I364	6/44	war loss 16/9/44
I365	8/44	war loss 28/11/44
I366	8/44	surrendered
I367	3/44	surrendered
I368	8/44	war loss 27/2/45
I369	10/44	surrendered
I370	9/44	war loss 26/2/45
I371	10/44	war loss 24/2/45
I372	11/44	war loss 18/7/45

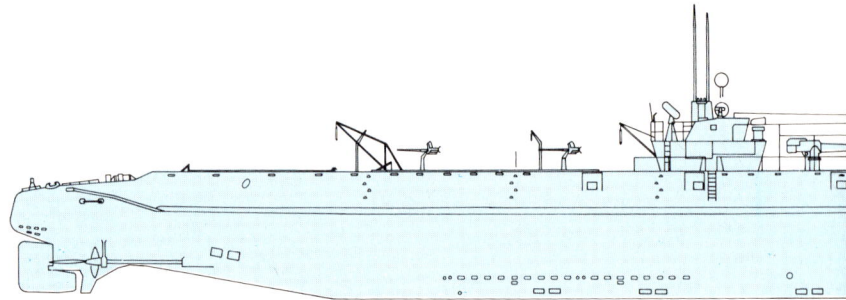

The *I361* Class, or Type D1, submarines were designed to carry supplies to isolated Japanese garrisons in the Pacific and had a surface radius of action of 15 000 nautical miles at 10 knots

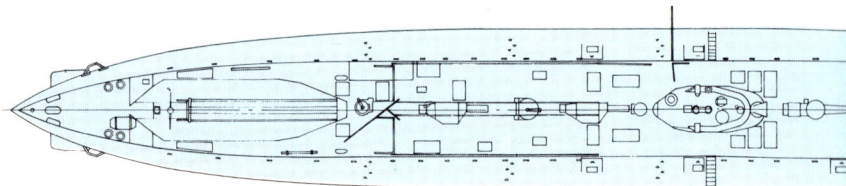

1373

Japanese submarine class, built 1944-45. This class was a development of the *I361* Class and was known as the Type D2. Apart from a slight increase in displacement the design was almost identical to the *I361*. Cargo capacity was increased at the expense of the vessel's radius of action by using some of the diesel-fuel tanks for the storage of other types of fuel. Originally the craft were to have been armed with two twin 76-mm (3-in) trench mortars and seven 25-mm (1-in) guns, but they were completed with a 140-mm (5.5-in) deck gun, and two 25-mm (1-in).

The loss of many of the islands they were to have supplied led to the cancellation of many of the submarines ordered to this design. Six were originally ordered from the Yokosuka navy yard under the 1943 Programme, but *I373-I378* were subsequently cancelled as were 140 units planned under the 1944 Programme.

Displacement: 1926/2240 tons (surfaced/submerged) *Length:* 74 m (242 ft 9 in) oa *Beam:* 8.29 m (29 ft 3 in) *Draught:* 5.03 m (16 ft 6 in)

Machinery: 2-shaft diesels/2 electric motors, 1750 shp/1200 hp=13/6.5 knots (surfaced/submerged) *Armament:* 1 140-mm (5.5-in); 2 25-mm (1-in) *Crew:* 60

No	fate
I373	war loss 13/8/45
I374	work ceased 3/45, scrapped

I400

Japanese submarine class, built 1943-45. These submarines were the largest in the world when completed, having been built expressly at Admiral Yamamoto's request for vessels to mount a long-range bombardment mission against the Panama Canal. The design finally arrived at combined the three roles previously covered by the Type A, B and C designs. The first design, which provided for two small bomber seaplanes to be carried on a displacement of 4550 tons, was revised to provide for three seaplanes. The redesigned hangar area also enclosed the aircraft armaments of four torpedoes, three 800-kg (1760-lb) bombs and eight 250-kg (550-lb) bombs. The displacement rose to 5223 tons. To keep the draught within the required limits the hull form was redesigned, and instead of the normal vertical double-hull arrangement a double hull on its side like a pair of spectacles was adopted.

Propulsion was provided by four diesels coupled two to a shaft, one set being installed in each of the hull cylinders. The submarines were to be equipped with snorkels, and the unconventional hull design meant that two separate sets of snorkel tubes had to be provided. The engines in the starboard hull were supplied by a set in fixed curved pipes in the conning tower; the port engines were fed by a second set on a mast which retracted into a well in the deck casing.

In spite of their size and unwieldiness these submarines achieved a reasonable performance. The radius of action and endurance were the highest of any submarine of the period, with sufficient supplies for 90 days and fuel for a surfaced radius of 37 500 nautical miles at 14 knots. The maximum submerged depth was 100 m (325 ft).

With the design complete, the first vessel was ordered under the 1942 Programme, though this Programme was subsequently cancelled. But for the personal intervention of Admiral Yamamoto the order would not have been replaced, as the Japanese admiralty had lost faith in large vulnerable submarines. Yamamoto insisted that 18 units be ordered in the new 1942 Programme, and five were laid down, the rest being cancelled in March 1945. The design of *I402* was altered during construction and she was completed as a refuelling submarine.

Displacement: 5223/6560 tons (surfaced/submerged) *Length:* 122 m (400 ft 3 in) *Beam:* 12 m (39 ft 4 in) *Draught:* 7 m (23 ft) *Machinery:* 2-shaft 4 diesels/electric motors, 7700 shp/2400 hp=18.75/6.5 knots (surfaced/submerged) *Armament:* 8 21-in (53-cm) torpedo tubes, 20 torpedoes; 1 140-mm (5.5-in); 10 25-mm (1-in) (3×3, 1×1); 3 seaplanes *Crew:* 144

No	completed	fate
I400	12/44	surrendered
I401	1/45	surrendered
I402	7/45	surrendered
I404	—	scrapped uncompleted
I405	—	scrapped uncompleted

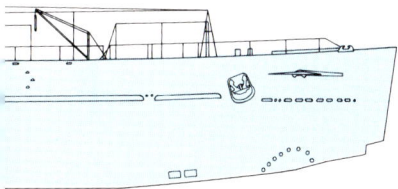

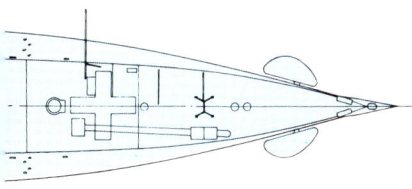

IAI Israeli aircraft

See **Arava, Kfir, Westwind**

IAI Israeli missiles   See **Gabriel**

I.A.R. 37/38/39

Romanian tactical bomber/reconnaissance aircraft. A single-bay unequal-span biplane designed at the Industria Aeronautica Romana at Brasov, the I.A.R. 37 flew for the first time in 1938, powered by an I.A.R. K14 IIc 14-cylinder radial (licence-built version of the Gnome-Rhône 14K Mistral Major) with a long-chord cowling. It was of wooden-frame fabric-covered construction, with fixed cantilever main wheels and a tail skid. The pilot, observer/bombardier and rear gunner sat in

I402 was a member of the *I400* Class, the largest submarines built up to that time. They were intended to launch their aircraft in an attack on the Panama Canal, but the scheme came to nothing

I.A.R. 80/81

tandem in a fully-enclosed greenhouse-style cockpit; transparent panels were fitted in the sides of the fuselage centre-section to give a better downward view. Armament comprised a 7.7-mm (0.303-in) machine-gun on a movable mounting in the rear of the cockpit and another retractable gun which fired downward and rearward through a ventral tunnel. Eight 50-kg (110-lb) or six 100-kg (220-lb) bombs were carried on underwing racks. Series production began in 1939; slight modifications included removal of the main-wheel spats, and minor changes to the rear half of the canopy, which opened upwards for firing of the rear gun.

The I.A.R. 37 was followed in 1940 by the basically similar I.A.R. 38, in which the observer/gunner was replaced by camera equipment and an operator. It was used for photo-reconnaissance duties only. Series production also began in 1940 of the I.A.R. 39, which was of the same overall construction as the other two aircraft but specialized in the light-bomber and close-support roles.

When production ended in 1942 a total of approximately 325 of these three aircraft had been built, and they continued to serve with the Romanian air force throughout the Second World War. Some I.A.R. 39s continued in use into the late 1940s for liaison and other second-line duties.

(I.A.R. 37) Span: 12.22 m (40 ft 1 in) *Length:* 9.50 m (31 ft 2 in) *Gross weight:* 3460 kg (7630 lb) *Maximum speed:* 335 km/h (208 mph)

I.A.R. 80/81

Romanian fighter aircraft. Design work on this all-metal low-wing single-seat monoplane began in late 1937 at the Industria Aeronautica Romana under the direction of Grossu-Viziru. The idea was to use as many components as possible from the Polish P.24E, which was at that time being built under licence in Romania. However, there was little similarity between the Polish fighter and the completed prototype, which flew for the first time in April 1939. Designated I.A.R. 80, the aircraft utilized the circular-section semimonocoque rear fuselage and tail assembly of the P.24E, but had new forward and centre fuselage sections of welded steel tubing. It was powered by a 940-hp I.A.R. K14-III C36 engine (licence-built Gnome-Rhône 14K Mistral Major radial) driving a variable-pitch three-blade propeller, behind which was installed the 403-litre (88.7-Imp gal) fuel tank. The cantilever low wing accommodated the hydraulically operated inward-retracting main undercarriage wheels, and the fixed tail skid was fitted with a hydraulic-pneumatic shock-absorber. An open cockpit was situated in the centre of the fuselage aft of the wings. (Production models were fitted with a rearward-sliding canopy.) Provision was made for four 7.92-mm (0.312-in) FN-Browning machine-guns to be mounted in the wings, firing outside the propeller arc.

After flight trials during 1939 it was decided to use the uprated 1025-hp I.A.R. K14-1000A powerplant, which in turn necessitated an increase in wing span, wing area and length. After the initial batch of 50 I.A.R. 80s, armament was increased by the addition of two 7.92-mm (0.312-in) FNs mounted one on each outer wing. Designated I.A.R. 80A, a

total of 90 of this modified type were built. In the I.A.R. 80B, of which 31 were built, two of the existing machine-guns were replaced by guns of 13.2-mm (0.52-in) calibre, and improved radio equipment was fitted.

At the same time, the new dive-bomber variant, designated I.A.R. 81, was being built. Based on the 80A, it had an increased wing span of 10.7 m (35 ft 1 in) and a centreline rack under the fuselage for one 250-kg (550-lb) bomb plus underwing racks for four 50-kg (110-lb) bombs. Fifty were built, together with 29 I.A.R. 81As which had the same armament as the 80B. The next variant to appear was the I.A.R. 81B long-range fighter, with two auxiliary underwing fuel tanks. Its armament comprised two 20-mm (0.79-in) Oerlikon (MG FF) or Ikaria cannon fitted in the wings, in addition to the four basic 7.92-mm (0.312-mm) FN machine-guns. Production of this version totalled 50 aircraft. The final model to appear was the I.A.R. 81C (of which 38 were built), equipped with four 7.92-mm (0.312-in) FNs and two 20-mm (0.79-in) Mauser MG 151 cannon, with provision for underwing or under-fuselage bombloads.

During 1942 it was decided to phase out production of the I.A.R. fighters in favour of the Messerschmitt Bf 109G. Production of the I.A.R. aircraft therefore ceased in January 1943, though less than 50 of the Messerschmitts had been assembled when the Brasov factory was destroyed by Allied air attack in April-May 1944.

The I.A.R. series were deployed by the Romanian air force on the Eastern Front as close-support aircraft/fighter-bombers between 1942-43. They also served on home defence duties, especially in the Bucharest and Ploesti oilfield areas. They remained in service after the war, and some I.A.R. 80s were converted to two-seat dual-control advanced trainers, designated I.A.R. 80DC. Others remained as the standard operational fighter, but after the declaration of the People's Republic on December 30, 1947, they were replaced by more modern Soviet types such as the Lavochkin La-7 and Yakovlev Yak-9.

(I.A.R. 80) Span: 10.5 m (34 ft 5 in) *Length:* 8.9 m (29 ft 2 in) *Gross weight:* 2550 kg (5620 lb) *Maximum speed:* 550 km/h (342 mph)

Ibis

German homing torpedo. Ibis was an experimental active homing torpedo which followed echoes from the target-ship's wake, and then pursued the target on a weaving course up the wake. The 'pings' were transmitted from the head of the torpedo at slightly less than 90° to the axis, and the echoes were received in the tail. Like the similar Fasen, Ibis (ibex) was dropped in favour of Geier in 1944, never having reached the production stage.

See also Fasen, Geier.

Ibuki

Japanese aircraft carrier (uncompleted). The Japanese shipbuilding industry's lack of capacity, and the indecision of the Imperial Japanese Navy's staff, were epitomized by Job No 300 of the 1941 Programme. Laid

down in 1942 as a repeat *Tone* Class heavy cruiser, the design was changed to that of an improved *Mogami* Class. *Ibuki* was launched at Kure on May 21, 1943, but work had to be suspended to enable the navy yard to undertake urgent repairs to damaged ships. Meanwhile the naval staff toyed with the idea of completing the ship as a high-speed oiler, but it was eventually decided that she would be a carrier, and in November 1943 she was towed to Sasebo navy yard for completion.

The hangar was located on the original upper deck, with the flight deck extending fore and aft over the cruiser-type forecastle and quarterdeck. The hangar accommodated 27 aircraft, and was connected with the flight deck by two large lifts. The island contained all the command and control positions, including the main gunnery-control director. As in most Japanese carriers, the funnel was separate, located below the starboard deck-edge abaft the island to discharge smoke horizontally. The main machinery was halved to two sets of turbines and shafts, but the maximum speed was not expected to be less than the *Mogami*'s 29 knots.

Somewhat surprisingly, only four medium-calibre DP guns were to be installed, but these were the new 76-mm (3-in)/60-cal guns with a high rate of fire and high muzzle velocity. Automatic AA armament was to have consisted of 16 triple 25-mm (1-in) mountings, and for defence against the successful US Navy dive-bomber it was intended to fit six multiple launchers for 12-cm (4.7-in) AA rockets.

Ibuki had been completed up to the flight deck and island by March 1945 (though not all machinery had been installed), when the decision was taken to suspend all further work. The carrier was towed to an anchorage near Sasebo and remained there for the duration, apparently escaping the attentions of the US Navy until after the end of the war. She was broken up at Sasebo in 1947.

The only Romanian fighter of indigenous design to be manufactured in quantity during the Second World War, the I.A.R. 80 used several components of the Polish P.Z.L. P.24E. The type entered service in early 1942

Displacement: 12 500 tons (standard) *Length:* 200.6 m (658 ft) oa *Beam:* 21.2 m (69 ft 6 in) wl, 23 m (75 ft 6 in) flight deck *Draught:* 6.3 m (20 ft 8 in) *Machinery:* 2 sets geared steam turbines, 2 shafts, 72 000 shp=29 knots *Aircraft:* 27 *Armament:* 4 76-mm (3-in) DP; 48 25-mm (1-in) AA; 168 12-cm (4.7-in) AA rocket launchers (6×28) *Crew:* 1015

Idzumi

Japanese protected cruiser. Starting life as the Chilean *Esmeralda,* she was laid down on April 5, 1881, launched on June 6, 1883, and completed on July 15, 1884. Like all Armstrong-designed cruisers of the period she was noteworthy for combining a heavy gun armament and high speed with a light displacement. *Esmeralda,* in fact, was the forerunner of these famous cruisers and her design laid the pattern for future protected cruisers. The main feature was the arched protective deck which ran the whole length of the ship below the waterline. Above the armoured deck was a cellular layer filled with cork, designed to assist buoyancy should the ship be pierced on the waterline.

All the guns were sited on the upper deck, with the hydraulically operated 10-in (254-mm) guns on the keel line. These had to be brought to a fore-and-aft position for loading with the hydraulic rammer behind a fixed steel screen shelter.

When the Sino-Japanese war broke out in 1894 Japan began negotiations for the purchase of *Esmeralda* from Chile, through the auspices of Equador. She was finally acquired in November 1894 and renamed *Idzumi,* but was not ready for service until after the war had ended. The great disadvantage of the design was the low freeboard, which resulted from mounting heavy guns on a hull of light displacement. The Japanese were not fully aware of this problem when they purchased the ship, and in the rough waters of the northern Pacific she earned the reputation of being a bad sea boat. Perhaps this judgement was unfair as she had been designed for the calmer waters of the southern Pacific. To improve her stability and seaworthiness the broadside 6-in (152-mm) guns were replaced by lighter 4.7-in (120-mm) guns in 1899. She was again refitted in 1901 when the two 10-in (254-mm) guns were replaced by 6-in (152-mm) quick-firing weapons and 18-in (46-cm) torpedo tubes replaced the 15-in (38-cm) models. She was also reboilered with Niclausse boilers. Thus armed and reboilered she took part in the Russo-Japanese war, being one of the first to sight the Russians at the Battle of Tsushima where she reported their position by wireless. She was finally removed from active operations in 1907.

Displacement: 2920 tons (normal) *Length:* 82.3 m (270 ft) pp *Beam:* 12.8 m (42 ft) *Draught:* 5.6 m (18 ft 3 in) *Machinery:* 2-shaft reciprocating, 6083 ihp=18.25 knots *Protection:* 25 mm (1 in) deck *Armament:* 2 10-in (254-mm)/30-cal; 6 6-in (152-mm)/26-cal; 2 6-pdr (57-mm) QF; 5 2-pdr (37-mm); 2 Gardner machine-guns; 3 15-in (38-cm) torpedo tubes *Crew:* 300

Idzumo

Japanese armoured cruiser class. *Idzumo* and *Iwate* were the second pair of armoured cruisers to be laid down by Armstrong at Elswick on the Tyne for the Japanese navy. Laid down some 18 months after the first pair (*Asama* and *Tokiwa*), they benefited from the technological advances that had taken place in the meantime.

New water-tube boilers of the Belleville type were fitted, and such was the general improvement in machinery design that a total saving in weight of some 300 tons was achieved without any loss of power. The fitting of 24 instead of the 12 boilers of *Asama* required the mounting of a third funnel in the *Idzumo,* and this was the main distinguishing feature between the two pairs of vessels.

The protection of *Idzumo* and *Iwate,* followed the same general layout as *Asama,* but was improved through the use of Krupp cemented armour plates as opposed to the Harvey nickel-steel plates of *Asama* and *Tokiwa.* Amidships the thickest section of the armoured belt was shortened by 2.7 m (9 ft) in *Idzumo,* while the upper belt was considerably shortened from 65.2 m (214 ft) in *Asama* to 53.3 m (175 ft) in *Idzumo* and 51.2 m (168 ft) in *Iwate.* Armament remained almost identical except for the omission of a bow torpedo tube and the addition of an extra 2½-pdr QF.

Following service in the Russo-Japanese war the two ships were rerated as coast-defence vessels under the Washington Treaty. All but six of the boilers were removed, reducing horsepower to 7000 and speed to 16 knots. The main deck 6-in (152-mm) and most of the QF guns were also removed, the vessels retaining four 8-in (203-mm), eight 6-in (152-mm), two (*Iwate,* one) 3-in (76-mm) AA, four (*Idzumo* only) 2½-pdr, five (*Iwate* only) 3-in (76-mm).

During the Second World War the vessels were further refitted, twin 5-in (127-mm) replacing the 8-in (203-mm) and four 6-in (152-mm) being removed. Both ships were surrendered in a damaged condition at the end of the war. They then mounted four 6-in (152-mm), four 5-in (127-mm) AA, three (*Idzumo,* one) 3-in (76-mm) AA, nine (*Idzumo,* 14) 25-mm (1-in), and two 13-mm (0.51-in).

Displacement: 9750 tons (normal) *Length:* 132.3 m (434 ft) oa *Beam:* 21 m (68 ft 9 in) *Draught:* 7.4 m (24 ft 3 in) *Machinery:* 2-shaft vertical triple-expansion steam engines, 14 500 ihp=20.75 knots *Protection:* 178-89 mm (7-3½ in) belt, 127 mm (5 in) upper belt, 63 mm (2½ in) deck, 152

Igo

Idzumo returns to port in December 1941 having sunk the British river gunboat HMS *Peterel* during the attack on Hong Kong

mm (6 in) turrets, casemates and barbettes, 356 mm (14 in) conning tower *Armament:* 4 8-in (203-mm)/40-cal (2×2); 14 6-in (152-mm)/40-cal (14×1); 12 12-pdr (76-mm) (12×1); 8 2½-pdr (42-mm) (8×1); 4 18-in (46-cm) torpedo tubes (submerged) *Crew:* 672

Name	laid down	launched	completed
Idzumo	5/98	9/99	9/00
Iwate	11/98	3/00	3/01

Igo

Japanese air-to-surface missiles. A series of ASMs was developed for the Japanese army late in the Second World War, although none saw operational service. Mitsubishi's radio-controlled Igo-1-A was powered by a rocket motor producing 240 kg (530 lb) of thrust for 75 seconds and was planned to be slung beneath the fuselage of the same manufacturer's Ki-67 bomber. Flight trials were carried out during the autumn of 1944, but the war ended before the weapon could be deployed.

The smaller Igo-1-B, also radio-controlled, was the responsibility of Kawasaki and was also test flown in late 1944 from a modified Ki-48-II bomber. The rocket motor generated 150 kg (330 lb) of thrust for 80 seconds. The planned launch platform was the Kawasaki Ki-102b assault aircraft. Though 180 missiles were built they failed to see service.

The last in the series, the Igo-1-C, was designed by the Tokyo Imperial University's Aeronautical Institute and used an acoustic seeker to home on to the noise of warships'

guns. Trials in the spring of 1945 are thought to have been successful, but the weapon was too late to enter production.

(Igo-1-A) *Length:* 5.77 m (18 ft 11 in) *Span:* 3.6 m (11 ft 10 in) *Weight:* 1400 kg (3090 lb)

(Igo-1-B) *Length:* 4.09 m (13 ft 5 in) *Span:* 2.6 m (8 ft 6 in) *Weight:* 680 kg (1500 lb) *Warhead:* 300 kg (660 lb)

(Igo-1-C) *Length:* 3.5 m (11 ft 6 in) *Diameter:* 500 mm (1 ft 8 in)

Ihoshima

Japanese small cruiser. *Ihoshima* and her sister-ship *Yashojima* were the ex-Chinese cruisers *Ning Hai* and *Ping Hai*. They were built to a Japanese design for Chinese specifications, the requirement being that they should be able to operate on the large Chinese rivers, hence the small displacement and low draught. Also included was the requirement that the vessels should be capable of operating two seaplanes, but although a large handling crane and hangar at the base of the mainmast were provided, it is doubtful whether the ships ever carried any seaplanes.

The first vessel, *Ning Hai*, was built by the Japanese at the Harima shipyard while the second, *Ping Hai*, was constructed by the Kiang Nan dockyard at Shanghai with mater-

ials, armament and machinery supplied by Japan and installed with Japanese assistance. With Sino-Japanese relations rapidly deteriorating, the delivery dates for the materials were constantly put back and construction was even halted for a while in 1933.

Both ships were serving on the Yangtse when war broke out. *Ping Hai* was sunk in shallow water on September 23, 1937, after a short engagement with Japanese gunboats. *Ning Hai* survived a little longer and was eventually captured intact on December 13, 1937.

Ping Hai was subsequently refloated and repaired by the Japanese and both vessels were transferred to the puppet Ching Wei Government in March 1940. They were requisitioned by the Japanese in 1943, rearmed, and commissioned into the Imperial navy as the *Ihoshima* (June 28, 1944) and *Yashojima* (September 25, 1944). The 140-mm (5.5-in) guns had been replaced with dual-purpose 127-mm (5-in) weapons. *Ihoshima* was sunk by the submarine *Shad* on September 19, 1944, and *Yashojima* by US naval aircraft on November 25, 1944.

Displacement: 2500 tons (normal) *Length:* 109.7 m (360 ft) oa *Beam:* 11.9 m (39 ft) *Draught:* 4.3 m (14 ft) *Machinery:* 2-shaft geared turbines, 9000 shp=22 knots *Armament:* 6 140-mm (5.5-in); 6 (*Yashojima* 3) 76-mm (3-in); 4 53-cm (21-in) torpedo tubes; 2 seaplanes *Crew:* 340

Name	laid down	launched	completed
Ihoshima (ex-*Ning Hai*)	2/31	10/31	7/32
Yashojima (ex-*Ping Hai*)	7/31	9/35	6/36

IK-2, Ikarus

Yugoslavian fighter aircraft. In 1934 the Yugoslavian air force gave its own country's engineers a chance to submit designs for a new single-seat, all-metal monoplane fighter. Ljubomir Ilić and Kosta Sivčev produced the IK-L1 (IK-1) prototype, which first flew on April 22, 1935, powered by an 860-hp Hispano-Suiza 12 Ycrs *moteur canon* engine (with a built-in 20-mm [0.79-in] HS 404 cannon firing through the propeller hub). It crashed during its third test flight when it spun after pulling out of a dive.

It was discovered that this accident was caused by separation of the wing fabric rather than by any basic defect in the design, and a second prototype, the IK-02, was produced with metal-skinned wings. The same engine was utilized, and two 7.92-mm (0.312-in) FN-Browning machine-guns were fitted in front of the enclosed cockpit, which was set back behind the high, braced wings. The IK-02 was flown for the first time on August 24, 1936, with slight streamlining modifications and improvements to the cockpit layout. After extensive trials an order was given in December 1937 for 12 production aircraft, to be designated IK-2. They entered service in early 1939, but only eight were actually airworthy when the Axis powers invaded on April 6, 1941. These eight, serving with the 107th Eskadrila at Bosanski Aleksandrovac, did not survive long after the seven-day battle for power against the Germans.

A projected two-seat trainer/reconnaissance variant, the IK-4, was abandoned following delays in the delivery of the fighter version.

Span: 11.40 m (37 ft 5 in) *Length:* 7.88 m (25 ft 10 in) *Gross weight:* 1857 kg (4094 lb) *Maximum speed:* 435 km/h (270 mph)

IK-3, Rogožarski

Yugoslavian fighter aircraft. With the assistance of Slobodan Zrnić, the Ilić and Sivčev team designed the IK-3, which was built by the Rogožarski factory. It was a single-seat, low-wing monoplane fighter of wood and metal construction, with all three undercarriage wheels retractable. The first flight took place in late May 1938, the aircraft being powered by an 890-hp Hispano-Suiza 12 Y-29 liquid-cooled engine. Twelve production models were ordered the following November, to be fitted with 980-hp Hispano-Suiza 12 Ycrs engines. Some structural strengthening was introduced, the rear fuselage section was modified, and a flat-glazed cockpit canopy was introduced. One aircraft was fitted with radio equipment. Armament comprised a 20-mm (0.79-in) Oerlikon FF cannon which fired through the propeller hub, and twin 7.92-mm (0.312-in) FN-Browning machine-guns which were installed in the upper engine cowling. Production began in the spring of 1939, but only six had been delivered by late March 1940, as the production programme had been delayed by lack of components. Delivery of the initial 12 was, however, completed by July of that year, six aircraft each being allocated to the 161st and 162nd Eskadrila of the Yugoslavian air force. The IK-3/2 two-seat dual-control

trainer did not get beyond the drawing-board stage.

Some success was achieved against Axis forces in the defence of Belgrade in 1941, but after the German occupation surviving IK-3s were destroyed, including a further 25 that were then under construction. (Also partially completed at that time was a prototype of the highly promising twin-engined IK-5 'heavy' fighter.)

One of the causes of IK-3 production delays had been the poor supply of engines, and various alternatives were explored, including the adaptation of one IK-3 to take a German DB 601A. (This aircraft was later destroyed by the Yugoslavs before it could be of any assistance to the Germans.) Work also began on a variant to be powered by an 1100-hp Hispano-Suiza 12 Y-51, and one IK-3 was to have been fitted with a 1130-hp Rolls-Royce Merlin II.

Two of the IK-3's designers, Sivčev and Zrnić, teamed up after the war with Svetozar Popović to produce the excellent S-49A and C fighters based on the IK-3 design.

Span: 10.30 m (33 ft 9 in) *Length:* 8 m (26 ft 3 in) *Gross weight:* 2630 kg (5800 lb) *Maximum speed:* 527 km/h (327 mph)

Ikadzuchi

Japanese destroyer class. This class of six destroyers was an improved version of the Argentine *Corrientes* Class, and was similar to, but larger than, the Thornycroft *Murakumo*. Extra bunkerage (110 tons as opposed to 80 tons in *Murakumo*) was pro-

Ikara antisubmarine missiles in the handling room of the Brazilian destroyer *Niteroi*

vided, and the higher-powered machinery required more space than that in the Thornycroft design, accounting for the 2.7-m (9-ft) increase in length. The indicated horsepower was increased from 5800 to 6000 to give an extra knot in speed at 307 tons displacement. These figures were exceeded on the three-hour trials by all six ships.

The 12-pdr gun was sited right aft, while the two single torpedo tubes on swivelling mounts on the keel line were fore and aft of the mainmast. The deck was fitted with rails to aid the handling of torpedoes to the tubes.

The vessels were all ordered from Yarrow's Poplar yard on the Thames under the 1896 and 1897 Estimates, and completed between 1899-1900. At some time in their career the forward 6-pdr gun was replaced by an additional 12-pdr.

Ikadzuchi and *Oboro* were both damaged during the Russo-Japanese war, the former by gunfire at the Battle of Tsushima on May 27, 1905, and *Oboro* by a mine off Port Arthur on November 2, 1904.

See also *Corrientes*.

Name	completed	fate
Akebono	7/99	scrapped 1921
Ikadzuchi	2/99	blew up 10/10/13
Inazuma	4/99	sunk collision 12/09
Niji	1/00	wrecked 29/7/00
Oboro	11/99	scrapped 1921
Sazanami	8/99	wrecked 10/11/13

Displacement: 305 tons (normal), 410 tons (full load) *Length:* 68.4 m (224 ft 6 in) *Beam:* 6.2 m (20 ft 6 in) *Draught:* 1.6 m (5 ft 3 in) *Machinery:* 2-shaft vertical triple-expansion steam engines, 6000 ihp=31 knots *Armament:* 1 12-pdr (80-mm); 5 6-pdr (57-mm); 2 18-in (46-cm) torpedo tubes (2×1) *Crew:* 55

Ikara

Australian antisubmarine missile. Ikara was developed jointly by the Australian Departments of the Navy and Supply from 1959 to provide a weapon which could attack submarines at longer ranges than was possible with the Mk 10 mortar. The missile was intended to have a longer range and to be lighter than the US Asroc, and to have a faster reaction time in all weathers and at night than was possible with a torpedo-carrying helicopter.

Potential targets are detected by sonar, which may be carried by the launch vessel or lowered into the water from a helicopter. The missiles are stored with torpedo attached but without wings or fins. These are fitted manually, but the rest of the loading sequence is automatic. The loaded launcher elevates and

Il-4, Ilyushin

Launch of an Australian Ikara antisubmarine missile from the frigate HMS *Leander*

trains under computer control, and after launch the missile climbs high enough to be tracked throughout flight by a shipboard radar. Ikara is acquired by a broad gathering beam, and is then followed by a narrow tracking beam which triggers an on-board transponder to receive positional information. In Royal Navy vessels the attack is controlled by a computer-based ADAWS (action data automation weapon system).

When the missile nears its target, which is tracked by the sonar, the torpedo is released on radio command and descends by parachute. Once in the water it homes on to its target in the normal way. The missile body flies clear of the area before ditching, so that the impact does not interfere with the torpedo's acoustic seeker.

Ikara serves with the navies of Australia, Britain and Brazil. A proposed lightweight development had been abandoned.

Length: 3.45 m (11 ft 4 in) *Span:* 1.52 m (5 ft)
Range: 24 km (15 miles) approx

Ikarus Yugoslav aircraft   See **IK-2**

Il-2, Il-10, Ilyushin Soviet ground attack aircraft   See **Stormovik**

Il-4, Ilyushin

Soviet bomber and multirole aircraft. In 1937 the best all-round bomber of the VVS (Soviet air forces) was the Ilyushin DB-3, an aircraft broadly comparable to an early He 111 or Hampden. In the summer of 1938 one of the many improved versions appeared with M-87A engines (a Tumanskii development of the French 14-cylinder Gnome-Rhône 14K Mistral Major) rated at 950 hp at up to 5000 m (16400 ft), driving VISh-23 variable-pitch propellers. The bluff, turreted nose had been replaced by a longer nose of improved aerodynamic form, with a roof hatch and multiple windows covering each side. At the tip of the nose was a simple Plexiglas cupola with a hand-held 7.62-mm (0.30-in) ShKAS machine-gun. The new nose reduced drag and weight and gave the navigator/bomb-aimer more room. Desig-

nated DB-3F (F for *forsirovannii*, boosted), this more efficient bomber was selected for state acceptance trials, which were successfully completed in June 1939.

The Ilyushin bureau switched immediately to manufacture of the DB-3F, supplies of the M-87A engine being forthcoming, and production of earlier DB-3 models ceased. Deliveries of the improved aircraft began in March or April 1940, and shortly afterwards the Soviet designation system by aircraft function (DB—*dalnii-bombardirovsh-chik*, long-range bomber) was abandoned and replaced by a system based on the leader of the responsible design bureau, and the DB-3F thus became the Il-4. It was destined to be the pre-eminent Soviet long-range bomber of the Second World War.

Though too late to see action in the Winter War against Finland, the Il-4 was serving in substantial numbers when Germany attacked the Soviet Union on May 22, 1941. There were probably almost 1000, backed up by survivors of the 1528 earlier DB-3 models. Deliveries seem to have been split roughly in the ratio 2 to 1 between the ADD (long-range air force) and the MA (naval aviation), there being numerous detail differences between the aircraft used by the two services.

Throughout the war the Il-4 was progressively changed and updated. In 1941 the whole programme was thrown into disarray by the advance of the German armies. It is not known whether Ilyushin's Il-4 production factory had to be evacuated (as was the case with more than half the aircraft plants operating in the summer of 1941), but the Tumanskii M-87A assembly line was evacuated to the Urals, and this virtually halted production of the engine for some three months. Equally serious was a crucial shortage of light alloy, that which was available being allocated to fighters and the Il-2 Stormovik. Ilyushin therefore began introducing wooden parts wherever he could to keep the Il-4 production going, beginning with the floor, the tail of the fuselage and the complete nose. Like all Soviet aircraft the Il-4 had a very hard life, operating from dirt or board airstrips and never enjoying the luxury of a hangar despite extremely severe weather. Most M-87A aircraft had simple hydraulic and electric sys-

tems, with Hucks starter dogs on the front of each propeller shaft.

Normal armament comprised three ShKAS, one in the dorsal turret and the others in the nose and twin-door rear ventral hatch; in aircraft built from early 1942 these were increasingly replaced by 12.7-mm (0.5-in) machine-guns. Some units operated with a crew of four, with two rear men to operate the guns, but the usual complement was only three. One of the best features of the Il-4 was its tremendous potential for carrying fuel and/or bombs. With full tanks, representing almost 28% of the gross weight, it was possible to carry a typical bombload of ten 100-kg (220-lb) bombs, hung on two DER-21 racks in the internal bay, over a range of 4260 km (2650 miles) at 264 km/h (164 mph). For shorter ranges three 500-kg (1100-lb) bombs could be hung externally, and in overload tactical roles both sets of internal and external loads could be carried together, a total of 2500 kg (5510 lb). The MA versions carried one (rarely, two) 43-36-AN or -AV torpedoes, or up to 2500 kg (5510 lb) of bombs, depth bombs or mines. Equipment included an APG-series autopilot, Tchaika radio compass and alcohol de-icing for the propellers and cockpit windshield.

By the late summer of 1942 production had been more than restored to its 1941 peak. During 1942 the M-87A engine was replaced by the M-88 series, derived by Shvetsov from the Gnome-Rhône 14R but with direct fuel injection, initially rated at 1000 hp. The 1100-hp M-88B form, with electric starter, was eventually adopted as standard for the Il-4. Another major change was the adoption of wooden construction for the complete outer wings, though the large ailerons continued to be made from light alloy with fabric covering. This was not allowed to reduce fuel tankage, and although structure weight probably increased, any reduction in cruising speed was barely measurable, and maximum speed fell by a mere 6 km/h (4 mph). With these changes output increased month by month until production of the Il-4 was terminated in 1944, when a total of 5256 had been built, not including DB-3s.

Details of the achievements of this impressive force are sparse, but enough information has seeped through the Iron Curtain to make it clear that the Il-4 did not languish on the ground. One of the earliest combat missions, and the only well-documented one, was the first Soviet raid on Berlin, on the night of August 7/8, 1941. A force of 15 early all-metal aircraft from the MA's 1st Mine-Torpedo Regiment was led by Colonel Preobrajensky from its base on Oezel (now Saaremaa) Island. It was said that they found Berlin brightly lit, though the city was blacked out on the many subsequent Il-4 attacks. Bombers of the ADD seldom went deep into Germany but bombed targets throughout the occupied areas, frequently operating by day and sometimes flying close-support missions. The Il-4 was the standard long-range torpedo-bomber with the MA. By 1943 very large numbers were serving as utility transports, glider tugs, strategic-reconnaissance aircraft and airborne-forces transports carrying external supply containers.

Numbers gradually decreased after 1945, the postwar AV-MF (navy) retaining some until 1949. The NATO reporting name was Bob. Small numbers were supplied to Poland, Yugoslavia and China. The planned successor, the Charomsky ACh-30B diesel-engined Il-6, with five 20-mm (0.79-in) ShVAK cannon and a crew of six, was abandoned in 1944 when the Il-4 design was judged obsolete.

Span: 21.44 m (70 ft 4 in) *Length:* 14.8 m (48 ft 7 in) *Gross weight:* 10 055 kg (22 170 lb) (typical) *Max speed:* 410 km/h (255 mph) (typical)

Il-12, Ilyushin Soviet transport aircraft
See **Coach**

Il-14, Ilyushin Soviet general-purpose transport aircraft
See **Crate**

Il-18, Ilyushin Soviet personnel transport aircraft
See **Coot**

Il-28, Ilyushin Soviet light bomber and patrol aircraft
See **Beagle**

Il-38, Ilyushin Soviet long-range maritime patrol aircraft
See **May**

Il-54, Ilyushin Soviet experimental bomber
See **Blowlamp**

Il-76, Ilyushin Soviet heavy transport aircraft
See **Candid**

Il-86, Ilyushin

Soviet strategic passenger transport. Having a layout similar to the Boeing 707 but on a larger scale, this impressive wide-bodied aircraft (NATO codename Camber) is in production for Aeroflot as the standard Soviet

passenger transport on trunk routes. A large number are being built, the Il-86 is also the Soviet Union's main troop transport. It is not known if any will serve full time with the V-TA, the military air-transport arm.

Powered by four 13 000-kg (28 660-lb) thrust Kuznetsov NK-86 turbofans, the Il-86 seats up to 350 passengers on one main deck. Three powered stairways fold down from the lower deck, where boarding passengers stow their baggage or equipment in large storage areas. Three fixed staircases then lead to the main deck. The underfloor areas also carry large quantities of cargo. There are three main landing gears, each with a four-wheel bogie, but it is not believed that the Il-86 is able to operate from unpaved airstrips.

Span: 48.06 m (157 ft 8 in) *Length:* 59.54 m (195 ft 4 in) *Gross weight:* 206 000 kg (454 150 lb) *Normal cruising speed:* 950 km/h (590 mph)

Ilyushin Soviet aircraft See **Beagle, Blowlamp, Candid, Coach, Coot, Crate, DB-3, May, Il-86, Stormovik**

Illinois

US battleship class. As the possibility of war with Spain increased in the latter part of the

nineteenth century, the US Congress continued to expand the navy. In June 1896 three more battleships were authorized, Nos 7-9, constituting the *Illinois* Class.

The construction of *Illinois* herself was held up because the Newport News yard was fully occupied with two battleships and so she was the last to commission, in September 1901, a year after *Alabama*.

The threat of a Spanish-American conflict ruled out the building of coast-defence battleships, and the new ships were based on the British *Majestic* Class, with good freeboard and a lighter secondary battery to reduce topweight and allow more armour. They also looked like the *Majestic*, with two tall funnels abreast and a two-storeyed battery amidships. The 13-in (330-mm) guns were reintroduced, though this was primarily a sop to certain US Navy officers, who had an exaggerated respect for large-calibre guns, and who bitterly criticized the omission of the 8-in (203-mm). The turret design was a great improvement over earlier American types, and resembled the British type with straight sides and a sloping face; it was fully balanced to avoid the vices of the *Indiana* type.

In December 1907 *Alabama* and *Illinois* left Hampton Roads with the rest of the Great White Fleet on its round-the-world tour, and did not return until 1909. In 1911 the

No and name	launched	built
BB.7 *Illinois*	10/1898	Newport News
BB.8 *Alabama*	5/1898	Wm Cramp, Philadelphia
BB.9 *Wisconsin*	11/1898	Union Iron Works, San Francisco

The *Illinois* Class battleship USS *Alabama* in late 1918, with only eight of the original 14 6-in (152-mm) casemate guns remaining

US Navy

Illinois

ships were refitted with cage foremast and mainmast. Four 3-in (76-mm) guns replaced most of the old 57-mm (2.24-in) and the torpedo tubes were removed.

During the First World War the ships served only as training vessels. In 1918 the six 6-in (152-mm) guns were removed and two 3-in (76-mm) AA guns were added. *Alabama* was sunk as a target during the Mitchell bombing experiments on September 27, 1921. *Wisconsin* was sold for scrap in 1922. *Illinois* served as a drill ship for the New York Naval Militia from 1921 onwards. In 1924 she was designated *IX-15*, and in January 1941 she was renamed *Prairie State*. She was scrapped in 1956.

Displacement: 11 565 tons (normal) *Length:* 114.38 m (373 ft 3 in) oa *Beam:* 22 m (72 ft 2 in) *Draught:* 7.16 m (23 ft 6 in) *Machinery:* 2-shaft triple-expansion, 12 000 ihp=17 knots *Protection:* 406-235 mm (16-9¼ in) belt, 356 mm (14 in) turrets, 254 mm (10 in) conning tower *Armament:* 4 13-in (330-mm)/35-cal (2×2); 14 6-in (152-mm)/40-cal QF (14×1); 16 57-mm (2.24-in) QF (16×1); 6 37-mm (1.46-in) QF (6×1); 4 0.30-in (7.62-mm) machine-guns (4×1); 4 18-in (46-cm) torpedo tubes (beam, above water) *Crew:* 536

USS *Illinois* in 1902 (below) and after her first refit (above) with cage masts, most of the original 57-mm (2.24-in) guns replaced by four 3-in (76-mm) guns and the torpedo tubes removed

Illustrious

British aircraft carrier class, built 1937-41. In 1935, the Admiralty took a radical step by deciding that the Royal Navy's next generation of aircraft carriers should be included in the same protection class as the big-gun units. This was to enable them not merely to stay afloat when hit but also to remain in action, by virtue of protection of their main armament, the aircraft complement.

Previous carriers had been armoured, but only on the lower hangar or main deck over machinery and magazines and in a waterline belt. The *Illustrious* Class ships were to have a hangar proof against 227 kg (500 lb) bombs or 152-mm (6-in) shells. This meant armouring the flight deck, and extending the vertical armour upwards to meet it. The flight deck between the lifts was 76 mm (3 in) thick and the hangar walls, like the belt, were 114 mm (4.5 in) thick. Both ends of the hangar could be closed off from the lift wells (elevator pits) by armoured doors. The hangar deck was proof only against splinters.

Although 5000 tons of armour was worked into the design, the displacement was limited by treaty to 23 000 tons—the same as *Ark Royal*, which had 3500 tons less armour. *Illustrious* was therefore built appreciably shorter than *Ark Royal* and, because the flight deck armour weighed 1500 tons, the second hangar deck was omitted to reduce the freeboard by 6.7 m (22 ft) and preserve stability. Designed aircraft capacity was reduced from 60 to 33, with a consequent saving in aircrew accommodation, aircraft-ordnance stowage and weight and aviation fuel, all of which contributed to keeping the displacement within the treaty limit.

Illustrious otherwise followed the general pattern established by *Ark Royal*. It featured a full-length flight deck, somewhat enlarged island and main gun armament of four pairs of 4.5-in (114-mm) dual-purpose twin turrets (unlike *Ark Royal*'s open mountings) located below flight-deck level on each side, fore and aft. Only one catapult was fitted, completely within the forward flight-deck structure, and two very narrow lifts which were unable to strike down aircraft without folding wings.

Like *Ark Royal*, the *Illustrious* Class had a three-shaft machinery installation, in order to economize on the size of the waterline beam. *Illustrious* was rather more powerful, but due to a slight increase in beam and a marked increase in draught, she was about a knot slower than *Ark Royal* on trials and two knots slower at sea.

Illustrious and *Victorious* were ordered in 1937 and *Formidable* and *Indomitable* later in the same year. *Indomitable* was completed to a slightly different design. Shortage of armour plate contributed to fairly long building times, and *Illustrious* was not completed until May 1940, *Formidable* in November 1940, and *Victorious* in April 1941.

Illustrious was launched on April 5, 1939, and sailed from the Vickers-Armstrongs yard at Barrow just over a year later. By the time she was accepted by the Royal Navy, on May 24, she had been fitted with a warning and fighter-control radar—the first to be installed in an aircraft carrier.

After a workup in the Bermuda area, *Illustrious* was despatched to join the Mediterranean Fleet, based at Alexandria. Between September 1 and December 31, 1940, her 18 Fairey Swordfish raided numerous Italian ports and airfields around the eastern Mediterranean, as well as striking shipping at sea. Undoubtedly her most successful operation was the attack on the Italian fleet in Taranto harbour on November 11-12, for which additional Swordfish were borrowed from *Eagle*: of the 20 aircraft which attacked, only two were lost, while the Italian battleship *Cavour* was sunk and *Littorio* and *Caio Duilio* had to be beached.

Although subjected to air attack on several

HMS *Illustrious* while part of the British task force in the Far East. During strikes against Japanese installations she became the target for suicide attacks, was damaged on April 6, 1944, and withdrew from operations

occasions, *Illustrious* remained undamaged until January 10, 1941, thanks largely to the efforts of her 15 Fairey Fulmar intercepters, which destroyed 25 Italian aircraft. On that day, she was attacked by Ju 87 Stukas off Malta and sustained seven direct bomb hits. Only one bomb, of 500 kg (1100 lb), penetrated the flight-deck armour, the remainder striking outside the hangar area. Still on fire, but under her own steam, *Illustrious* reached Malta, where she remained for emergency repairs until January 23. Further repairs were undertaken at Alexandria and on March 20 she left Egypt for Norfolk navy yard, Virginia.

She spent six months in dockyard hands, returning to the United Kingdom in December 1941. Modifications to her radar and armament were carried out after her arrival and she was not ready to begin working up until the end of February 1942. This workup was cut short by the need for carriers to take part in the occupation of the Vichy French naval harbour of Diego Suarez, at the northern end of Madagascar, and *Illustrious* sailed for the Indian Ocean on March 23, 1942. On May 5, she and *Indomitable* began three days of operations against the Vichy air and naval forces while British and Commonwealth troops landed and captured the town. *Illustrious*'s 21 Swordfish sank two submarines and an armed merchant cruiser and shared in sinking a large sloop; the 20 Grumman Martlet fighters also saw action, shooting down seven Vichy aircraft.

Illustrious remained in the Indian Ocean for the remainder of 1942, undertaking one diversionary operation, to distract Japanese attention from the south-west Pacific at the time of the Guadalcanal landings in August. In September, her aircraft covered the occupation of southern Madagascar, achieving their task without firing their guns or dropping bombs. For this operation, she had embarked 45 aircraft (18 Swordfish, 21 Martlets and six Fulmars); 41 of these could be stowed in the hangar, leaving four Martlets permanently parked on deck. Permanent deck parking had never been favoured by the Royal Navy, although it had always been a US Navy procedure, but it had to be adopted in order to embark as many aircraft as possible for operations.

Leaving the Indian Ocean in January 1943, *Illustrious* was refitted in the UK between February and June. In July, she took part in a diversionary operation off Norway, where her Martlets shot down two flying boats, and in August she sailed to join the Mediterranean Fleet. By now she had embarked 12 of the new Fairey Barracudas, 28 Martlets and ten Supermarine Seafires, the latter parked on deck. Even if there had been room for them in the hangar, they could not be struck down the narrow lifts. Between September 9-11, *Illustrious* and *Formidable* provided generally uneventful fighter patrols over a force of escort carriers which were supporting the invasion of Salerno. Thereafter, both carriers left the Mediterranean, *Formidable* to refit and *Illustrious* to prepare for another Indian Ocean deployment.

She arrived in Ceylon from Britain on January 31, 1944, with 21 Barracudas and 28 Vought F4U Corsairs embarked. Because of the lack of overhead clearance in *Illustrious*, the American-built fighters' rounded wingtips

Illustrious after the war. She remained in service and was used for trials with jet aircraft

had had to be clipped to enable them to be spread and folded in the hangar. The new air group first saw action on April 19 when, in company with *Saratoga*, strikes were launched against Sabang, Sumatra. A month later, on May 17, the two carriers attacked Surabaja, Java, harbour and oil refineries, *Illustrious* having replaced her Barracudas with 18 Grumman TBF Avengers for this one operation.

Saratoga left after this operation and on June 21 *Illustrious* undertook a solo strike against the Andaman Islands. For this operation, she embarked an extra 14 Corsairs at the expense of six Barracudas: this was the greatest number of aircraft ever operated from *Illustrious* and at one time on May 21 she had 51 of the 57 airborne.

After another raid on Sabang, on July 25, in company with *Victorious*, she left for a refit at Durban and did not return to Trincomalee until November 2. In anticipation of forthcoming deployment to the Pacific, the Barracudas had given way to the faster and longer-ranged Avengers, and the number of Corsairs had been increased to 36.

The first strike was against Sumatran oil installations on December 20, but bad weather led to disappointing results. On January 24 and 29, 1945, however, *Illustrious* was part of the carrier force which made devastating raids on the Palembang refineries, her contribution being 24 Avenger and 52 Corsair offensive sorties on the two days.

The force, designated the British Pacific Fleet, proceeded from the launching area to Sydney, which was to be the rear base for Pacific operations. *Illustrious* had been damaged by friendly AA fire on January 29 and had experienced propeller shaft vibration during the passage to Sydney and required docking for repairs and investigation of the centre shaft. The latter proved to be defective and the propeller was removed, reducing her maximum speed to 24 knots. The other three carriers of the fleet had sailed by the time *Illustrious* undocked, but she rejoined

them before they left the forward base at Manus for operations in support of the American invasion of Okinawa.

Between March 26 and April 13, *Illustrious* launched 443 combat sorties on nine strike days. Targets included airfields in the Sakishima Gunto Archipelago and on Formosa. Suicide aircraft attacked on April 1 and 6. *Illustrious* was the target on the second occasion, and although her automatic AA weapons deflected the kamikaze so that it only clipped the island, the explosion of the bomb under water caused damage, the extent of which was not realized at the time. She was relieved by *Formidable* on April 14 and retired to the US forward base at Leyte, where divers examined the hull and reported that the outer plating and internal frames were cracked. Temporary repairs were effected and *Illustrious* returned to Britain via Sydney, her speed now restricted to 19 knots.

She was taken in hand for refit on return at the end of June, the work being expected to take four months. The end of the war in mid-August resulted in her completion being delayed until June 1946, the alterations being more extensive than originally planned. The forward end of the flight deck was extended and remodelled, the catapult was modified to launch heavier aircraft. The aviation-fuel capacity was increased by 30%, overcoming one of the most serious disadvantages of the class—the 229 750 litres (50 540 Imp gal) which had been barely adequate for 33 aircraft was just not sufficient for more than 50.

Between 1946 and the end of 1954, *Illustrious* was employed as the Home Fleet trials and training carrier, only once or twice embarking front-line squadrons for exercises. During this period, the initial deck-landing trials with the Royal Navy's first generation of jet aircraft were carried out aboard *Illustrious* but, unlike her sister ship *Victorious*, she was not considered for modernization. Laid up in reserve in December 1954, she was sold for scrapping on November 3, 1956.

Displacement: 23 000 tons (standard), 29 110 tons (full load) (from 1946 26 000 tons [standard], 31 630 tons [full load]) *Length:* 225.5 m (740 ft) (from 1946 229.6 m [753 ft 3 in]) *Beam:* 29.2 m (95 ft 9 in) *Draught:* 8.8 m (29 ft) *Machinery:* 3 sets geared steam turbines, 3 shafts, 113 300 shp=30.5 knots approx *Aircraft:* 33 *Armament:* 16 4.5-in (114-mm) DP (8×2); 88 2-pdr (40-mm) AA (6×8, 5×8); 3 40-mm (1.57-in) Bofors AA (3×1); 52 20-mm (0.79-in) Bofors AA (52×1) *Crew:* 1229 (from 1946, 1997)

Ilya Mourometz, Sikorsky

Soviet heavy bomber. In 1913 the world's first four-engined aeroplane, the Le Grand, was designed and built by two Russians, Igor Sikorsky and G I Lavrov. It flew for the first time on May 13 of that year. Three months later Sikorsky commenced work on an even larger four-engined transport version, which he named Ilya Mourometz after a legendary Russian hero of the tenth century. Powered by four 100-hp Argus engines, this remarkable biplane had a fully enclosed fuselage incorporating a glass-windowed pilot's cockpit, a passenger cabin, a luxury private cabin, and an upper deck or balcony where a washroom was provided. Fuselage doors gave access to the wings for in-flight engine maintenance. The fuselage was lit by electricity from wind-driven generators, and warmed by pipes in the cabin corners which utilized heat from the engine exhausts.

In April 1914 a second Ilya Mourometz was built, virtually identical to the first except for the installation of 140-hp engines in the two inboard locations. To test and demonstrate his designs, Sikorsky decided on what was for the period an ambitious cross-country flight from Petrograd to Kiev, a distance of some 1130 km (700 miles). Setting off on June 29, 1914, the crew of three slept, ate and took turns at the controls, reaching their objective safely next day in spite of having had to extinguish a fire and recover from a 365-m (1200-ft) spin en route. Later renamed Kievsky, this aeroplane opened the Russian air offensive against Germany, and survived until 1917.

Ten examples of a military version were ordered by the Imperial Russian Air Service in early 1914, and on the outbreak of war further orders increased the overall total to 73 machines intended for war use. These were built in at least five differing variants, the largest and fastest of which was the E-1, powered by four 220-hp Renault engines with a maximum speed when loaded of 137 km (85 mph). To exploit the huge bomber's war potential a special self-contained unit was

formed—the Eskadra Vozdushnykh Korablei (squadron of flying ships)—under the command of Major-General M V Shidlovski, which made its first bombing sorties from its Polish base at Jablonna on February 15, 1915. From then until the 1917 revolution the massive bombers flew a total of 422 raids, during which they dropped over 2000 bombs and destroyed 40 enemy aircraft. This outstanding record was all the more remarkable considering that during those three years only one bomber was lost to enemy action (on September 12, 1916), though two others were destroyed in flying accidents.

Although it was cumbersome in appearance, and needed firm control in flight, the Ilya Mourometz was well constructed and capable of absorbing considerable damage. That it was no easy target for an opposing fighter was demonstrated on a raid in March 1916 when three of the bombers, IM-5, IM-7 and IM-9, were attacked by 12 enemy fighters. Gunners in the bombers shot down three of the fighters, and the surviving attackers broke off the action. Normal defensive armament comprised four hand-operated machine-guns, although up to seven gunners were sometimes carried. A useful bombload of up to 680 kg (1500 lb) could be handled with ease. In May 1915 one machine successfully lifted a single 454-kg (1000-lb) bomb in an experimental trial. A variety of powerplants was fitted to various machines, including Argus, Sunbeam, Salmson and Renault engines. At least one Ilya Mourometz was fitted with a huge float undercarriage.

When the Czarist regime was overthrown in the revolution of 1917 most of the Ilya Mourometz aircraft were still intact and operational. Most, if not all, were quickly destroyed to prevent their being used by the revolutionaries or the Germans, at least 30 machines being deliberately destroyed at Vinnitza in February 1918. Igor Sikorsky emigrated to the US, and became renowned as a flying boat and helicopter designer.

(Type V) *Span:* (upper wing) 29.79 m (97 ft 9 in) *Length:* 17.09 m (56 ft 1 in) *Gross weight:* 4595 kg (10 130 lb) *Maximum speed:* 121 km/h (75 mph)

IMAM Italian aircraft
See **Ro 37, Ro 43, Ro 44, Ro 57, Ro 58**

IMP

US machine-pistol. The IMP (individual multipurpose weapon) is one of the lightweight survival weapons which has been developed for the US Air Force during the 1970s. The original specification called for a weapon with a 100-m (110-yards) lethal range, a maximum weight of 0.68 kg (1 lb 8 oz), a maximum length of 33 cm (13 in), a magazine capacity of at least seven rounds, and a semiautomatic action. The work was undertaken by the US Air Force Armament Laboratory which evolved the unusual configuration of the IMP in which the firer's arm acts as part of the butt.

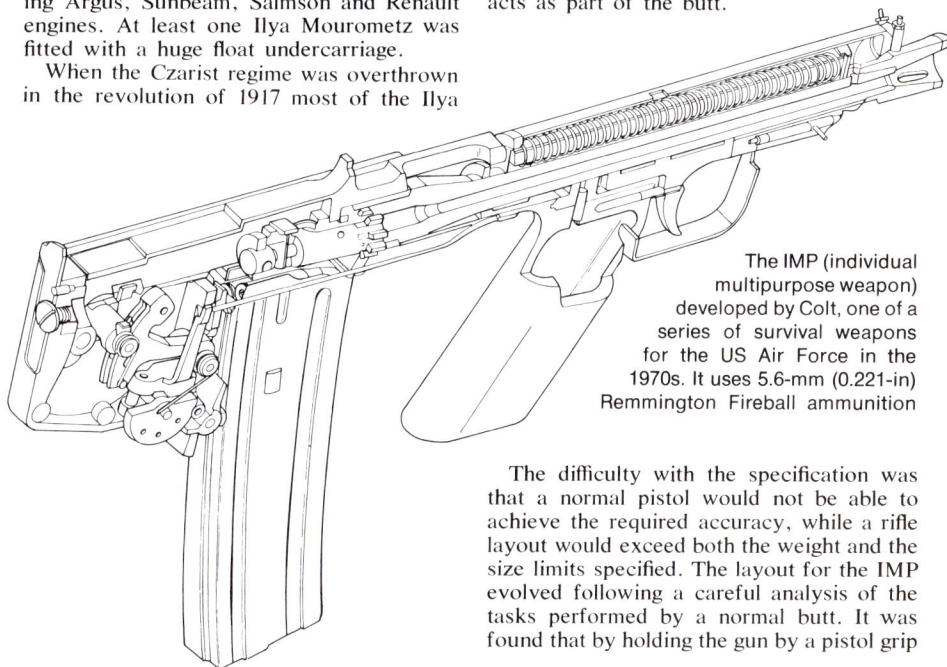

The IMP (individual multipurpose weapon) developed by Colt, one of a series of survival weapons for the US Air Force in the 1970s. It uses 5.6-mm (0.221-in) Remmington Fireball ammunition

The difficulty with the specification was that a normal pistol would not be able to achieve the required accuracy, while a rifle layout would exceed both the weight and the size limits specified. The layout for the IMP evolved following a careful analysis of the tasks performed by a normal butt. It was found that by holding the gun by a pistol grip

The Ilya Mourometz Type V heavy bomber designed by the prolific Igor Sikorsky for the Imperial Russian Air Force in 1913

Impavido

at or near the muzzle, and supporting it along the inside of the outstretched right arm, the weapon could be held quite steady and the recoil force easily absorbed.

To achieve the necessary performance an existing Remington 0.221-in (5.6-mm) Fireball round is used. The weapon is similar to a long-barrelled pistol, with a forehand grip and the action and magazine located at the extreme rear. There are normal sights. When shooting, the magazine is steadied on the right arm by the left hand. Only four have been made (all by Colt) and there do not seem to be any more orders, but this interesting idea may have possibilities for future light weapons.

Weight unloaded: 1.81 kg (4 lb) *Calibre:* 0.221-in (5.6-mm) Fireball *Length:* 403 mm (15.87 in) *Barrel length:* 254 mm (10 in) *Magazine:* 30-round box *Rate of fire:* 500 rds/min (cyclic) *Muzzle velocity:* 732 m/sec (2400 ft/sec)

Impala, Atlas South African licence-built version of Aermacchi M.B.326 trainer/light strike aircraft   See **M.B.326**

Impavido

Italian destroyer class. Two guided-missile destroyers were authorized under the 1956-57 and 1958-59 Programmes, the first missile-armed ships to be built for the Italian navy. *Impavido* (D.570) was launched at Riva Trigoso on May 25, 1962, and *Intrepido* (D.571) was launched at Livorno on October 21 the same year. On her sea trials *Impavido* reached 34.5 knots in light condition. In general the design follows that of the *Impetuoso* Class, though the *Impavido*s have more sheer to the forecastle, a bigger superstructure and taller funnels. The same twin 5-in (127-mm) of US Navy pattern is mounted forward, and a single-arm Tartar missile-launcher is mounted on a circular deckhouse at the after end of the superstructure. There are also four single 76-mm (3-in)/52-cal automatic guns abreast of the after funnel and triple Mk 32 torpedo tubes for antisubmarine torpedoes on either side of the bridge.

During 1974-76 both ships were modernized, and the bulky fire-control director was replaced by an Elsag (Elettronica San Giorgio) Argo NA 10 system. Two SPG-51 directors are fitted to control the Tartar missiles, together with an SPS-12 search radar and SPS-39 3-D long-range surveillance radar. They are also fitted with a hull-mounted SQS-23 sonar and a flight deck for operation of an antisubmarine helicopter, but have no hangar or maintenance facilities.

Since entering service in 1963-64 both ships have been actively employed with NATO forces in the Mediterranean and Atlantic. The Tartar missile system is to be replaced by Standard, but this will involve no outward alterations.

Displacement: 3201 tons (standard), 3851 tons (full load) *Length:* 131.3 m (430 ft 9 in) *Beam:* 13.6 m (44 ft 7½ in) *Draught:* 4.5 m (14 ft 9 in) *Machinery:* 2-shaft geared steam turbines, 70 000 shp=33 knots *Armament:* 1 RIM-24 Tartar SAM launcher; 2 5-in (127-mm)/38-cal DP (1×2); 4 78-mm (3-in)/62-cal AA (4×1); 6 32.4-cm (12.75-in) torpedo tubes (2×3) *Crew:* 335

Aldo Fraccaroli

Above: Intrepido with Impetuoso in the background in March 1971. Below: Impavido, with her sister Intrepido, became the first missile-armed warships to serve with the Italian navy

Giorgio Arra

Imperator Aleksandr II

Russian battleship class, built 1885-92. The two ships comprising the class, *Imperator Aleksandr II* and *Imperator Nikolai I*, were laid down in St Petersburg between 1885 and 1886. They were commissioned into the Russian Baltic Fleet, but by the beginning of the twentieth century they were obsolescent.

At the outbreak of the Russo-Japanese war of 1904, it was decided to send the Russian Baltic fleet to the Far East to strengthen the hard-pressed Russian squadrons at Port Arthur and Vladivostok. The Baltic fleet was placed under the overall command of Admiral Zinovi Rodzhestvenski, and spent the summer of 1904 refitting for the long voyage to the Far East.

Following the refit, *Nikolai I* sailed as the flagship of Rear-Admiral Nebogatov's squad-

ron. During the battle of Tsushima on May 27, 1905, when the numerically superior but inefficient Russian fleet was defeated by Japanese forces under Admiral Togo Heinachiro, *Nikolai I* suffered light damage. She became the flagship of the remnants of the Russian fleet after Rodzhestvenski was badly wounded and taken off the sinking *Kniaz Suvorov*. On the day following the action she surrendered to Japanese destroyers and torpedo boats, and was escorted to Sasebo. The Japanese reconstructed her and she entered service as *Iki* in 1906, serving as a gunnery training ship. From 1910-15 she served on coastal-defence duties and as a training ship for boy seamen. After being stricken she was used as a target ship, and was sunk by the new battlecruisers *Kongo* and *Hiei* in October 1915.

Aleksandr II was also refitted and rearmed

for service in the Far East, but the collapse of Port Arthur meant that she never left the Baltic. In 1906 she became flagship of the Baltic Fleet Training Squadron, and in 1911 became a gunnery training ship. In February 1917 she was renamed *Zara Svobody*, and three years later was damaged by British coastal motorboats taking part in the attack on Kronstadt during the 'war of intervention' against the new Bolshevik regime. She was stricken in 1922 and scrapped.

Displacement: 9244-9440 tons (normal), 9672-9927 tons (full load) *Length:* 10ᵣ.64 m (346 ft 7 in) oa *Beam:* 20.42 m (67 ft) *Draught:* 7.85 m (25 ft 9 in) max *Machinery:* 2-shaft reciprocating steam, 8000 ihp=15 knots *Protection:* 356 mm (14 in) belt, 254 mm (10 in) turrets, 63 mm (2.48 in) deck *Armament:* (*Imperator Aleksandr II* [1908]) 2 12-in (305-mm)/30-cal (1×2); 4 8-in (203-mm)/45-cal (4×1); 8 6-in (152-mm)/45-cal (8×1); 4 4.7-in (120-mm) (4×1); 4 47-mm (1.85-in) (4×1); 2 37-mm (1.46-in) (2×1); 4 machine-guns (4×1); (*Imperator Nikolai I* [1910]) 2 12-in (305-mm)/40-cal (1×2); 6 6-in (152-mm)/40-cal (6×1); 6 4.7-in (120-mm)/40-cal (6×1) *Crew:* 611-648

Imperator Nikolai I

Russian battleship, built 1914-17. She was ordered in 1914 as a larger and faster version of the *Imperatritsa Maria*, and was launched at the Russud yard at Nikolayev on October 18, 1916. In 1917, while only 40% complete, she was renamed *Demokratiya* and work continued on her until the approach of the German armies in 1918. She suffered repeated sabotage from the Germans and the White Russian forces, and after the civil war was beyond repair and was scrapped.

Displacement: 27 627 tons (normal), 29 500 tons approx (full load) *Length:* 182 m (597 ft) oa *Beam:* 28.8 m (94 ft 6 in) *Draught:* 9 m (29 ft 6 in) *Machinery:* 4-shaft steam turbines, 29 700 shp=23 knots *Protection:* 305-203 mm (12-8 in) belt, 305 mm (12 in) turrets, 76-38 mm (3-1.5 in) deck *Armament:* 12 305-mm (12-in)/52-cal (4×3); 20 130-mm (5.1-in)/55-cal (20×1); 4 45-cm (17.7-in) torpedo tubes (submerged, beam) *Crew:* 1250 approx

Imperator Petr Veliky

Russian battleship built 1869-75. This venerable turret-ship had been relegated to training duties by the beginning of the twentieth century, and in 1907 she was completely rebuilt as a training ship. Her appearance changed completely from a low-freeboard ship of the monitor type to a high freeboard ship with a broadside battery and two funnels.

After reconstruction had been completed at the Franco-Russian Works in St Petersburg she joined the Baltic Training Squadron as a gunnery training ship, and served with that unit until the February revolution of 1917. Renamed *Respublikanetz* by the Kerensky Government, she was scrapped in 1922.

Displacement: 9665 tons (normal), 9790 tons (full load) *Length:* 100.96 m (331 ft 3 in) oa *Beam:* 19 m (62 ft 4 in) *Draught:* 8.3 m (27 ft 3 in) *Machinery:* 2-shaft reciprocating steam, 8258 ihp=13 knots *Armament:* 4 8-in (203-mm)/50-cal (4×1); 12 6-in (152-mm)/45-cal (12×1); 12 3-in (76-mm) QF (12×1); 4 57-mm (2.24-in) QF (4×1); 8 47-mm (1.85-in) QF; 2 37-mm (1.46-in); 6 machine-guns *Crew:* 374

Imperatritsa Maria

Russian battleship class. These three Dreadnoughts ordered for the Black Sea Fleet were similar to the *Gangut* Class building in the Baltic, but were slightly smaller and slower. *Imperatritsa Maria* was launched by the Russud yard in 1913, followed by *Imperator Aleksandr III* from the same yard and *Imperatritsa Ekaterina II* from Nikolaiev

State yard in 1914. *Imperatritsa Maria* commissioned in June 1915, followed by *Imperatritsa Ekaterina II* three months later, but *Imperator Aleksandr III* was not commissioned until early 1917.

Imperatritsa Maria and *Imperatritsa Ekaterina II* took part in several actions in the First World War, including bombardments of Turkish shore positions. On October 20, 1916, *Imperatritsa Maria* blew up while at anchor in the northern harbour of Sevastopol. Although sabotage was suspected, the most likely cause was deterioration of her cordite. She was refloated upside down in 1917 but was scuttled in 1920 to avoid capture by rebel forces. In 1927 she was refloated once more and scrapped.

After the February revolution of 1917, *Imperator Aleksandr III* was renamed *Volya* while *Imperatritsa Ekaterina II* became *Svobodnaya Rossiya*. The latter was scuttled at Novorossiisk by Soviet forces on June 18, 1918, but *Volya* was captured by the Germans and renamed *Volga*. She was taken over by the British in 1919, and for a while there was talk of shipping one of her triple 12-in (305-mm) gun turrets back to England for testing. Instead she was handed over to the White forces and renamed *General Alekseyev*, and when White resistance collapsed in 1920 she led the exodus to Bizerta, where she lay until 1936 when the French government sold her for scrap.

Displacement: 22 800 tons (normal), 24 000 tons (full load) *Length:* 168 m (551 ft 2 in) oa *Beam:* 27.3 m (89 ft 6 in) *Draught:* 8.3 m (27 ft 3 in) *Machinery:* 4-shaft steam turbines, 26 500 shp=21 knots *Protection:* 305-203 mm (12-8 in) belt, 305 mm (12 in) turrets, 76-38 mm (3-1.5 in) deck *Armament:* 12 305-mm (12-in)/52-cal (4×3); 18 130-mm (5.1-in)/55-cal (18×1); 4 76-mm (3-in) QF (4×1); 4 47-mm (1.85-in) QF (4×1); 4 machine-guns; 4 45-cm (17.7-in) torpedo tubes (submerged, beam) *Crew:* 1252

The Russian Dreadnought *Imperatritsa Maria*. Her 12 305-mm (12-in) guns were used to bombard Turkish installations during the First World War. She was severely damaged in 1916 by a mysterious explosion

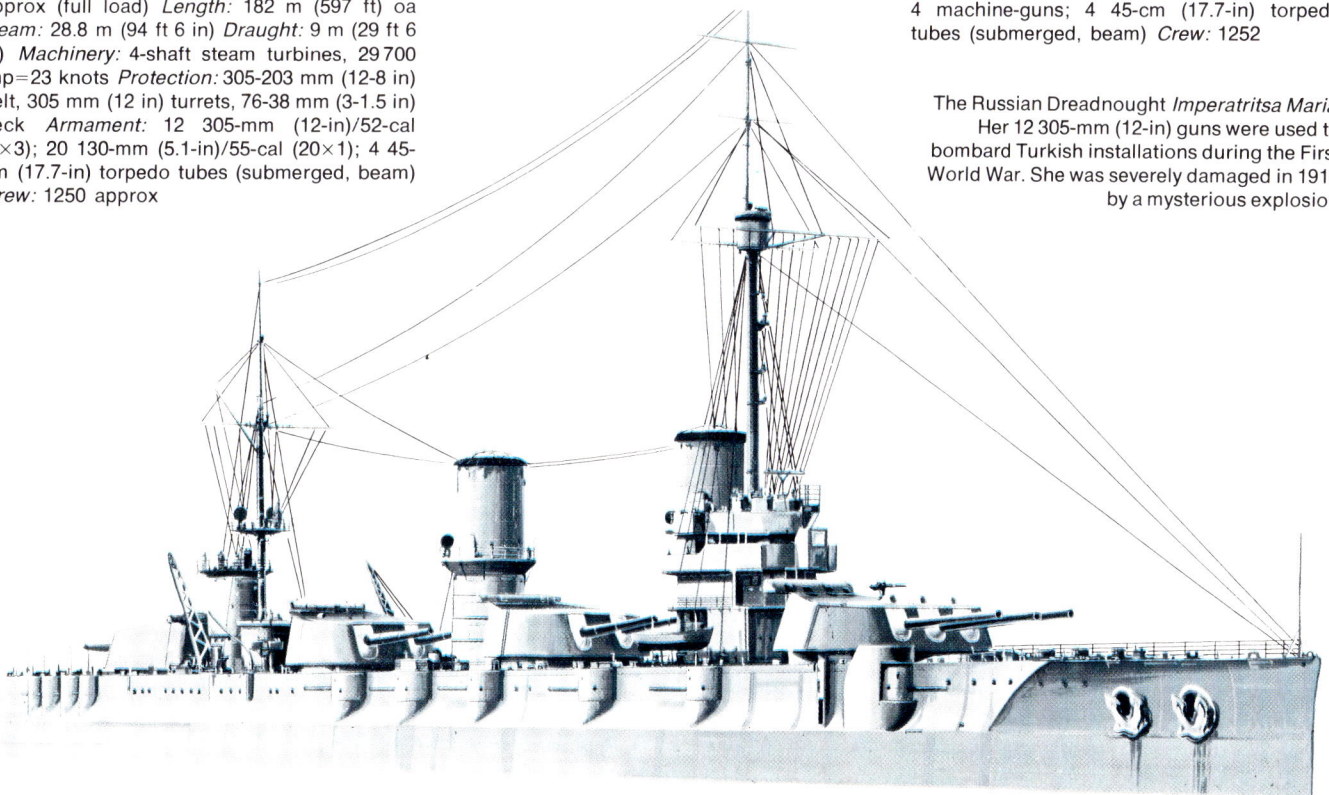

Impetuoso

The Italian destroyer *Impetuoso*. With her sister the *Indomito* she was among the first warships built by the Italians in the 1950s

Impetuoso

Italian destroyer class. As the first instalment of a massive rearmament programme, which was partially funded by US money, Italy began to rebuild her naval forces in 1952. The first destroyers ordered were a pair of ships broadly based on the *Gearing* Class, but with more beam to allow a greater weight of antisubmarine and antiaircraft armament.

The armament was conventional: two twin 127-mm (5-in)/38-cal guns forward and aft, and quadruple and twin 40-mm (1.57-in) Bofors AA guns disposed on the beam amidships. The fire control and the guns were supplied from the US; an Italian Menon triple-barrelled antisubmarine mortar was installed in B position; depth-charge racks were installed on the quarterdeck; and single Mk 25 53-cm (21-in) A/S torpedo tubes were installed on the beam between the funnels.

Indomito was launched on August 7, 1955, from the Ansaldo yard, Livorno, and *Impetuoso* from the Cantieri Navali dell'Tireno yard on September 16, 1956. Both ships exceeded 35 knots on trials. They have been refitted since 1966, the principal alteration being the replacement of the Mk 25 single torpedo tubes by triple Mk 32 tubes. A search radar (type SGS/6B) and SFS/6O fire-control radar are fitted, with Mk 34 radars for the Mk 51 40-mm (1.57-in) directors. The hull-mounted sonar is an SQS/11. By the late 1970s these ships had become obsolescent, lacking a good AA defence, and were due for decommissioning and replacement by more modern destroyers.

Displacement: 2755 tons (standard), 3800 tons (full load) *Length:* 127.6 m (418 ft 8 in) oa *Beam:* 13.3 m (43 ft 8 in) *Draught:* 5.3 m (17 ft 5 in) *Machinery:* 2-shaft geared steam turbines, 65 000 shp = 34 knots *Armament:* 4 127-mm (5-in)/38-cal DP (2×2); 16 40-mm (1.57-in)/56-cal AA (2×4, 4×2); 1 triple Menon A/S mortar; 2 53-cm (21-in) torpedo tubes (2×1) *Crew:* 315

Implacable

British aircraft carrier class. Although *Implacable* and *Indefatigable* are usually described as the fifth and sixth units of the *Illustrious* Class, or as improved *Indomitables*, the 1938 design of fleet carrier to which they were built was quite new. Apart from standard displacement and beam, which were limited by treaty and by dock-gate dimensions, only the well-proven external layout and main armament remained unchanged.

The naval staff had demanded greater speed and an increased aircraft complement, compared with *Indomitable*. Existing machinery could not give the extra power needed for 32 knots on three shafts and so an extra set of boilers, turbines and a fourth shaft had to be squeezed into the width allowed for three in earlier fleet carriers. The extra hangar space was found by extending the lower hangar further forward than in *Indomitable*. As the hull was extended by only 7.9 m (26 ft) and the hangar was 14 m (46 ft) longer, internal accommodation was very cramped and required considerable rearrangement.

The Royal Navy had not really wanted to reduce the thickness of the hangar walls in *Indomitable*, and in the new class the thickness was increased to 51 mm (2 in) and at the same time the lower hangar deck was armoured over the machinery. The extra armour required topweight compensations and so the height of the lower hangar was reduced by 61 cm (2 ft), both hangars now having overhead clearance of 4.26 m (14 ft). The lifts were identical to those in *Indomitable*, but a new type of catapult was installed. All the flight-deck machinery was intended to handle aircraft of up to 9070 kg (20 000 lb)

weight. A considerable 'stretch' was thus built into the class, since the Royal Navy's heaviest aircraft weighed barely half this figure in 1939.

The main external differences between the *Implacable* Class and their predecessors were the much enlarged funnel and longer island. The fire-control director, previously mounted above the bridge, was moved down to a position abaft the funnel and a multiple pom-pom was shifted from the flight deck abaft the island to below the port deck-edge, both changes being made to improve stability.

Implacable was ordered in 1938 and *Indefatigable* a year later. Construction was halted in 1940 by order of Churchill and even after it was resumed at the end of the year little priority was given to completion. *Implacable* took five years to build and was not commissioned until August 28, 1944, by which time her sister was fully operational and actually at sea in combat.

Indefatigable was completed by the John Brown Clydeside yard on May 3, 1944, and after trials which included the first deck landings on a British carrier by a twin-engined aircraft (the de Havilland Mosquito), she worked up at Scapa Flow. Since the low hangars prevented her from embarking Corsairs and since insufficient Hellcats were available, her fighter wing had to be equipped with Supermarine Seafires. Though Seafires were excellent intercepters, their low fuel capacity made them indifferent general-purpose fighters, and fuselage and undercarriage weaknesses made them poor carrier aircraft. As well as the 24 Seafires, *Indefatigable* embarked 21 Barracudas and the first squadron of Fairey Firefly two-seat fighters to go to sea.

The first operation, a fighter sweep off Bergen on August 3, 1944, was aborted by low cloud, but a week later the fighters covered a minelaying strike by Grumman Avengers from two escort carriers. Later in the month, all the Home Fleet's operational carriers took part in a series of strikes on the German battleship *Tirpitz* lying in her Kaafjord, Norway, anchorage. Attacks were delivered on August 22, 24 and 29, but the enemy's smoke screen resulted in only two hits being scored, one by an *Indefatigable* aircraft on August 24. On return from this operation, the carrier was modified for Pacific operations.

The Seafire wing was transferred to *Implacable*, which made her operational debut on October 19, when her Fireflys found *Tirpitz* at Tromsö. On October 26, *Implacable* began a three-day antishipping operation off Norway, in which her aircraft sank seven ships and damaged 14 others, as well as driving a U-Boat aground as a total loss.

Returning to land *Indefatigable*'s fighter wing and to work up her own, *Implacable* spent a month in the Scapa Flow area before going back to the Norwegian coast. On November 27, 11 Barracudas supported by 24 fighters attacked a convoy sinking two ships and damaging four others and two escorts, at no cost to the carrier aircraft. Soon afterwards *Implacable* sustained serious damage to her forward hull plating in a gale, and after launching one further mission on December 8 she had to return for dockyard repairs.

Indefatigable had meanwhile arrived in Ceylon to join the Eastern Fleet. Between November 19 and New Year's Day 1945, she worked up with the other armoured carriers of the fleet, all of which were now armed with Grumman Avengers in place of Barracudas. *Indefatigable* now possessed 40 Seafires out of a total air group of 73 aircraft.

Her first operation was a strike on the Pankalan Brandan oil refinery at Medan on January 4, 1945, in company with *Indomitable* and *Victorious*. This strike was a great success, as were two attacks on the Palembang refineries on January 24 and 29, while on passage to Sydney, where the redesignated British Pacific Fleet arrived on February 10.

A month later, the main body sailed for the combat area, off the Sakishima Gunto. The operation, with the British carrier force covering the Okinawa invasion against interference from the direction of Formosa, began on March 26. No enemy attacks were delivered against the fleet until April 1, when *Indefatigable* was the first British carrier to be hit by a kamikaze. This was a Mitsubishi Zero which hit the flight deck at the base of the island and broke up on the 76-mm (3-in) deck armour, causing 29 casualties. The fire on the deck was extinguished in 15 minutes and aircraft were landing within 35 minutes. An hour later, the ship was fully operational once again.

Strike missions were flown by the Avengers and Fireflys on 12 days up to April 20, while the Seafires provided the majority of the fleet's low- and medium-level fighter patrols. These intercepters suffered heavy losses through landing accidents. No fewer than 21 were written off and six damaged beyond the ship's capacity to repair them. The losses were made good during replenishments at sea and during a week spent at Leyte. In the second phase of the operation, which lasted during May 4-25, only nine Seafires were lost from all causes. Avenger and Firefly losses were light throughout and *Indefatigable* contributed over 1800 of the

British Pacific Fleet's total of 5335 sorties between March 26 and May 25, 1945.

Implacable left the United Kingdom on March 10, 1945, and arrived at Sydney in mid-May, while the other carriers were off Sakishima. Before they returned, she left again for a 'training strike' on Truk, the bypassed Japanese naval base which now served as a target for units completing working up. (It was so used in a dummy run by the B-29 which was to undertake the first A-bomb raid.) *Implacable*'s 21 Avengers, 12 Fireflys and 48 Seafires flew 216 sorties against the main islands in the atoll on June 14-15, bombing, rocketing, and spotting for cruiser bombardments. The carrier proceeded to Manus, New Guinea, to await the fleet, whose next target was to be Japan itself. *Indefatigable*'s auxiliary machinery broke down shortly before the force left Sydney on June 28, and her first meeting with her sister ship, on July 7, was brief as the other ships were leaving Manus as she entered.

Implacable, *Formidable* and *Victorious* launched their first missions against Japan on July 17 and the honour of being the first British aircraft to fly over the Japanese home islands fell to the Fireflys of *Implacable*'s 1771 Squadron. *Indefatigable* joined in on July 24, and on that and five more days up to August 10, the four British carriers flew 2291 sorties. Airfields, the railways system, shipyards, factories, naval bases and coastal shipping were all attacked. Operations reached a climax on August 9, when 258 British strike sorties delivered over 120 tons of ordnance. *Indefatigable* and *Implacable*, with their larger air groups, were responsible for nearly two-thirds of the total, their

HMS *Implacable* at anchor in Scapa Flow during her service with the Home Fleet in 1944. She transferred to the Far East in May 1945

Seafires taking part in the offensive missions as well as providing defensive patrols.

Indefatigable remained to operate with the US 3rd Fleet when *Implacable* and the two other carriers departed for Australia after the strikes of August 10. She flew 78 sorties on August 14, in spite of bad weather, and the next day launched eight Fireflys for an offensive sweep, followed by six Avengers and eight Seafires sent to attack an airfield. The strike was intercepted by Zeros but the Seafires shot down eight of the fighters, and damaged three more, for the loss of one Seafire. This was officially the last combat of the war, for at the same time news of the Japanese surrender was received by the fleet.

Indefatigable remained with the American fleet until September 2, 1945, and was present at the surrender in Tokyo Bay. She returned to Sydney a fortnight later after a deployment which had sent her at sea for 64 days.

Both *Implacable* and *Indefatigable* remained with the British Pacific Fleet after the war, the latter making one cruise to Japan to bring back Allied prisoners of war before re-embarking her squadrons for a cruise to New Zealand. *Indefatigable* left Sydney at the end of January 1946 and reached Portsmouth on March 15. *Implacable* followed three months later, returning to the United Kingdom on June 3, 1946.

Indefatigable made one trooping voyage to the Far East during the second half of 1946 and then paid off into reserve, but *Implacable* recommissioned immediately for service as the Home Fleet's deck-landing training ship. Although an air group was allocated to her in late 1947, the two squadrons were experiencing considerable teething troubles and it was not until March 1949 that she embarked 13 de Havilland Sea Hornets and 12 Blackburn Firebrands. These were reinforced in the autumn of 1949 by the four de Havilland Sea Vampires of the Jet Fighter Evaluation Unit, which operated successfully from the carrier during a cruise to Gibraltar. In the summer of 1950 the 12 Fairey Barracudas of the Navy's only dedicated antisubmarine squadron joined for an exercise. In September 1950, she was placed in reserve, her future to be decided.

Meanwhile *Indefatigable* had been refitted as a training ship, her hangars being too low for modern aircraft but ideal for conversion to classrooms and messdecks. From 1950 she served in this role, being joined by *Implacable* from January 1952. In August 1954 both carriers paid off for the last time. *Implacable* was scrapped in late 1955 and her sister followed a year later.

Displacement: 23 450 tons (standard), 32 110 tons (full load) *Length:* 233.6 m (766 ft 6 in) *Beam:* 29.2 m (95 ft 9 in) *Draught:* 8.9 m (29 ft 4 in) *Machinery:* 4 sets geared steam turbines, 4 shafts 150 935 shp=32 knots *Aircraft:* 81 *Armament:* 16 4.5-in (114-mm) DP (8×2); 52/(*Indefatigable* 44) 2-pdr AA (3×4, 5×6/1×4, 5×8); 61/(*Indefatigable* 55) 20-mm (0.79-in) (61×1/55×1) *Crew:* 2300 approx

INA

Brazilian submachine-gun. The INA (in full, Metralhadora de Mao 0.45-in INA 953) takes its name from the initial letters of the makers, Industrias Nacional de Armas of São Paulo.

The INA is a modified version of the Danish Madsen Model 1950 and it is made under licence in Brazil in 0.45-in (11.43-mm) calibre instead of the more normal 9-mm (0.354-mm). There are some slight divergencies from the Madsen design, notably in the alteration of the position of the cocking handle from the top of the body to the right-hand side. There are some other small changes internally, probably to take account of the different characteristics of the ammunition, but in all general respects the INA is just a Madsen in a larger calibre.

It has been made in quantity and is the standard issue of the Brazilian armed services and police. The weapon has also been exported to other South American countries.

Calibre: 0.45-in (11.43-mm) *Ammunition:* 0.45 in M1911 (0.45 in ACP) *Weight unloaded:* 3.40 kg (7 lb 8 oz) *Length:* (stock extended) 794 mm (31.26 in), (stock retracted) 546 mm (21.5 in) *Barrel length:* 214.6 mm (8.45 in) *Operation:* simple blowback *Magazine:* 30-round detachable box *Rate of fire:* 650 rds/min *Muzzle velocity:* 228 m/sec (750 ft/sec) approx

Indefatigable

British battlecruiser class. These ships were essentially repeats of the *Invincible* Class, Britain's first battlecruisers, but were 7.6 m (25 ft) longer to provide for a wider spacing of the wing turrets, and 0.46 m (18 in) broader. They had more powerful machinery to maintain the same speed with the larger hull. Other variations from the earlier ships included moving the belt further aft, which improved the protection to the after magazines but left the bow unprotected, reducing the thickness of the lower deck from 51-38 mm (2-1.5 in) to 25 mm (1 in), and mounting three fewer torpedo tubes. The intention in moving the wing turrets was to allow for better arcs of fire when firing across the beam, but in practice these arcs were greatly reduced by the effects of blast on the superstructure. Wing turrets were, in any case, to prove of little tactical value as they

could hardly ever fulfil their intended purpose of providing full broadside as well as 75% ahead or astern fire.

The result was a design with the same speed, same armament and almost the same armour as the *Invincibles*, but over 1000 tons larger and with weaker deck protection. Thus at a time when Germany had started to build battlecruisers, and there was an obvious need for ships of superior design, the Admiralty ordered vessels which were in some respects inferior to the *Invincible* designed two years earlier. The only valid excuse for this was that the Admiralty's design department was already fully occupied on other projects and did not have the time to produce a new battlecruiser design. The one saving grace of the new ships was that they were cheap; *Indefatigable* was, ton for ton, the cheapest capital ship to be built in the twentieth century.

The name-ship *Indefatigable* was ordered under the 1908 Programme and built by Devonport dockyard, while her two sister ships *Australia* (built by John Brown) and *New Zealand* (built by Fairfield) were paid for by the governments of the countries after which they were named. *Indefatigable* was laid down in February 1909, launched in October 1909, and completed in February 1911. *New Zealand* and *Australia* were laid down in June 1910, launched in July and October 1911, and completed in November 1912 and June 1913 respectively. All three exceeded their designed power and achieved between 26.3 and 26.9 knots during their eight-hour full-power trials. *Indefatigable* was completed with a fire-control position on her mainmast, but smoke from the funnels made this position unworkable and it was omitted from the other ships. During 1914-15 all the ships were fitted with main-armament directors on a platform below the foretop, and an AA gun was mounted on the after superstructure.

On completion, *Indefatigable* joined the 1st Cruiser Squadron (reclassified 1st Battlecruiser Squadron in 1913) and she remained with this force until transferred to the

HMS *Indefatigable* just before Jutland in 1916 where she was lost with all but two of her crew

Mediterranean in December 1913. After the outbreak of war she took part in the search for the *Goeben* and the blockade of the Dardanelles before being recalled to Home Waters where she joined the 2nd Battle-cruiser Squadron of the Grand Fleet in February 1915. On May 31, 1916, during the Battle of Jutland (Skagerrak) *Indefatigable* took part in the initial engagement between the opposing battlecruiser forces. Shortly after 1600 hours, after having been engaged for some time with the German battlecruiser *Von Der Tann*, she was hit by a salvo of three shells which fell across the upper deck abreast the after turrets. A large explosion followed as one of the after magazines exploded, and she turned out of line to starboard, sinking by the stern. A second salvo then fell across her forward turrets, followed by another explosion as one of her forward magazines detonated. She quickly rolled over and sank leaving only two survivors from the 1024 crew.

New Zealand had neither the trained men nor facilities to maintain a battlecruiser, and their ship was presented to the Royal Navy on completion. She was sent on a ten-month world cruise, which included a three-month visit to her home country, before joining the 1st Battlecruiser Squadron of the Home Fleet in January 1914. In January 1915 she took part in the Dogger Bank action and shortly afterwards was transferred to the 2nd Battlecruiser Squadron. During the Battle of Jutland (Skagerrak) she was hit on X turret but received minimal damage and had no casualties. After Jutland she transferred to the 1st Battlecruiser Squadron, but returned to the 2nd Battlecruiser Squadron in September 1916 and remained with this force until the end of the war.

Australia arrived in her home country in October 1913 to take up duty as flagship of the Royal Australian Navy. On the outbreak of war she became flagship of the North America and West Indies Station and in January 1915 transferred to the Grand Fleet where she joined her two sisters in the 2nd Battlecruiser Squadron, with which she served until the end of the war. On April 22, 1916, she collided with *New Zealand* in fog and was in dock for repairs until June 5, missing the Battle of Jutland. Modifications to both *New Zealand* and *Australia* during 1917-18 included the addition of searchlight towers around the middle funnel, enlarging and modifying the bridge and foretop and fitting aircraft platforms on the wing turrets. Both ships were listed for disposal under the terms of the Washington Treaty of 1922, and *New Zealand* was sold for scrap in that year. *Australia*, which had continued her service as flagship of the RAN in 1919, was sunk ceremoniously off Sydney in April 1924 in accordance with the terms of the Washington Treaty on Naval Limitations.

Displacement: 18 500 tons (load), 22 080 tons (full load) *Length:* 179.8 m (590 ft) oa *Beam:* 24.4 m (80 ft) *Draught:* 7.9 m (25 ft 11 in) *Machinery:* 4-shaft direct-drive steam turbines, 44 000 shp=25 knots *Protection:* 152 mm (6 in) belt, 178 mm (7 in) turrets and barbettes, 64-25 mm (2.5-1 in) deck *Armament:* 8 12-in (305-mm) (4×2); 16 4-in (102-mm) (16×1); 2 18-in (46-cm) torpedo tubes (submerged) *Crew:* 800 (peace time)

Independence

US aircraft carrier class, built 1942-43. In 1941 at the outbreak of the war in the Pacific, the US Navy possessed only seven fast carriers for fleet operations, and although 13 more (of the *Essex* Class) had been ordered in 1940 and 1941 only half-a-dozen of these could be expected to be operational before the end of 1943. As an emergency measure the US Navy in March 1942 ordered that nine light cruisers of the *Cleveland* Class should be completed as light carriers, capable of operating 45 aircraft. Five of the hulls had already been laid down, and three of the light carriers were commissioned by the end of March 1943. The last was laid down in November 1942 and was completed 13 months later. All were built by the New York Shipbuilding Corporation.

The original cruiser hull was completed up to the flush weather deck. Interior arrangements were altered to permit installation of bomb magazines, the ship command and control offices (which would normally have been situated in the bridge structure) and extra accommodation for personnel and stores. The hangar occupied a third of the length of the original weather deck, between two large rectangular lifts. The wooden flight deck formed the roof of the hangar, extending for 160 m (525 ft), leaving the forecastle and quarterdeck open. A diminutive island was located at the starboard deck-edge. The funnels were abaft the island in two pairs, angled outward with only short vertical portions to give a height of not more than 4.3 m (14 ft). Two parallel catapults were flush-mounted in the forward end of the flight deck.

The standard displacement of 11 000 tons was 1000 tons more than that of the *Cleveland* Class cruisers. Most of the excess was carried high up, and to restore stability shallow external bulges had to be added at and below the waterline, increasing the beam by 1.5 m (5 ft). In the first two ships, *Independence* (CVL.22) and *Princeton* (CVL.23), the cruiser's belt armour was omitted, but it was incorporated in all subsequent ships, having a thickness of 51 mm (2 in), increasing to 127 mm (5 in) outboard of the magazines. Deck armour was between 76-51 mm (3-2 in) thick, on the hangar and main decks.

The first four ships were originally armed with 22 40-mm (1.57-in) Bofors and five single 20-mm (0.79-in) Oerlikon AA guns distributed around the deck-edges and on the open forecastle, as well as a single 5-in (127-mm) 38-cal dual-purpose gun on the quarterdeck. The 5-in was removed in 1944 and replaced by a quadruple 40-mm mounting (and was fitted in the last five ships from completion) and the Oerlikons were doubled up.

The hangar was disappointingly small: only 65.5 m (215 ft) long and 17.7 m (58 ft) broad, it was smaller than those of the *Sangamon* and *Commencement Bay* Classes of escort carriers. The introduction of the large Grumman F6F Hellcat fighter and TBF Avenger torpedo-bomber resulted in the elimination of dive-bombers from the light carriers' air groups, so that the normal complement was 33 aircraft. There was a constant campaign within the Navy for the removal of the torpedo-bombers, but not until July 1945 was this implemented, too late to see action.

The name ship was laid down as the light cruiser *Amsterdam* in 1941, renamed *Independence* in March 1942 and launched on August 22 of the same year. Commissioned on January 15, 1943, she worked up in the Caribbean from the spring and arrived at San Francisco in early July. Most of August was spent at Pearl Harbor, exercising with the first two *Essex* Class carriers *Essex* and *Yorktown*.

The three carriers undertook their first strikes on September 1, 1943, when their aircraft attacked Marcus Island, 1600 km south-east of Tokyo. Five weeks later, on October 5-6, six of the new fast carriers, including three *Independence* Class ships out of the four which were then operational (*Independence, Princeton, Belleau Wood* and *Cowpens*) carried out an effective series of training strikes on Wake Island.

On November 11, *Independence* took part in a raid on Rabaul, New Guinea, with *Essex* and *Bunker Hill*. While the carriers' fighters were away escorting the strike, shore-based US Navy fighters patrolled over the task group, the Hellcats of VF-33 landing aboard *Independence* to refuel. The Japanese did attack but lost heavily without scoring any hits.

A week later, the task group began pre-invasion strikes on Tarawa, Gilbert Islands, continuing on November 19-20, the latter being the day of the landings by the Marines, who suffered the heavy losses that made Tarawa a byword. That evening, Mitsubishi Betty torpedo-bombers from the Marshall Islands attacked, and one of the six which broke through the defences scored a hit on *Independence*'s starboard quarter. In addition to the hole caused by the explosion, her bottom plates were badly damaged, a propeller shaft was bent and machinery spaces were flooded by a ruptured fire main. She was towed to Funafuti, where she was repaired sufficiently to enable her to return to Pearl Harbor and San Francisco under her own steam, arriving at the latter on January 2, 1944.

On July 4 she began her workup as a night carrier. Her fighter-direction organization and her radar outfit had been revised for this role during the refit and, in place of the 24 Hellcat day fighters and nine Avengers which were the standard load of a light carrier, she had embarked only five 'straight' F6F-3 Hellcats and 14 F6F-3N night fighters, as well as eight TBM-1D Avengers, equipped with a new lightweight high-definition radar.

Independence was in action again on September 6, 1944, when the whole of Task Force 58—eight large and eight light carriers—began preparatory strikes before the invasion of Peleliu. Lack of Japanese air opposition, by day or night, resulted in the virtual abandonment of *Independence*'s night role during the month which followed, her aircraft joining in the task force's mass daylight strikes on the Caroline Islands, the Palaus and the southern Philippines. When the carriers began their most daring operation to date, the neutralization of Okinawa and Formosa prior to the invasion of Leyte, *Independence* reverted to the night role and on October 12, her Hellcat night fighters were rewarded with five kills in four hours.

She continued to serve in a primarily defensive role during the Leyte operations

Independencia

later in October. On October 24, after the air-sea battle of the Sibuyan Sea, her Avengers shadowed the Japanese battle fleet which was to engage the escort carriers off Samar Island on the following day. Their warning was, however, ignored by the fleet commander, Admiral Halsey, who was diverted by the presence of the Japanese carriers, also being shadowed by *Independence*'s aircraft. The shadowers directed the main strike for a dawn attack but took no further part in the battle of Cape Engano, which saw the destruction of four Japanese carriers.

Thereafter *Independence* took part in operations off Luzon and accompanied Task Force 38 on its raiding cruise in the South China Sea between January 10-20, her aircraft delivering night attacks on Formosa, Hong Kong and Cam Ranh Bay, Indo-China, as well as scoring more night air-to-air kills. For this operation, *Enterprise* was also being used in the night carrier role, and when the task force withdrew she was joined by *Saratoga* which took *Independence*'s place in the 'night task group'. The light carrier left the forward area on January 30, 1945, bound for Pearl Harbor, where she was to refit and reconvert to the day role.

Independence rejoined the fast carrier force at Ulithi on March 13, 1945, and sailed on the following day to strike at Japan, prior to the opening of the Okinawa campaign. Between March 23 and June 10, her aircraft flew combat sorties on 41 days. Although carriers in company were attacked and damaged by the many kamikaze raids during this period, she escaped unharmed. A month was allowed off operations before Task Force 38 sailed again, to undertake sustained strikes against the Japanese home islands. The coming of the typhoon season and the need to remain clear of the cities of Hiroshima and Nagasaki on August 6 and 9, when the atomic bombs were dropped, reduced to 12 the number of 'strike days' between July 10 and VJ-Day, August 15, 1945. During this period, TF38's aircraft, assisted by those of the British Pacific Fleet, destroyed what little remained of the Imperial Japanese Navy and inflicted serious damage on the shipbuilding and transportation industries.

After the surrender in Tokyo Bay on September 2, *Independence* returned to San Francisco in slow time, calling en route at Guam and Pearl Harbor. Between November 15 and January 28, 1946, she was engaged on Operation Magic Carpet, returning service personnel from the Pacific islands to the US. In June 1946, she steamed to the Marshall Islands and on July 1 was moored only 800 m (0.5 miles) from ground zero during the Bikini air-burst A-bomb test. She survived this and the July 25 underwater test, although damage was very severe. On July 28 she was formally decommissioned, and some while later the radioactive hulk was towed to San Francisco for exhaustive examination and tests. By now useless for any other purpose, *Independence* was finally sunk on January 29, 1951, during US Navy weapons trials off the California coast.

Displacement: 11 000 tons (standard), 14 300 tons (*Independence* and *Princeton* 14 000 tons) (full load) *Length:* 202 m (662 ft 6 in) oa *Beam:* 21.8 m (71 ft 6 in) wl, 33.4 m (109 ft 6 in) oa *Draught:* 7.9 m (26 ft) *Machinery:* 4 sets geared steam turbines, 4 shafts 100 000 shp=31.5 knots *Aircraft:* 33 *Armament:* 26 40-mm (1.57-in) AA (2×4, 9×2), 10-12 20-mm (0.79-in) AA *Crew:* 1570

Independencia

Argentine coast-defence battleship class, built 1889-93. Two small battleships were

No and name	completed	fate
CVL.22 *Independence* (ex-CL.59 *Amsterdam*)	1/43	sunk in weapons trials 30/1/51
CVL.23 *Princeton* (ex-CL.61 *Tallahassee*)	1/43	sunk by bomb 24/10/44
CVL.24 *Belleau Wood* (ex-CL.76 *New Haven*)	3/43	transferred to France as *Bois Bellau* 9/53; returned and scrapped 1962
CVL.25 *Cowpens* (ex-CL.77 *Huntington*)	5/43	scrapped 1962
CVL.76 *Monterey* (ex-Cl.78 *Dayton*)	6/43	scrapped 1970
CVL.27 *Langley* (ex-CL.85 *Fargo*)	8/43	transferred to France as *Lafayette* 6/51; returned and scrapped 1964
CVL.28 *Cabot* (ex-CL.79 *Wilmington*)	7/43	transferred to Spain as *Dedalo* 8/67 (in service 1978)
CVL.29 *Bataan* (ex-CL.99 *Buffalo*)	11/43	scrapped 1959
CVL.30 *San Jacinto* (ex-CL.100 *Newark*)	12/43	stricken 1970

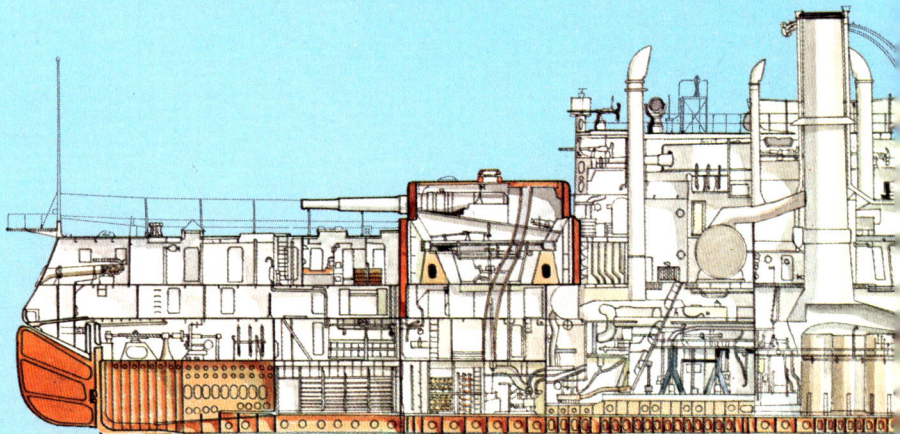

ordered from the Laird shipyard, Birkenhead, and were named *Independencia* and *Nueve de Julio*. They were armed with two 240-mm (9.4-in) Krupp guns, one mounted forward and the other aft, and four 4.7-in (120-mm) Elswick quick-firers at the corners of the superstructure. In 1925-27 both ships (*Nueve de Julio* having been renamed *Libertad*) were converted from coal to oil fuel, and were rerated as gunboats. Although still in service on the outbreak of the Second World War, they had become obsolete. They were laid up during the course of the war, and were subsequently sold for scrap.

Displacement: 2336 tons (normal) *Length:* 73.15 m (240 ft) pp *Beam:* 13.11 m (43 ft) *Draught:* 3.96 m (13 ft) max *Machinery:* 2-shaft reciprocating steam, 3000 ihp = 13 knots *Protection:* 203 mm (8 in) belt, 51 mm (2 in) deck, 203 mm (8 in) barbettes *Armament:* 2 240-mm (9.4-in)/35-cal (2×1); 4 4.7-in (120-mm)/40-cal QF (4×1); 4 47-mm (1.85-in) QF (4×1); 2 37-mm (1.46-in) (2×1) *Crew:* 225

Indiana

US battleship class, built 1890-96. After a long struggle to create a worthwhile navy out of the useless coast-defence force which had existed since the Civil War, Congress was persuaded to authorize three battleships in June 1890. In deference to the coast-defence lobby, however, they still had to be designated as seagoing coast-line battleships.

No and name	launched	built
BB.1 *Indiana*	2/1893	Cramp, Philadelphia
BB.2 *Massachusetts*	6/1893	Cramp, Philadelphia
BB.3 *Oregon*	10/1893	Union Iron Works, San Francisco

The design was produced by the Navy Department and slightly modified by William Cramp, the builders of the lead-ship. The ships had two twin 13-in (330-mm) turrets, four twin 8-in (203-mm) wing turrets, four 6-in (152-mm) guns amidships and six torpedo tubes above the waterline. Although the Americans were proud of the fact that the *Indiana* Class carried a heavier armament than foreign contemporaries of equal size, they had too little freeboard or endurance for ocean work and were overloaded. Nevertheless they were a considerable technical achievement, and made good use of the new Harvey face-hardened steel armour.

Problems were encountered with the main gun turrets. The Navy Department preferred the old cylindrical 'pillbox' turret, and in order to secure the maximum elevation for the guns without making the ports too large, the designers had to place the 13-in mounting close to the outer edge of the turret, thereby placing the turret's centre of balance 1.2 m (4 ft) from its axis. As a result, the ship listed sharply when the guns were trained on the beam. On one occasion *Indiana*'s guns broke loose in a storm, and it took over 100 men to secure them. It was found that the 8-in guns could not be fired within 10° of the centreline as the blast from their muzzles concussed the men in the sighting hoods of the 13-in turrets.

The ships served in the Spanish-American war, during which *Oregon* made a famous 22530-km (14000-mile) dash from the Pacific coast round Cape Horn to join the fleet blockading Cuba. She further distinguished herself in the chase after Admiral Cervera's squadron at the battle of Santiago.

In 1909-11 all three ships were given a cage mainmast, and the 6-in (152-mm) guns were replaced by 12 3-in (76-mm). Being obsolete, they played little part in the First World War, and were stricken after the Armistice of 1918. In March 1919, *Indiana* was renamed *Coast Battleship No 1* to release her name for a new battleship, and was sunk as a bombing target on November 1, 1920. *Massachusetts* became *Coast Battleship No 2* at the same time, and was sunk on November 22, 1920, by shore batteries at Pensacola, Florida. *Oregon* was spared on account of her fame, and was rerated as hulk *IX-22* in January 1924, before being lent to the State of Oregon as a memorial in June 1925. The loan was revoked by Presidential order in October 1942 in deference to hysterical demands for scrap metal, and *IX-22* was towed out to Guam for use as an ammunition-storage hulk. There she lay until March 1956, when she was sold for scrap.

Displacement: 10288 tons (normal) *Length:* 107 m (351 ft) oa *Beam:* 21.1 m (69 ft 3 in) *Draught:* 7.3 m (24 ft) mean *Machinery:* 2-shaft triple-expansion, 9000 ihp = 15.5 knots *Protection:* 457 mm (18 in) belt, 381 mm (15 in) turrets, 432 mm (17 in) conning tower *Armament:* 4 13-in (330-mm)/35-cal (2×2); 8 8-in (203-mm)/34-cal (4×2); 4 6-in (152-mm)/40-cal (4×1); 20 57-mm (2.24-in) QF; 6 37-mm (1.46-in) QF; 4 Gatling machine-guns; 6 18-in (46-cm) torpedo tubes (1 bow, 1 stern, 4 beam) *Crew:* 473

Indigo-MEI, Sistel

Italian surface-to-air missile. The Italian army has ordered Indigo-MEI to protect armoured columns and mechanized infantry and to defend fixed installations such as bridges, fuel dumps and ammunition stores. Each battery will comprise four vehicles, all based on the M548 tracked chassis: a search and tracking unit, two six-round launcher units, and a reload unit carrying 12 rounds.

The prototype search and tracking vehicle is fitted with Thomson-CSF radars, a Mirador pulse-Doppler surveillance set and an Eldorado tracker, with an Officine Galileo computer. The French radars will be replaced by Selenia equipment in production vehicles. The trailer-mounted version of Indigo uses a

Left and Below: USS *Indiana*, one of three battleships built in the late 19th century which saw action during the Spanish-American war. Like her sisters *Massachusetts* and *Oregon* she had poor sea-going properties with too little freeboard and inadequate endurance for ocean work. However, her four 13-in (330-mm) guns made her a formidable coast defence vessel. None of the ships played any real part in the First World War while the *Oregon* survived the Second World War as an ammunition storage hulk and was scrapped in March 1956

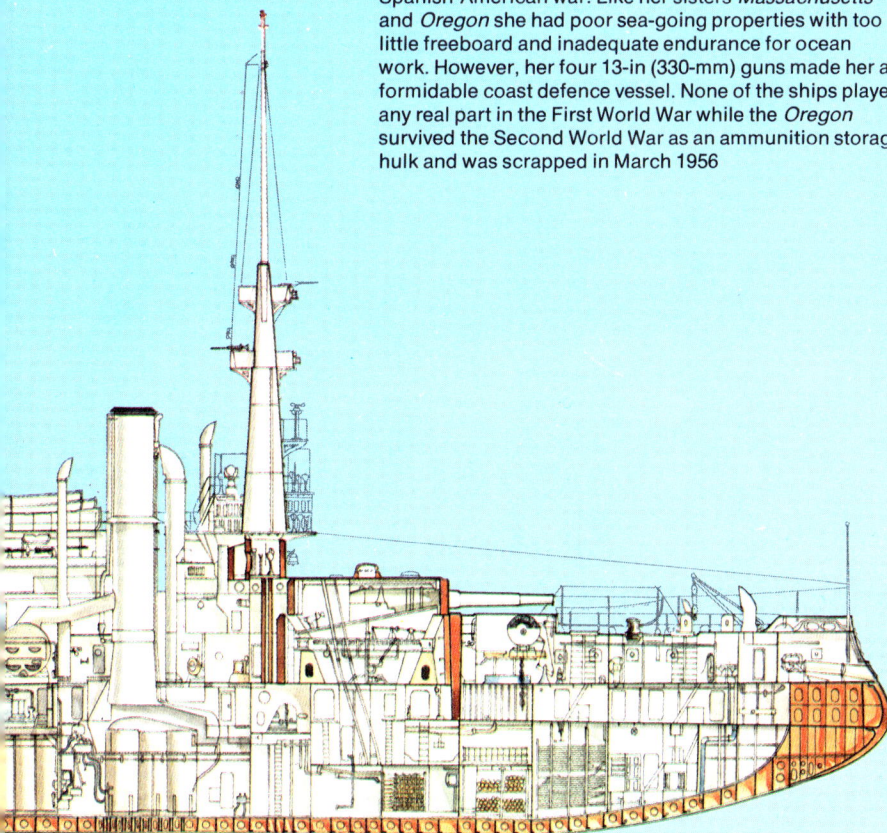

Indomitable

Contraves Superfledermaus fire-control radar and has been undergoing trials with the Italian army since 1973 but will not be ordered for deployment. The proposed Sea Indigo naval variant has also been abandoned.

Indigo is designed to intercept aircraft flying at up to Mach 1.3 virtually down to ground level. Targets are tracked either by the radar or with the aid of an optical sight, and radio commands are transmitted to the missile in flight to bring it on to an interception course.

See also Sea Indigo

Length: 307 cm (10 ft) *Span:* 81 cm (2 ft 8 in) *Diameter:* 19.5 cm (7.7 in) *Weight:* 120 kg (264 lb) *Range:* 10 km (6 miles) *Maximum altitude:* 5000 m (16 400 ft) *Warhead:* 22 kg (48 lb 8 oz) fragmentation

Indomitable

British aircraft carrier. Ordered as the fourth unit of the *Illustrious* Class, *Indomitable* was laid down in November 1937 at Barrow. Shortly afterwards, the Admiralty revised the design, so that the new ship would be able to operate 45 aircraft instead of 33. The extra stowage space could only be obtained by adding an extra hangar deck, above the existing hangar. It was found that by reducing the thickness of the hangar walls from 114 mm (4.5 in) to 38 mm (1.5 in) it was possible to raise the 1500-ton armoured flight deck by 4.3 m (14 ft) without reducing the stability of the ship. A full-length hangar 4.3 m (14 ft) high, was inserted into this space and only the after third of the original 4.9-m (16-ft) high hangar was retained, served by the after lift. The forward lift was widened by 50%, to 10 m (33 ft), to accommodate unfolded or non-folding aircraft. The extra volume made available by the sacrifice of the forward third of the lower hangar was used to accommodate personnel, workshops and stores, space for which had been extremely cramped in the *Illustrious* Class. Storage for 113 600 litres (25 000 Imp gal) of aviation fuel was added, at the expense of 350 tons of the ship's fuel-oil capacity, and the aircraft ordnance magazine capacity was increased by nearly 50%, to meet the requirements for the additional aircraft.

There was little external difference between *Indomitable* and *Illustrious,* apart from the increased freeboard. *Indomitable* was fractionally longer—227.1 m (745 ft) as against 225.5 m (740 ft)—but there was no difference in the layout of armament or the island and, with the same type of boilers, the funnel was identical.

Indomitable was completed on October 10, 1941, and sailed almost immediately for a workup in the West Indies. This was cut short when she ran aground off Jamaica and she was unable to sail as planned for the Far East, where she was to have joined *Prince of Wales* and *Repulse*. Her air group consisted of 24 Fairey Albacore torpedo-bombers, 12 Fairey Fulmars and nine Hawker Sea Hurricanes. The last were non-folding and could use only the forward lift and upper hangar.

Arriving in the Indian Ocean in January 1942, *Indomitable* ferried RAF Hurricanes to Java towards the end of that month and then flew off 48 more Hurricanes to Ceylon in February. Two of the latter remained on board, where they were modified and retained by 880 Squadron. During the Japanese carrier raids on Ceylon in early April *Indomitable*'s Albacores had actually sighted the enemy fleet. Following the raid, the Eastern Fleet withdrew to Mombasa, where it could provide support neither to India and Ceylon, nor to the hard-pressed Americans and Australians in the Coral Sea and southwest Pacific, and the Japanese were not even persuaded to divert any of their major naval units to guard against a foray from Mombasa. In May 1942, *Indomitable* and *Illustrious* assisted in the occupation of Diego Suarez, and in June *Indomitable* exercised with the RAF off Ceylon.

While three modern carriers were thus underemployed in the Indian Ocean, two small old carriers *Eagle* and *Argus* greatly helped in the defence of a Malta convoy. Another convoy was scheduled for August, and *Indomitable* was brought back to European waters to join the escort, arriving at Gibraltar at the beginning of the month. Prior to her departure, she had re-equipped her Fulmar squadron with Sea Hurricanes and had embarked nine Grumman Martlets to give her a total of 31 fighters; *Eagle* and *Victorious*, the other carriers with the force, had 41 Sea Hurricanes and Fulmars between them. Operation Pedestal, the most famous of all the Malta convoys, was subjected to heavy attacks by the Luftwaffe and Regia Aeronautica on August 12, 1942. *Eagle* had been sunk by a U-Boat on the previous day, but the two surviving carriers put up such a strong defence that when they left the convoy that evening only one of the 14 merchant ships had been damaged. *Indomitable*'s fighters had shot down 27 enemy aircraft for the loss of only four of their own number.

Shortly after parting company with the convoy, however, the Fleet came under attack, and Ju 87 Stuka dive-bombers concentrated on *Indomitable*, scoring two hits. One 500-kg (1100-lb) bomb penetrated the flight-deck armour near the forward lift and the other struck abaft the after lift, where there was no armour. *Victorious* recovered the aircraft which were airborne, while *Indomitable* fought her fires and headed for Gibraltar. Repairs in the United States took four months, and it was not until February 1943 that she was able to begin working up again.

This commission, for which she embarked 15 Albacores and 40 non-folding Seafires (ten aircraft over her designed complement) was even shorter than the first. In late June 1943, she joined *Formidable* in the Mediterranean and from July 10 the two carriers covered the Allied invasion of Sicily, guarding against a sortie by the Italian fleet. This did not materialize, but on the night of June 15-16, a Ju 88 torpedoed *Indomitable* in the port side, causing serious damage to the port boiler room and extensive flooding. *Indomitable* returned for her third repair at Norfolk navy yard and was not ready to join the fleet until the following April.

By June 1944, *Indomitable* was with the Eastern Fleet, based on Ceylon. By this time, the *Illustrious* Class was equipped with Vought F4U Corsairs, but the lack of headroom in *Indomitable*'s upper hangar, and lack of space in the lower meant that she could not embark enough of this type of fighter, and

she was supplied instead with Grumman F6F Hellcats, which had rearward, instead of upward, folding wings. At first, 24 Hellcats were embarked, with 24 Barracudas, but the number was increased to 29 in late 1944.

Indomitable and *Victorious* delivered strikes on Sumatra—on the port of Emmahaven (now Telukbajur) and cement works at Indaroeng on August 29, 1944, and on the Sigli railway yards on September 18—though neither attack was an outstanding success. On October 17 and 19 the same two carriers struck at the Nicobar Islands. Japanese aircraft attempted to close the force on this occasion, and *Indomitable*'s Hellcats scored their first victories, destroying three Nakajima Oscar fighter-bombers.

The Barracudas were disembarked after this operation and were replaced by 21 Grumman Avengers. After working up to establish new strike tactics, *Indomitable* and *Illustrious* made an unsuccessful attempt to attack the oil refinery at Medan, Sumatra, on December 20. Bad weather caused the failure of this operation, but another strike on January 4, 1945, by aircraft from *Victorious*, *Indefatigable* and *Indomitable* was entirely successful. The carrier offensive against Japanese-occupied oil refineries in Sumatra was concluded on January 24 and 29, 1945, by strikes from four ships against Pladjoe and Soengi Gerong; like that on Medan, these were completely successful.

The British Pacific Fleet (BPF) now continued to Sydney to prepare for operations in support of the invasion of Okinawa. The fleet's task was the neutralization of Japanese airfields in the Sakishima Gunto, between Okinawa and Formosa, and the carriers flew strikes on 12 days between March 26 and April 20. Only on April 1 and 6 did Japanese aircraft manage to get through the fighters to attack the fleet, but on neither occasion was *Indomitable* herself a target. After a week's replenishment at Leyte, the fleet returned to the Sakishima area on May 4. The kamikazes promptly attacked, hitting first *Formidable* and then *Indomitable*: the former was out of action for six hours, but *Indomitable*'s assailant simply slid up the armoured deck and over the side, causing no damage. When the BPF finally withdrew from the Okinawa area, on May 25, another 11 days of strikes had been provided over the islands, bringing the total to 24 in the two phases. Nearly 1000 tons of bombs and 950 rockets had been released and half a million rounds of aircraft ammunition fired: *Indomitable*'s 15 Avengers and 33 Hellcats had flown over 1100 sorties, the fighters destroying 16 enemy aircraft.

The war was now virtually over for *Indomitable*. Being in need for a short refit, she remained at Sydney when the other carriers left to strike at the Japanese Home Islands in July. She was ready for operations later in the month and left in mid-August to take part in the reoccupation of Hong Kong. On August 31 and September 1, her aircraft flew their last combat missions, against Japanese suicide boats at Hong Kong.

Indomitable returned to the United Kingdom in November 1945. Her aircraft had been thrown overboard off Sydney and the hangars were used as vast dormitories for British personnel returning from Australia. Early in 1946 she started out for the Far East again, for another trooping voyage, repeating

Above: HMS *Indomitable* in 1941. A Fairey Fulmar is making a low pass, while Sea Hurricanes are parked on the deck. *Below: Indomitable* with Avengers during trials in Chesapeake Bay. With *Formidable* she made up part of the British Pacific Fleet hitting Formosa and Okinawa

Indomito

Indomito

the same voyage again later in the year.

Between 1947 and 1950, *Indomitable* was in reserve and then refitting, being equipped with modernized radar and armament and having her catapults, arrester wires and lifts strengthened to allow her to operate the last generation of piston-engined Royal Navy aircraft. During the next three years, she operated Fairey Fireflies, Hawker Sea Furies, de Havilland Sea Hornets and Blackburn Firebrands and, from 1951, the first British embarked search and rescue helicopter flight. Throughout this time she served with the Home Fleet. Her last major public appearance was the Coronation review of the fleet, held at Spithead in June 1953. Four months later, she was reduced to reserve and lay in the Clyde until October 1955, when she was finally disposed of for scrap.

Displacement: 23 000 tons (standard) 29 730 tons (full load) *Length:* 227 m (745 ft) *Beam:* 29.2 m (95 ft 9 in) *Draught:* 8.7 m (28 ft 8 in) *Machinery:* 3 sets geared turbines, 3 shafts, 113 250 shp=30.5 knots *Protection:* 114 mm (4.5 in) main belt; 114 mm (4.5 in) hangar sides; 63.5-76 mm (2.5-3 in) deck *Aircraft:* 45 *Armament:* 16 4.5-in (114-mm) dual purpose (8×2); 40 2-pdr AA (5×8); 12 40-mm (1.57-in) AA (12×1); 60 20-mm (0.79-in) (60×1) *Crew:* 2100 approx

Indomito

Italian destroyer class. In January 1910 the Italian navy ordered their first six turbine-driven destroyers from Pattison's yard, Naples. The design was drawn up by Luigi Scaglia and resembled contemporary British destroyers, with three funnels and two single 45-cm (17.7-in) torpedo tubes amidships. However they carried a 120-mm (4.7-in) gun on the forecastle and four 76-mm (3-in) guns at the break of the forecastle and on the quarterdeck. On completion, the torpedo armament of *Ardente* and *Ardito* was doubled by the provision of twin tubes in place of the singles, while *Indomito* was given an extra pair of single tubes at the break of the forecastle. In 1919 the four survivors were given a standard armament of five 102-mm (4-in), one 2-pdr pom-pom and two twin 45-cm (17.7-in) torpedo tubes.

On December 4, 1915, *Intrepido* was sunk off Valona by a mine laid by the German U-Boat *UC 14*. Her sister *Impetuoso* was torpedoed on July 10, 1916, by the Austro-Hungarian submarine *U 17* in the Otranto Straits. *Impavido* (recognition letters IV), *Indomito* (ID), *Insidioso* (IS) and *Irrequieto* (IR) were reclassified as torpedo boats in October 1929 and discarded in 1937-38, three of the four remaining members of the class being scrapped.

Insidioso was not scrapped, and in March 1941 she was rearmed and reinstated. She served as a target for submarines at Pola and as an escort in the Adriatic. On her capture by the Germans at Pola in September 1943 she was renumbered *TA.21*. She was damaged in August 1944 and was sunk by a torpedo dropped by an Allied aircraft on November 5, 1944.

Displacement: 672 tonnes (normal), 772 tonnes (full load) *Length:* 73 m (239 ft 6 in) oa *Beam:* 7.33 m (24 ft) *Draught:* 2.46 m (8 ft) *Machinery:* 2-shaft steam turbines, 16 000 shp=32 knots

Irrequieto as a torpedo boat in 1937. She was commissioned as an *Indomito* Class destroyer

Armament: 1 120-mm (4.7-in)/40-cal QF; 4 76-mm (3-in)/40-cal QF (4×1); 2 45-cm (17.7-in) torpedo tubes (2×1); (from 1919) 5 102-mm (4-in)/35-cal (5×1); 1 40-mm (1.57-in)/39-cal AA; 4 45-cm (17.7-in) torpedo tubes (2×2); (*Insidioso* 1941) 1 102-mm (4-in)/45-cal; 4 20-mm (0.79-in) AA (4×1); 2 13.2-mm (0.52-in) machine-guns (2×1) *Crew:* 69-79

Infanta Maria Teresa

Spanish cruiser class, built 1888-91. In the latter part of the nineteenth century, Spain's remaining possessions in the Caribbean and the Far East were seriously threatened by the expansionist policies of both the US and Germany. Spain therefore built up a considerable force of small cruisers and gunboats for local defence and policing duties, and a smaller force of much larger cruisers intended for mobile defence and to protect the sea lanes between her colonies and the home country. Because Spain could not afford a battleship fleet, the large cruisers were designed to be as powerful as possible, and *Infanta Maria Teresa* and her sisters *Almirante Oquendo* and *Vizcaya* were quite large cruisers for their day, with thick armour and a relatively powerful armament.

They were similar to the earlier British *Orlando* Class, with a narrow waterline belt and two large guns placed fore and aft. The 280-mm (11-in) Hontoria guns were mounted singly in barbettes, and were protected with 38-mm (1.5-in) armoured cupolas. The 140-mm (5.5-in) guns were mounted behind thin shields on the broadside amidships, with the end guns in sponsons sited for firing directly ahead or astern. Two of the torpedo tubes were mounted one on either side of the bow, and the others were on the beam and at the stern. The compound 305-mm (12-in) belt extended from bow to stern, and there was a complete 50-mm (2-in) protective deck.

They were handsome, flush-decked vessels, with two raked masts and funnels, and were fitted out for service in tropical waters. In order to avoid excess heat building up in the 'tween-deck spaces, the upper decks were made entirely of wood, without the customary steel deck beneath. Unlike the slightly later Spanish cruisers, they were built reasonably quickly. All were constructed at Bilbao, and *Infanta Maria Teresa* was laid down in 1888. She was launched on August 30, 1890. *Vizcaya* was launched on July 8, 1891, and *Almirante Oquendo* on October 4 of the same year. *Infanta* entered service in 1893, followed shortly by the other two. Most of their service was seen in tropical waters, but they were also extensively used on goodwill and ceremonial visits to European countries and to the US. Indeed, *Vizcaya* was at New York when the USS *Maine* blew up in Havana harbour on February 15, 1898. She immediately sailed to join her sisters and the incompletely armed *Cristobal Colon* at the Cape Verde Islands to form Admiral Cervera's 'Flying Squadron'. These four cruisers were the only ones available, since all other major units were either still completing or undergoing major refits.

Against Cervera's wishes, the 'Flying Squadron' sailed for Cuba on May 19, and soon after their arrival were blockaded in Santiago harbour by a superior US squadron. There they remained until the approach of the US Army forced the squadron to attempt a breakout on July 3, 1898. The large expanse of unarmoured side above the belt and the light armour protecting the main and secondary armament provided little protection against the US shells, and the absence of a steel upper deck made the upperworks almost untenable after the wooden planks had caught fire and burnt away. After half an hour, *Infanta* and *Oquendo* were both beached in flames, and half-an-hour later *Vizcaya* also had to run ashore. *Oquendo* and *Vizcaya* were unsalvable, but the US Navy raised the *Infanta* on August 6, 1898, with the intention of taking her back to the US. On November 1, 1898, while under tow, she foundered off the Bahamas and was finally abandoned several days later on November 16.

Displacement: 7000 tons *Length:* 103.7 m (340 ft 2 in) *Beam:* 19.8 m (65 ft) *Draught:* 6.6 m (21 ft 8 in) *Machinery:* 2-shaft compound reciprocating, 13 700 ihp=20 knots *Protection:* 305 mm (12 in) belt, 52 mm (2 in) deck, 250 mm (9.8 in) barbettes *Armament:* 2 280-mm (11-in); 10 140-mm (5.5-in); 8 6-pdr (57-mm); 8 37-mm (1.46-in); 2 machine-guns; 6 35.6-cm (14-in) torpedo tubes *Crew:* 497

Ingeniero Hyatt

Chilean torpedo boat class. Five 140-ton boats, *Ingeniero Hyatt, Cirujano Videla, Ingeniero Mutilla, Guardia Marina Contreras* and *Teniente Rodriguez*, were built during 1896-98 by Yarrow to a conventional design, with three 3-pdr guns and three deck-tubes. They were all scrapped in the 1920s, by which time they were completely worn out.

Displacement: 140 tons (normal) *Length:* 46.5 m (152 ft 7 in) *Beam:* 4.6 m (15 ft 1 in) *Draught:* 2.4 m (7 ft 10 in) *Machinery:* 1-shaft reciprocating steam, 2200 ihp=27 knots *Armament:* 3 47-mm (1.85-in) QF (3×1); 3 36-cm (14-in) torpedo tubes (3×1) *Crew:* 28

Ing Mechanik Zver'ov

Russian torpedo boat class. The German Schichau yard built the first three boats in 1900-01 (*Bestrachni, Besposchadni, Beschumni*) and these were followed in 1905-06, the time of the Russo-Japanese war, by a further ten: *Boyevoi, Bditelni, Burni, Lt Sergeev, Kapt Yurassovski, Ing Mechanik Zver'ov, Ing Mechanik Dimitiev, Vnimatelni, Vnushitelni, Vinoslivi*. They were all smaller editions of the *Emir Bucharski* type, with one or two 75-mm (2.95-in) guns and three torpedo tubes.

During the First World War these boats served in the 7th Torpedo Boat Division, which played an important role in the defence of Abo and the Åland Islands. *Kapitan Yurassovski* and *Lt Sergeev* served in the Siberian flotilla with *Bestrachni, Besposchadni* and *Beschumni*, but in 1916-17 all but the *Beschumni* were transferred to the Arctic flotilla. They were all employed mainly on patrol and escort duties.

Bditelni was mined on November 27, 1917, and most of the others were scrapped in 1922-23. Four survived under new names: *Zemchujni* (ex-*Ing Mechanik Zver'ov*), *Rosal II* (ex-*Ing Mechanik Dimitriev*), *Martynov* (ex-*Vnushitelni*), *Artemov* (ex-*Vinoslivi*). All four were scrapped about 1931-32 when the new *Shtorm* Class came into service.

See also *Emir Bukharski*.

Displacement: 380 tons (normal) *Length:* 63.63 m (208 ft 9 in) oa *Beam:* 7 m (23 ft) *Draught:* not known *Machinery:* 3-shaft reciprocating steam, 6000 ihp=28 knots *Armament:* 1/2 75-mm (2.95-in) (1/2×1); 6 machine-guns (6×1); 3 45-cm (17.7-in) torpedo tubes (3×1) *Crew:* 95

Ingram

US submachine-guns. Gordon B Ingram became a small-arms manufacturer after he was demobilized from the US Army at the end of the Second World War. He had acquired a good practical knowledge of arms and believed that reliability could be achieved by simplicity of design, and effectiveness in combat by automatic fire.

Ingram began designing submachine-guns at a time when the current US weapon was the M3. His prototype weapon, designated M5, appeared in 1946, but did not enter production. It was a conventional submachine-gun with a wooden butt, a tubular, perforated barrel and used the Reising 12-round magazine. Three years later, together with some friends, he set up the Police Ordnance Company to make a submachine-gun especially for police use. Designated the Model 6, this weapon had blowback operation and was chambered for the 9-mm (0.35-in) Parabellum and .45 (11.4-mm) ACP cartridge, with .38 (9.6-mm) ACP as a further alternative. The weapon was fairly light, although it was fitted with solid wooden furniture and a moderately heavy finned barrel. The design was simple, and the chief feature was the lack of a selector lever. Semiautomatic firing was carried out by pulling the trigger back to an intermediate position. Fully automatic fire was achieved by pulling the trigger completely back. The Model 6 came in three versions: the Police, with the forehand grip closely resembling that on the Thompson M1928 submachine-gun; the Guard, with a straight forearm, and a military bayonet-equipped version, with a full stock carried along to the muzzle.

Sales were good: customers included some police forces in the United States, the US Constabulary in Puerto Rico, the Cuban navy, and the Peruvian army. It is estimated that 15 000 in .45 ACP were sold in the US and 8000 in Peru. The Peruvian army not only bought the military, bayonet-equipped version, but established a plant to make it under licence with the designation P.O.C. Model 6. The .45 ACP Model 6 appeared to be the most popular; the 9-mm Parabellum and the .38 ACP made scarcely any impact in the US.

The Model 7 was a failure and was hardly distinguishable from its predecessor, except that it fired from a closed bolt position. Its successor, Model 8, was an improved Model 6, and in 1954 the Thailand government invited Ingram to Bangkok to lay out a production line. It was an abortive project. In 1959 a prototype Model 9 appeared. It was an improved version of the Model 8 with a steel butt stock of the M3 pattern.

Ingram appears to have left the armaments industry for the next ten years, but in 1969 he was working for Sionics, an Atlanta, Georgia, company specializing in rifle silencers. Sionics produced a silencer used on the 7.62-mm (0.30-in) rifle which showed good results in Vietnam. By 1969 the company was enlarged and became the Military Armament Corporation of Powder Springs, Georgia. With the new company Ingram developed his Model 10, the weapon by which his name is best known.

The Model 10 (and its variant Model 11) contrasts with the previous submachine-guns designed by Ingram. It is short, compact and easy to shoot with, despite a high rate of fire. The outline is smooth, with no projections to catch in clothing or undergrowth. The weapon can be fired equally well left- or right-handed. Both the M10 and M11 are of the same basic design and differ only in the weight and length dictated by the cartridge used—Model 11 weighs 1.59 kg (3 lb 8 oz),

but the difference in length is marginal. Model 10 is chambered for the .45 (11.4-mm) ACP or 9-mm (0.354-in) Parabellum cartridge. Model 11 takes the short cartridge .38 (9.6-mm) ACP. Fire is automatic and semiautomatic. The weapons are short since the bolts are of the wrap-round type, with the bolt face and the fixed firing pin located well back to allow the greater part of the bolt to envelop the breech. At the same time, the bolt design helps to keep the centre of gravity over the pistol grip during the firing of a short burst. Thus the magnitude of the oscillation produced by the reciprocating action of the bolt is kept down. The box magazine is an integral part of the pistol grip, and the gun can be fired with one hand if need be. There is no specially designed forehand grip. The wire stock pulls out for firing from the shoulder, and is retracted for hip firing.

The cocking handle is located on top of the receiver and, like the early Thompson submachine-gun, has a U-notch to allow an unimpeded line of sight. Rotation of the cocking handle through 90° locks the bolt when it is in the closed position. The sights, therefore, cannot be used when the bolt is locked. Located on the right of the trigger guard and forward of the trigger is a second safety catch. When this is pulled to the rear, the bolt is locked in either the forward or the cocked positions.

Models 10 and 11 are externally threaded at the muzzle to take the Military Armament Company suppressor. In contrast with conventional silencers this allows the bullet to attain full supersonic velocity, but the emergent gas velocity is reduced to a subsonic level. It is claimed that the device makes the location of the weapon difficult to pinpoint from the sound of firing alone. Someone at the target position would only hear the crack of the supersonic bullet as it passed. The MAC suppressor for the Model 10 weighs 0.545 kg (1 lb 3 oz) and is 291 mm (11.4 in) long. The corresponding figures for the Model 11 are 0.455 kg (1 lb) and 224 mm (8.8 in).

The Model 10A1 is another variant. It is specially designed to be manufactured with the simplest machine tools. The bolt is made of steel sheet, pressed into a box shape and filled with lead, so that only the barrel needs to be machined. It might be expected that this 'economy' weapon would be remarkably cheap and readily find a market. Yet sales have been disappointing. The demand for short-range submachine-guns thus appears to be almost over, although there will always be a small demand from specialist customers. The trend now favours the light rifle: the Ingram gun came about ten years too late.

(Model 6) *Calibre:* .45 (11.4-mm) ACP (automatic Colt pistol) *Weight:* 3.29 kg (7 lb 4 oz) *Length:* 762 mm (2 ft 6 in) *Barrel length:* 229 mm (9 in) *Operation:* Blowback *Magazine:* 30-round detachable box *Rate of fire:* 600 rds/min *Muzzle velocity:* 274 m/sec (900 ft/sec)

(Model 10) *Calibre:* .45 (11.4-mm) ACP; 9 mm (0.354 in) Parabellum *Weight:* 2.84 kg (6 lb 4 oz) *Length:* 267 mm (10.5 in) excluding stock *Barrel length:* 146 mm (5.75 in) *Operation:* Blowback *Magazine:* 30-round box (.45 ACP), 32-round box (9-mm Parabellum) *Rate of fire:* 1145 rds/min (.45 ACP), 1090 rds/min (9-mm Parabel-

International Harvester

lum) *Muzzle velocity:* 274 m/sec (900 ft/sec) (.45 ACP), 366 m/sec (1200 ft/sec) (9-mm Parabellum)

International Harvester

US M75 armoured personnel carrier. After the Second World War the US Army issued a specification for a tracked APC to replace the ageing, but still useful, M3 half-track. The specification called for a fully-tracked vehicle armoured against small arms, artillery splinters and light aircraft bomb fragments and capable of carrying ten men and a crew of two. There was also to be sufficient flexibility in the design to allow it to be used as a reconnaissance vehicle or a command post if needed. Furthermore it was to make use of the chassis of the T43 cargo tractor, though this was largely disregarded in the final models and components from the running gear of the M41 Walker Bulldog tank were incorporated.

Development started in 1946 and the final design was authorized for production in 1951. Manufacture was split between International Harvester and FMC and by 1954 1730 vehicles had been completed. Unfortunately the M75 proved unsuccessful, and almost before the last one was off the production line plans were afoot for its replacement and it was only a short time before it was being phased out in favour of the M59.

The chief difficulties with the M75 were its cost and size. It was inordinately expensive to build and equally so to maintain. The designer had interpreted the specification in such a way as to construct a remarkably high hull, apparently sitting right on top of the tracks, yet this large volume could not float nor had it any NBC filtration system. The hull was of welded steel and the driver was at the left front, provided with a fairly elaborate cupola and vision blocks. The engine and transmission driving front sprockets were on his right. On top of the hull was another cupola for the commander and two escape hatches for the passengers. The main entrance and exit doors were in the rear.

Some experiments were made with different armament arrangements, but the only model to be issued to the US Army carried a 0.5-in (12.7-mm) Browning on the commander's cupola. When the M75 was taken out of US service it was sold to Turkey, Greece and Belgium.

Weight: 18 828 kg (41 500 lb) *Length:* 5.19 m (17 ft) *Width:* 2.84 m (9 ft 4 in) *Height:* 3.04 m (10 ft) *Armour thickness:* 25—9.5 mm (1-0.3 in) *Powerplant:* Continental AO-895-4 6-cylinder air-cooled gasoline *Speed:* 71 km/h (44 mph) *Range* 185 m (115 miles)

Intrepid

British destroyer class. Constructed under the 1935 Programme the *Intrepid* or 'I' Class were repeats of the 'H' Class destroyers of the previous year's programme. They were however fitted with quintuple instead of quadruple torpedo tubes, a new streamlined bridge (fitted experimentally in *Hereward* and *Hero*), and were equipped for rapid conversion to minelayers. They were laid down in 1936, launched during 1936-37 and completed during 1937-38.

Wartime alterations included the fitting during 1940 of a 12-pdr AA gun in place of the after torpedo tube mounting and the removal of the mainmast to clear its arc of fire. Later they were fitted with air warning radar and, except for the early war losses, surface warning radar. During 1942-43 *Icarus*, *Impulsive* and *Isis* were converted to escort vessels having B gun (A gun in *Icarus*) replaced by a Hedgehog A/S weapon, Y gun and the 12-pdr AA removed to provide space for additional depth-charge stowage and equipment, and an HF/DF mast added aft. All the surviving members of the class also had their 0.5-in (12.7-mm) guns removed and six 20-mm (0.79-in) (6×1) AA guns fitted.

On completion the class was formed into the 3rd Destroyer Flotilla and joined the Mediterranean Fleet where they remained until transferred to the Western Approaches command on the outbreak of the Second World War. In December 1939 *Icarus*, *Impulsive*, *Intrepid* and *Ivanhoe* were fitted for minelaying and joined the newly formed 20th (minelaying) Flotilla. During the following months they took part in several minelaying operations, mainly off Norway, and saw action during the Norwegian campaign and the Dunkerque evacuation.

On September 1, 1940, *Ivanhoe* struck a mine off Texel (a Dutch island in the North Sea) and was extensively damaged. She proceeded under her own power for a short time and was then taken in tow but on the following morning was further damaged during an air attack. She was abandoned shortly afterwards and sunk by a torpedo from the destroyer *Kelvin*. The remaining three ships were converted back to fleet destroyers and joined the 3rd Flotilla with the Home Fleet. *Icarus* and *Impulsive* remained in Home Waters and served as escorts for Soviet convoys and in the North Atlantic. They were also present during the Normandy landings. The *Intrepid* transferred to the Mediterranean Fleet where she was bombed and

HMS *Ivanhoe,* an *Intrepid* Class destroyer lost early in the war when she hit a mine off Texel in September 1940 and was sunk by the *Kelvin*

sunk in Leros harbour (a Greek island in the Dodecanese) on September 27, 1943.

The other four ships of the class joined the 3rd Flotilla, Home Fleet in December 1939 and also took part in the Norwegian campaign. On July 16, 1940, *Imogen* was lost in collision with the cruiser *Glasgow* while operating in the Pentland Firth. The remaining three, *Ilex*, *Imperial* and *Isis* transferred to the Mediterranean Fleet where they saw considerable action. *Imperial* was sunk on May 29, 1941, by her own forces after a steering failure (following earlier damage) during the evacuation of Crete. *Ilex* and *Isis* were both seriously damaged in 1941 and were out of action while under repair until the end of 1942 when they returned to the Mediterranean. *Isis* later transferred to Home Waters and was sunk off Normandy on July 20, 1944, by a German midget submarine. The surviving ships *Icarus*, *Ilex* and *Impulsive* were sold for scrap during 1946-48. During the war, ships of the class helped sink ten German and Italian submarines.

Icarus, *Ilex*—built by John Brown
Imogen, *Imperial*—built by Hawthorn Leslie
Impulsive, *Intrepid*—built by White
Isis, *Ivanhoe*—built by Yarrow

Displacement: 1370 tons (standard), 1890 tons (full load) *Length:* 98.45 m (323 ft) oa *Beam:* 10.06 m (33 ft) *Draught:* 2.59 m (8 ft 6 in) *Machinery:* 2-shaft geared steam turbines, 34 000 shp=35.5 knots *Armament:* 4 4.7-in (120-mm) (4×1), 8 0.5-in (12.7-mm) AA (2×4); 10 21-in (53-cm) torpedo tubes (2×5) *Crew:* 145

Intrepida

Argentine fast patrol boat class. Two gun- and torpedo-armed patrol boats were ordered from Lürssenweft, Vegesack, the Netherlands, and delivered in late 1974. *Intrepida* (P.85) and *Indomita* (P.86) are armed with the Seeaal (sea eel) wire-guided torpedo aft, and the OTO-Melara 76-mm (3-in) gun forward. Four MTU diesels give a speed of 40 knots. A twin 81-mm (3.2-in) Oerlikon rocket launcher is also provided for launching flares

and smoke canisters. These vessels are the first foreign fast patrol boats to have the Seeaal torpedoes, which are fired aft from two single tubes, as in the similar West German navy vessels.

Displacement: 240 tons (standard) *Length:* 50 m (164 ft) oa *Beam:* 7.3 m (24 ft) *Draught:* 2.5 m (8 ft 2½ in) *Machinery:* 4-shaft diesel, 12 000 bhp=40 knots *Armament:* 1 76-mm (3-in)/62-cal; 2 40-mm (1.57-in)/70-cal (2×1); 2 53-cm (21-in) torpedo tubes (2×1) *Crew:* 35

Intruder, Grumman A-6

US carrier-based all-weather attack aircraft. During the Korean war of 1950-53, Allied airpower was found to be incapable of meeting the demands made upon it. The most pressing need was for a tactical attack aircraft capable of delivering weapons with precision at any time and in any weather. An official history of the US Navy and Marine Corps in that war states that, though there was 'an hourly need' for such aircraft 'the requirement and the state of the art were miles apart at that time'. Subsequent rapid development of improved radars, computers,

navigation systems and cockpit displays swiftly reduced the gap, and in May 1956 the marine corps issued a detailed requirement for an all-weather close-support attack bomber. The Marines obtained their aircraft through the navy, and the Bureau of Aeronautics added some requirements of its own such as carrier equipment so that the new aircraft could become part of the navy's seagoing airpower. The design competition of May-September 1957 was won on the last day of that year by Grumman's design 128. Eight aircraft were ordered for evaluation with the designation A2F-1 Intruder, which was changed to A-6A in the 1962 scheme.

As originally conceived the Intruder featured jet deflection (as did most of the 11 competing proposals, and the original scheme for the Buccaneer). The British designers dropped the feature at an early stage, but the first A2F flew at Calverton on April 19, 1961, with the jet pipes of the two 3855-kg (8500-lb) Pratt & Whitney J52 turbojets arranged to hinge down through 23°, reducing stalling speed by 11 km/h (7 mph). This was not considered worthwhile, and the pipes of production aircraft are fixed at a downward inclination of 7°. The airbrakes in the wake of

Below: A Grumman A-6 Intruder with the Condor air-to-surface electro-optically guided missile

An Intruder equipped with mockups of Agile missiles during trials. A-6 can also carry Snakeye, Walleye, Bullpup, Hobos and Harpoon missiles

Invader, Douglas A-26/B-26

the nozzles are also absent in most production subtypes, though all models have had split upper and lower airbrakes at the wingtips. The folding wings have virtually full-span flaps along both leading and trailing edges, with roll control by 'flaperon' spoilers.

The pilot and bombardier/navigator occupy a lofty and comfortable cockpit. The pilot has a superb view of the left hemisphere while the right-seat man sits lower down and slightly to the rear. The canopy slides rearwards under hydraulic power. The capacious nose is filled with avionics, and the A-6A had Diane (digital integrated attack navigation equipment) which combined many facets of 1956 technology and included a Norden APQ-92 search radar and a navy-developed APQ-88 track radar, together with other equipment, all linked by a Litton computer. One of the best-appreciated items was the new Kaiser display which presented the crew with a picture of the scene ahead with other information superimposed on it. With Diane, navy and marine crews acquired new capability, and were for the first time able to place their bombload of up to 6804 kg (15 000 lb) dead on target at any time.

When the A2F (A-6A) was designed it was expected to carry a nuclear weapon and two drop tanks, or possibly three bombs of 907 kg (2000 lb) each, but by the time the Intruder entered service in February 1963 it had been cleared to carry numerous loads of up to the structural limit of 1633 kg (3700 lb) on each of its five pylons. In addition to the navy's range of conventional bombs, the A-6 can carry Snakeye, Walleye, Bullpup, Hobos, Standard ARM, Harpoon and Tomahawk missiles, and will later carry the night attack missile version of the AGM-65 Maverick, in conjunction with Tram (target recognition attack multisensor).

By December 1969 Grumman had delivered 482 A-6A Intruders. Many served in Vietnam and were (apart from the brief participation of the USAF F-111A) the only aircraft capable of penetrating hostile airspace at all times and making a blind first-pass attack on a point target. The first combat missions were flown in early July 1965 by navy squadron VA-75 from the carrier *Independence*. By this time there were several hundred qualified navy and marine crews, but their effectiveness was limited by poor serviceability of what was proving to be a complex and problem-ridden aircraft. Part of the trouble was that the technology was by then ten years old, and the A-6 did not incorporate much of the compact and reliable solid-state microelectronics that became available after 1959. Serviceability in 1965-66 was not higher than an average 35% in any A-6 unit, and it was rare to find a squadron achieving better than 100 maintenance man-hours per flight hour.

Gradually the situation improved, mainly by refining and changing the hardware. Nineteen A-6As have been modified to carry the Standard ARM antiradar missile and are redesignated A-6B. The A-6C has a turret under the forward fuselage so that the right-seat man can train FLIR (forward-looking infrared) and LLTV (low-light TV) equipment, giving detailed pictures of targets not discernible on the radar. The 12 A-6Cs are also converted A-6As.

By far the most important new model is the

A-6E, first flown in February 1970. This has a completely new multimode radar (APQ-148, previously APQ-112) replacing the two older radars. IBM provide the ASQ-133 solid-state computer, and there are 12 other completely new or redesigned subsystems. Like A-6As delivered from 1963, they have J52-8A engines, uprated to 4218 kg (9300 lb).

By 1976 Grumman had delivered 58 new E-models, and was well into a programme to rebuild all remaining A-6As in the inventory to a total A-6E strength of 318. In 1974 a further improvement flew on an A-6E when Tram began a long programme of flight testing. Tram's under-fuselage turret contains new electro-optics including a very advanced FLIR and a laser. The FLIR and other sensor inputs are combined and presented on a new kind of display by a Hughes DRS (detecting/ranging set) and the net result is what A-6E/Tram crews claim to be the finest cockpit equipment for air-to-surface operations. It can study land surfaces, acquire targets marked by ground lasers, and deliver conventional or laser-guided weapons. The A-6E Tram also has many other new or expanded capabilities, including the Cains (carrier-aircraft inertial navigation system) and automatic carrier landing. It has been matched with the long-range Condor missile, which was flight tested on A-6Es, but was subsequently cancelled.

In May 1966 the first KA-6D Intruder tanker began flight testing. At that time the standard carrier-based tanker was the KA-3B Skywarrior, but it was evident that the Intruder could make a better conversion while retaining some attack capability. The KA-6D proved a most successful conversion, and a total of 62 were delivered, all rebuilt A-6As. The basic aircraft is simplified, with most of the all-weather attack sensors and subsystems removed. In the rear fuselage a flight refuelling (FR) hosereel is fitted, and the four wing pylons carry 1750-litre (385 Imp gal) tanks or ECM pods. Tacan (tactical air navigation system) is fitted to facilitate hook-ups between aircraft in bad weather. Shortly after takeoff a KA-6D can transfer more than 9525 kg (21 000 lb) of fuel; at a distance of 463 km (290 miles) it can transfer 6800 kg (15 000 lb). These versatile aircraft act not only as tankers for A-6 and other squadrons (all Intruders have a socket for a large fixed FR probe above the nose on the centreline) but also as long-loiter air-sea-rescue control platforms or as visual attack aircraft.

Among the original production Intruders of 1962 were 12 aircraft for the Marine Corps modified for ECM support missions. Designated EA-6A, they were minimum-change aircraft, and though many major subsystems of the A-6A were deleted the EA-6A retained a partial attack capability. Major ECM payloads were added in a large fairing on the fin, on the wingtips, and in four pods (each powered by a ram-air windmill turbo-generator) on the wing pylons. The EA-6A has more than 30 antennae to detect, locate, classify, record and jam hostile radiations. By 1967 all 12 were in action in south-east Asia, and they proved to be of the greatest value both as lead ships for other aircraft and as defence-suppression platforms. It is believed that their capabilities extended to interfering with the in-flight guidance of SA-2 Guideline SAMs, making the latter fly aim-

lessly or even turn back to their launchers. (However, there has been no report of similar interference with later SAM systems, such as SA-6.) Subsequently 27 EA-6As were accepted by the Marine Corps, six being rebuilds. The name Intruder is not always used with these aircraft, and the completely redesigned EA-6B electronic-warfare aircraft is named Prowler.

Span: 16.15 m (53 ft) *Length:* 16.64 m (54 ft 7 in) *Gross weight:* 27 500 kg (60 630 lb) *Maximum speed:* 1035 km/h (643 mph)

Invader, Douglas A-26/B-26

US multipurpose bomber. The Invader was designed to a 1940 USAAC requirement for a multipurpose light bomber, capable of making high-speed low-level and medium-height precision attacks whilst carrying a strong defensive armament. Intended to replace the Douglas A-20 Havoc, its basic design was similar—a three-seat shoulder-wing monoplane, with large underwing nacelles for the two 2000-hp R-2800-27 Pratt & Whitney

The Douglas A-26B Invader with a solid nose mounting six 0.50-in (12.7-mm) machine-guns. It could also carry an internal bombload of 1815 kg (4000 lb) and up to 905 kg (200 lb) of bombs or eight 5-in (127-mm) rockets slung under the wings. With this formidable ground-attack capability they were recalled for use in Vietnam in the early 1960s but withdrawn after accidents and the arrival of more modern types

Double Wasp radial engines. Three prototypes were ordered in June 1941 and the first, the XA-26, was flown on July 10, 1942. It was designed as an attack bomber and carried an internal bombload of 1360 kg (3000 lb). The aircraft was armed with two remote-controlled 0.5-in (12.7-mm) guns in dorsal and ventral turrets, plus two more guns in the transparent nose section. The crew consisted of pilot, navigator/radio operator and gunner.

The XA-26A second prototype was a night-fighter model, with a solid nose enclosing an AI (airborne interception) radar system. Armament consisted of four 20-mm (0.79-in) cannon in a ventral tray plus four 0.5-in guns in an upper turret. The XA-26B third prototype was also a night-fighter version, but with a shorter nose housing a single 75-mm (2.95-in) cannon.

The first production model was designated A-26B and officially named Invader. It was powered initially by two 2000-hp R-2800-27 engines, but the -79 was installed on later aircraft. This had a water injection system which boosted power and performance at high altitudes. An internal bombload of 1815

kg (4000 lb) was carried, with provision for underwing points which could carry an additional 905 kg (2000 lb) of bombs, eight 5-in (127-mm) rockets and two drop-tanks, or 16 rockets. Six 0.5-in guns (eight on later models) were installed in the solid nose, and two more guns of the same calibre were fitted in each of the ventral and dorsal turrets. The dorsal turret could be locked into the forward-firing position and operated by the pilot. Douglas factories produced 1355 A-26Bs, of which 1150 came from the Long Beach plant and 205 from Tulsa. Deliveries began during early 1944 and A-26B Invaders made their operational debut with the Ninth Air Force in Europe on November 19, 1944.

The next production version was the A-26C, with a wider fuselage, dual controls and a transparent 'bombardier' nose equipped with only two 0.5-in guns, although the dorsal and ventral turret guns were retained. With the exception of five manufactured at Long Beach, all 1091 A-26Cs were constructed at Tulsa. As deliveries did not begin until 1945, they saw less service (in their case primarily in the Pacific) during the Second World War.

A few modified aircraft, designated FA-26C, were used in the reconnaissance role. Others were equipped with radar bomb-sights under the front fuselage section, and 141 were converted to US Navy JD-1s for target-towing duties.

The XA-26D was a one-off modification of an A-26B with eight 0.5-in guns in a solid nose and six additional guns of the same calibre in two underwing packs. A production order for 750 26Ds was cancelled after VJ-Day, as were 445 A-26Bs, 2809 A-26Cs, and 1250 A-26Es (which was to have been an updated development of the C model). In 1945 the XA-26F was flown as an engine test-bed. It was a converted B model with a General Electric J31 turbojet installed in the rear fuselage, but no production was undertaken.

The 9th and 12th Air Forces had been equipped with Invaders, and following the amalgamation of the units in 1946 as Tactical Air Command (TAC), these aircraft still continued to be supplied. By June 1948 the A (for attack category) prefix was dropped, and the A-26 became the B-26 (which had been the

Invader, Douglas A-26/B-26

A-26B Invaders in formation. Invaders serve in the forces of a large number of central American states and also with Portugal and Zaire

wartime designation for the Martin Marauder). USAFE (United States Air Forces Europe) used the B-26B (A-26B) and B-26C (A-26C) from bases in Germany after this date. There was also an unarmed RB-26C variant, for day and night reconnaissance work, which was equipped with cameras and photoflares.

B-26s saw action for the second time on June 27, 1950, during the Korean war. They equipped three squadrons of the 3rd Bombardment Group at Iwakuni and the 542nd Bombardment Group (later the 17th) at Itazuki. A number of modifications were made to these aircraft: the operational gross weight was increased to 17 465 kg (38 500 lb); they utilized the eight-gun solid nose of the XA-26D plus three more 0.5-in guns in each wing and the usual four sited in the two turrets; bombload was still 1815 kg (4000 lb) carried internally, supplemented by 14 5-in (12.7-cm) rockets, napalm bombs or droptanks under the wings. B-26Cs used in Korea had the same underwing stores as the B but were fitted with H₂S radar in the fuselage, and were extremely effective on night bombing raids.

Invaders phased out of TAC service in Europe were returned to the United States

and served with the Air Force Reserve and Air National Guard. In 1962 they were recalled to operational duty against the Viet Cong in South Vietnam. After 12 months' service, during which several accidents had occurred, it was realized that the Invader was past its prime as a front-line aircraft. However, the On Mark Engineering company, which had been converting B-26s for commercial use, obtained a USAF contract for a COIN (counter-insurgency) variant, the YB-26K. The airframe was strengthened and refurbished, and the powerplant was changed to two 2500-hp R-2800-103W radials. Provision was made for a greater internal fuel load and permanent wingtip tanks were fitted. Eight underwing pylons could carry most of the 2495 kg (5500 lb) of stores (including the wingtip fuel) and three guns were installed in each wing. Nose sections were interchangeable between the two-gun bombardier type and the eight-gun solid version. A reconnaissance camera was fitted as standard equipment and six 455-kg (1000-lb) st JATO (jet assisted takeoff) bottles could be attached under the fuselage, to reduce the lift-off distance needed on the often hastily-prepared and frequently-damaged runways in their area of operation. Approximately 70 of these

B-26K conversions were ordered after the first flight on May 26, 1964. The majority of these were used in Vietnam under the designation A-26A, although some were supplied to other countries under the US military assistance programme.

Other Invader conversions, designated TB-26B and TB-26C, were used as trainers with Air Force Reserve and Air National Guard units. CB-26Bs were transports and VB-26Bs were VIP transports with USAF Headquarters. DB-26Cs (and Navy JD-1Ds) were airborne control aircraft used to launch and direct target drones.

In the mid-1970s, B-26Bs and B-26Cs were still in service with the air arms of Brazil, Chile, Colombia, the Dominican Republic, El Salvador, Guatemala, Honduras, Indonesia, Mexico, Nicaragua, Peru, Portugal and Zaire. Some 18 of the Brazilian aircraft had then been converted to B-26K standard.

(A-26B) *Span:* 21.3 m (70 ft) *Length:* 15.2 m (50 ft) *Gross weight:* 15 875 kg (35 000 lb) *Maximum speed:* 570 km/h (355 mph)

(B-26K) *Span:* 21.8 m (71 ft 6 in) *Length:* 15.2 m (50 ft) *Gross weight:* 19 670 kg (43 370 lb) *Maximum speed:* 640 km/h (397 mph)

Soviet paratroops jump from an ASU-85 airborne assault gun during an exercise in February 1969. The ASU-85 mounts an 85-mm SD-44 gun

Before the Second World War the Russians had few if any self-propelled guns. Some truck-mounted AA guns had been seen at the May Day parade and during fighting in the Russo/Finnish War rather crude SP antitank guns based on the Komsomolets armoured utility tractor were deployed at Viipuri. The SU-57 also used the Komsomolets, but left the gun crew almost totally exposed bar a frontal shield.

Encounters with German SP guns during 1941-45 gave Russian designers some useful ideas and by the end of the war they had not only caught up, but surpassed the Germans in designing and mass producing vehicles which mounted guns up to 122-mm (4.8-in), more than able to destroy rival AFVs. Since 1945 they have continued to produce a useful range of SP equipments including air-portable antitank guns. A more recent introduction has been fully armoured 122-mm (4.8-in) and 152-mm (6-in) SP guns with 360° traverse similar to the US M109 SP Howitzer.

One feature of modern SP guns which is retained from the Second World War is a direct fire and antitank capability, whatever the calibre of the main armament. They can operate in a chemically or nuclear contaminated environment and the 122-mm howitzer is amphibious.

SU-45/SU-57

It was not until 1942 that Soviet self-propelled guns became a real threat to German armour. During the Russo/Finnish war the SU-45 had used the ubiquitous Kom-

The ISU-152 used the Josef Stalin heavy tank chassis to mount a 152-mm (6-in) M1937/43(ML-20S) gun-howitzer in a hull similar to that of the ISU-122 SP gun

somolets tractor to mount a box-like structure with a crew of three and a 45-mm (1.8-in) antitank gun normally fitted into a BT-7 tank. The SU-57 also used the Komsomolets chassis but mounted a 57-mm (2.24-in) antitank gun M1941 and saw extensive service in the opening months of the war.

SU-37

The T-70 light tank was used for two SP equipments, the SU-37 AA gun and the SU-76 antitank gun. The former had a turret that could be rotated through 360° but only 32° for firing while the gun elevated from −2° to 87°.

The T-70 was the only standardized SP AA mounting used during the war, though trucks were pressed into service equipped with three Maxim MMGs as AA guns. Before the war, parades had displayed a mobile 76-mm (3-in) gun, but little is known of these in action.

An SU-76 or 3rd Ukrainian Front in a hide position prior to Russian assaults on German positions near Lake Balaton, Hungary in 1944

Novosti

SU-76

The SU-76 was widely used during the war. It was originally intended as a tank destroyer, but thicker armour on German tanks led to its relegation to infantry support work. It was well suited to this task, carrying 60 rounds and a gun that fired HE (muzzle velocity 680 m/sec [2230 ft/sec]), HEAT (muzzle velocity 325 m/sec [1065 ft/sec]), APHE (muzzle velocity 655 m/sec [2151 ft/sec]), and HVAP (muzzle velocity 965 m/sec [3167 ft/sec]). Its chief weakness was that it had no overhead cover for the crew compartment. Later versions (the SU-76M) had new engines and overhead cover.

SU-85/D-S85

The SU-85 not only had full armour protection, but used the well-tried T-34 medium tank chassis and the 85-mm (3.35-in) AA gun which after adaptation became the D-S85. It fired either APHE (muzzle velocity 790 m/sec [2598 ft/sec]) or HVAP (muzzle velocity 1030 m/sec [3379 ft/sec]). When the T-34 was rearmed with the 85-mm gun SU-85 crews went over to the SU-100.

SU-100

The SU-100 was the last SP antitank gun based on the T-34 chassis. Its 100-mm (3.95-in) gun was later used in the T-54 tank and was a great improvement. With an elevation

An SU-85 rumbles down a street in the German town of Allenstein in 1944. It used a T-34 chassis and an adaptation of the 85-mm AA gun designated D-S85 or D-S85A

Early versions of the SU-76 had an open crew compartment which made them vulnerable to air-burst shells or hand grenades.

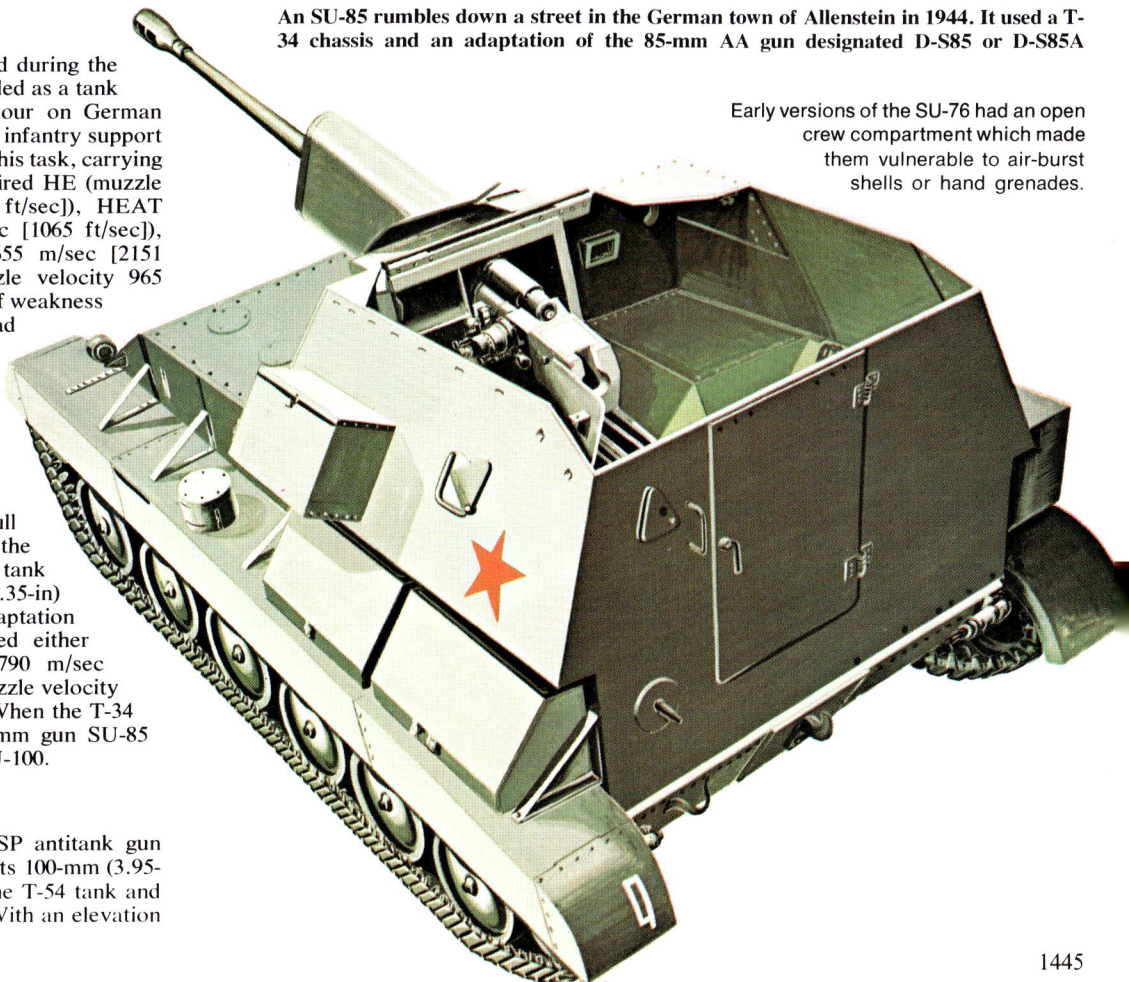

The SU-100 had an M1944 D-10S antitank gun with a 12.7-mm DShK antiaircraft machine-gun mounted on the cupola

Novosti

SU-76 SP guns wait at a start line on the Eastern Front. They are equipped with unditching poles for recovery from soft ground

The SU-122 used the successful 122-mm M1938 Field Howitzer on a T-34 chassis as a close-support gun for infantry and armour assaults

Above: ISU-122 had a top speed of 37 km/h (23 mph) on roads and 23 km/h (14 mph) cross country. The IS chassis was used for two versions of the 122-mm gun, the A-19S and later the D-25S which had a muzzle-brake. Though crudely finished by Western standards the ISU-122 and ISU-152 gave the Russians SP guns that were more than a match for enemy armour and devastating against bunkers and field defences

from −2° to +17° it fired APHE (muzzle velocity 920 m/sec [3017 ft/sec]) and HVAP (muzzle velocity 1000 m/sec [3281 ft/sec]).

Below: SU-122 SP guns pass through the Narva Gate in Leningrad during the German seige

ISU-122

The climax in Soviet SP design came with the ISU-122. It used the IS tank chassis and mounted a 122-mm (4.8-in) gun. The first model, which appeared in 1944, had a modified M1931/7 Corps gun designated A-19S while the D-25S fitted to later versions was an identical gun except for a large muzzle-brake. It fired APHE ammunition with a muzzle velocity of 915 m/sec (3000 ft/sec) and many vehicles mounted a 12.7-mm (0.5-in) DShK heavy machine-gun on top of the fighting compartment. The ISU-122 continued in service after the war and was, like the SU-100 passed on to Warsaw Pact and friendly nations. An SU-100 captured by British forces at Suez was shipped to Britain at the close of the expedition in 1956.

ASU-57/ASU-85

Current Soviet SP equipments reflect two tactical requirements. Air portability and fire power. The ASU-57 airborne assault gun has a Ch-51M 57-mm (2.24-in) gun with 30

rounds. It can be carried slung under helicopters or air-dropped. The fighting compartment is open and the vehicle is capable of speeds of up to 45 km/h (28 mph). The ASU-85 is a bigger version with an enclosed compartment and an SD-44 85-mm (3.35-in) gun with 40 rounds. It too can be air-landed or parachuted and is capable of 44 km/h (27 mph). It is NBC-proofed and has been fitted with an IR night-fighting light and retrofitted with target-acquisition and ranging aids.

122-mm SP Howitzer M1974

Among the latest SP equipments to be deployed by Warsaw Pact countries are the 122-mm (4.8-in) SP Howitzer M1974 and the 152-mm (6-in) SP Gun M1973. The M1974 is based on the PT-76 tank chassis and has an amphibious capability. Armament consists of one 122-mm gun with HE and HEAT ammunition with a gun crew of two and a driver. Normally used some distance behind the front line it can also be used in a direct-fire role.

152-mm SP Gun M1973

The M1973 has a 152-mm (6-in) gun and a 12.7-mm (0.5-in) AA gun. Ammunition type is not known but it can be assumed to be conventional. The crew with driver consists of four men. It is normally used behind the front line but can be brought forward.

ZSU-23-4

The ZSU-23-4 has been used in action in the Middle East and consists of four 23-mm (0.9-in) AA cannon with 1000 rounds, with a Gun Dish radar on a PT-76 tank chassis. It is not amphibious but it is capable of 44 km/h (27 mph). It has a crew of four housed in a box-like turret and hull.

ZSU-57-2 SP AA guns on parade in Moscow during May Day celebrations in 1959. This equipment uses a chassis based on a shortened version of the T-54 tank but cannot wade or swim

ZSU-57-2

The big brother of the ZSU-23-4 is the ZSU-57-2, which has twin 57-mm (2.24-in) antiaircraft guns with 316 or 360 rounds. It has a crew of six and like the 23-4 has been widely deployed within the Warsaw Pact and friendly nations. However, it lacks radar and swimming or deep wading capability. The gun can also be used against light armour where it can pierce a thickness of 106 mm (4.2 in) at 500 m (550 yards).

COMPARATIVE DATA—SOVIET SELF-PROPELLED GUNS

Gun	vehicle	chassis	crew	weight (kg/tons)	date
57-mm AA Gun M1941	SU-57	Komsomolets	3	4032/4	1940
76.2-mm Field Gun M1942	SU-76	T-70	4	10 987/10.9	1942
37-mm AA Gun M1939	SU-37	T-70	3	10 575/10.5	1943
85-mm AA Gun M1939	SU-85	T-34	4	29 736/29.5	1943
100-mm AT Gun M1944	SU-100	T-34	4	32 256/32	1944
122-mm Howitzer M1938	SU-122	T-34	5	45 662/45.3	1943
122-mm M1931/37	ISU-122	IS	4	45 662/45.3	1944
152-mm Gun M1937	ISU-152	IS	4	46 700/46	1944
57-mm CH-51M	ASU-57	ASU-57	3+6	3350/3.3	1957
85-mm SD-44 Gun	ASU-85	ASU-85	4	14 000/13.78	1962
122-mm D-74	122-mm SP Gun M74	PT-76	3	20 000/19.68	1974
152-mm M1955 (d-20)	152-mm SP	152-mm SP	4	N/A	1973
23-mm ZU-23 AA Gun	ZSU-23-4	PT-76	4	14 000/13.78	1955
57-mm S-68 AA Gun	ZSU-57-2	T-54	6	28 100/27.65	1957

The dramatic signature of a rocket barrage. The smoke and dust attracted retaliatory fire

When Germany invaded Russia in 1941 she had a fairly accurate picture of most of the current Soviet equipment. There were, however, two big surprises, the T-34 medium tank and the multi-rail rocket launchers nicknamed Stalin Organs or Katyusha. The latter name, Katyusha, translated as 'Little Katy' and was adopted by the Russians for their M-8 launcher and then used loosely for other similar equipments.

Rocket barrages were fearful experiences for their victims, with from 12 to 16 18-kg (40-lb) warheads exploding almost simultaneously in a comparatively small target area. However, as with all rocket weapons the scream of the rocket and its surface blast were the most frightening features, and as long as a soldier could keep his head down and remain calm under fire casualties resulting from rocket barrages were likely to be less heavy than under conventional artillery fire.

The advantage of rocket projectiles for the Russians, and also subsequently for the Germans was that they were easy to make and did not need an elaborate gun carriage. A conventional GAZ or ZIS 1½-ton or 2½-ton truck or a Lend-Lease US 6×4 could be simply fitted with a frame for the 132-mm (5.2-in) or 82-mm (3.2-in) rockets with a 10° traverse and +15° to +45° elevation, loaded up with rockets and driven to a launch site.

Mobility was an important feature since counter-battery fire could be prompt and rocket units had to get into and out of action quickly. However, in the latter years of the war rocket units could operate with increasing immunity and for some set-piece actions a heavier 300-mm (11.8-in) projectile was brought forward in its packing frame launcher and fired by remote control.

Since the end of the Second World War the Russians have continued to develop rocket artillery, improving on the basic multi-rail truck-mounted launcher. In addition short-range battlefield support missiles like the Frog and Scud have been developed which can carry a variety of warheads including chemical, HE, nuclear and possibly radar or heat seeking sensors.

82-mm

First used by Soviet forces at Orszy in July 1941, the 82-mm (3.2-in) rocket was most usually propelled by some form of solvent-less cordite, though a more crude black powder was occasionally used. All the rockets deployed by Soviet forces were fin stabilized and were fired electrically via primers in the rocket venturi using power from a battery in the cab which was protected by a steel sheet over the roof. The operator could ripple fire the rockets by using a rotary switch box, and the minimum that could be fired was two rockets. The rails of the M-8 launcher were perforated steel beams 188-cm (74-in) long mounted on a tubular-steel frame. Fourteen rockets were fitted above the top rail, with 12 slung below and a further ten slung below the bottom rail.

132-mm

Just after the 82-mm (3.2-in) rocket had been introduced into service it was followed by the 132-mm (5.2-in), which subsequently became the longest serving Soviet artillery rocket. The M-13 launcher carried 16 132-mm rockets, eight on top and eight below. The rails were 488-cm (192-in) long on a tubular frame similar to that of the M-8. Elevation was up to 45° with traverse either 10° or 20°. The sights were standard MP41 used for mortars.

300-mm

The 300-mm (11.8-in) rocket, which saw action at Stalingrad, came in an M-30 frame which doubled as a packing and launching frame. The rockets were positioned for set-piece barrages like the German schweres Wurfgerät 40 or 41.

310-mm

By 1944 the Soviets had produced a more sophisticated launcher, the M-31, which was used with the 310-mm (12.2-in) rocket. The 310-mm was first produced in 1943 and could be fired from a frame as well as the M-31 launcher. The mobile launcher consisted of two banks of six rectangular launching frames on a mounting similar to the M-8 and M-13. Like the other launchers it was mounted on a variety of trucks which were provided with jacks at the rear of the chasses for additional stability.

During the siege of Leningrad home-made versions were produced in the city including projectiles in 280-mm (11-in) and 120-mm (4.7-in) calibres but little is known about these projectiles.

122-mm BM-21

Since the Second World War Soviet multi-barrelled launchers have been improved with the 122-mm (4.8-in) BM-21. Mounted on the Ural-375 or Tatra 813 truck in a bank of 4×10

Soviet 132-mm (5.2-in) rockets in position on their truck-mounted M-13 launchers ready to fire

An M-13 truck-mounted launcher for 16 132-mm (5.2-in) rockets, eight on top and eight below, travelling at speed on its way to the front

tubes the BM-21 can be loaded in ten minutes and fired in either salvo or ripple. The launcher has an elevation from 0° to 50° and a traverse through 120°. In action the vehicle is parked at an oblique angle to the line of launch to avoid blast damage to the cab.

132-mm BM-13-16

The BM-13-16 132-mm rocket launcher is based on the Z1L-151 truck and mounts 16 barrels. It is capable of 140° traverse and takes from five to ten minutes to reload. The Z1L-151 truck has a top speed of 60 km/h (37 mph) on roads when fully loaded. The rockets weigh 77.5 kg (170.8 lb) and have a range of 9000 m (9850 yards).

140-mm M1965

The 140-mm RPU-14 bears a considerable resemblance to German towed launchers from the Second World War. This 16-tube launcher takes 4 minutes to reload and is used by Soviet Marine and airborne troops in its light role. It is used widely in the Warsaw Pact forces, though the Polish army have developed their own eight-tube WP-8 firing the same spin-stabilized rocket.

200-mm BMD-20

The BMD-20 mounts four 200-mm (7.9-in) rockets on a Z1L-151 chassis and since the rockets weight 91.4 kg (205 lb) it takes ten

minutes to reload. It can be fired in either ripple or salvo and has a massive blast effect in the target area.

240-mm BM-24

The 240-mm (9.4-in) BM-24 may be an ungainly short-ranged weapon, but it has a very substantial blast effect. Crews can reload the 12 tubes, which are mounted on Z1L-157 trucks or AT-S tracked vehicles, in three to four minutes. Captured BM-24s were used by the Israelis during the 1973 war in the Middle East, and they have also been deployed in Africa by Cuban forces. The frame elevates from 0° to 45° and has a 105° traverse.

COMPARATIVE DATA – SOVIET ROCKET ARTILLERY

Rocket	length (cm/in)	weight (kg/lb)	range (m/yards)	muzzle velocity (m/sec/ft/sec)
82-mm	59.6/23.5	8/17.6	5500/6017	315/1033
132-mm	142/55.9	42.5/93.7	8500/9300	355/1165
310-mm	176.5	94.6/208.6	4800/5250	255/837
122-mm	3226/1270	45.8/100.9	20 500/22 420	N/A
132-mm	1473/580	77.5/170.8	9000/9850	350/1148
140-mm	1085/427	39.6/87.3	9810/10 730	400/1312
200-mm BMD 20	3110/1224	91.4/201.5	20 000/21 870	N/A
240-mm BM-24	129/50	109/240.3	10 200/11 150	465/1525
250-mm BM-25	5822/2292	455/1003.1	39 000/32 800	N/A

Igniter
assembly

Solid
rocket
fuel

Left and below: The 3-in (76-mm) AA
rocket used a variant of the AA shell
time fuze which was set before firing
and had an electrically fired solid fuel
rocket motor. Though it was a crude
missile it could fill the sky with
fragments and could be deployed by
day or night in all weathers

When Britain began rearming in 1935 it was
soon apparent that there would be considerable delay in providing enough antiaircraft
guns to form a satisfactory defence. The
research department of Woolwich arsenal was
therefore asked to investigate the possibility of
developing a rocket weapon, the only specification being that whatever was produced had to
have a time of flight to 4570 m (15000 ft)
comparable with the 3-in (76-mm) AA shell.

What information existed on rockets was
of no value in this context, and design had to
begin at first principles. Fortunately; a suitable propellant, a solventless cordite, was in
production and could be extruded in large
sticks. This, in turn, dictated the size of the
rockets, since the smallest diameter stick
thought capable of propelling a useful size of
rocket was 2 in (51 mm) while the largest the
machinery could extrude was 3 in (76 mm).
These two sizes were chosen for trials and
eventually became the standard sizes of
rocket.

In late 1935 preliminary ballistic tests with
the 2-in charge were conducted in order to
determine some of the basic characteristics
and it was soon apparent that in order to
achieve the desired velocity the charge would
have to be quite large, implying a long, thin
rocket. This led to the need for fins on the
rear end since such a long projectile could not
be spin-stabilized. By 1937 good progress had
been made and, in order to ensure a warhead
with sufficient lethality to damage a full-sized
bomber, a design for a 3-in rocket was in
hand.

During the first few months of 1939 an
extensive trial of over 2500 rockets was

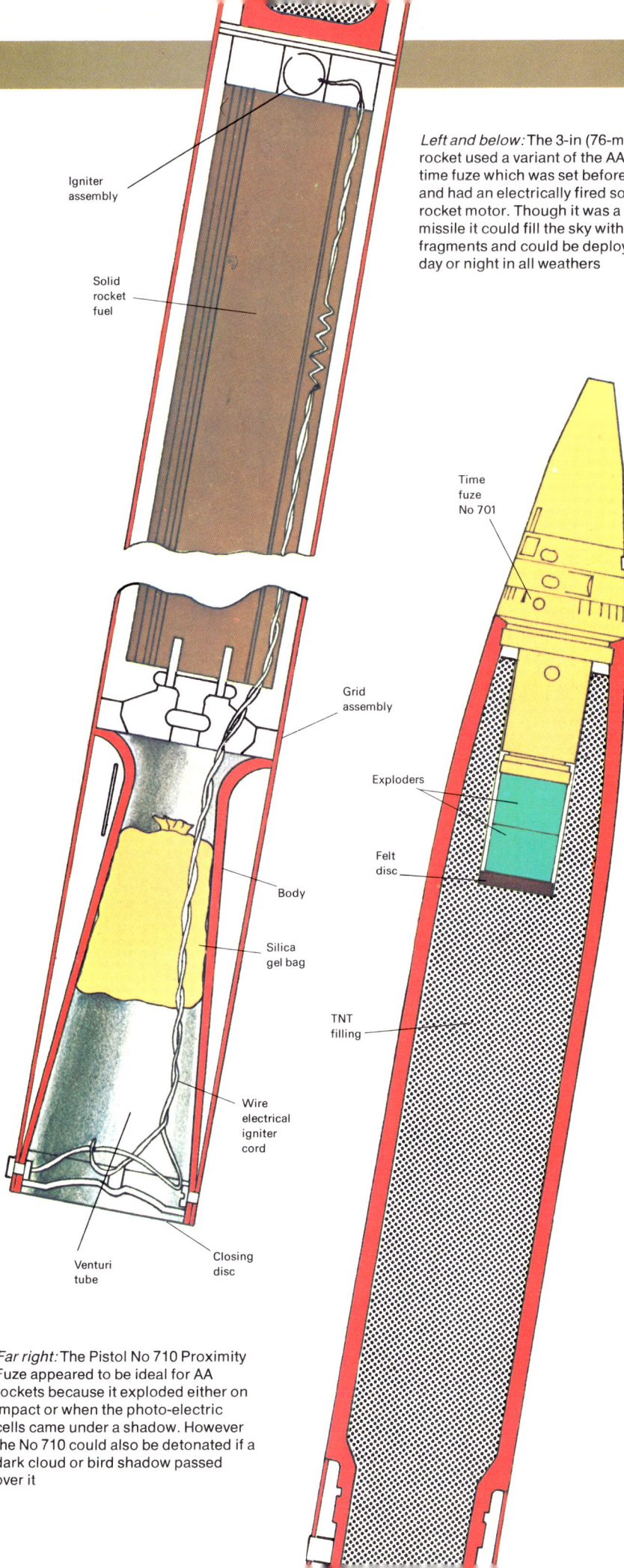

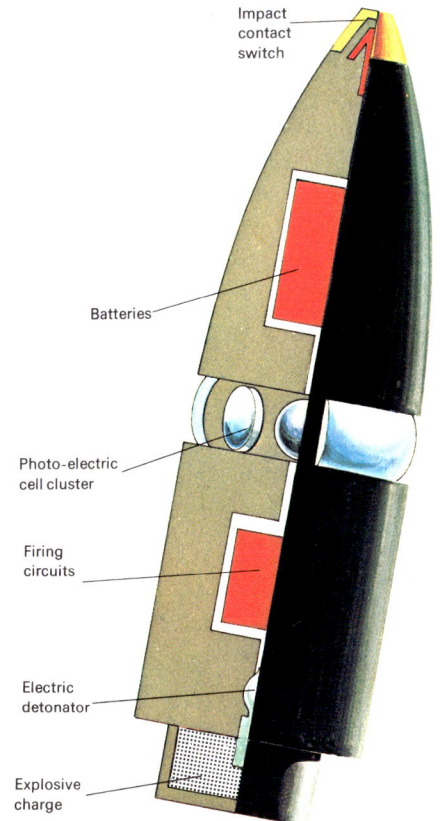

Time
fuze
No 701

Grid
assembly

Exploders

Felt
disc

Body

Silica
gel bag

TNT
filling

Wire
electrical
igniter
cord

Impact
contact
switch

Batteries

Photo-electric
cell cluster

Firing
circuits

Electric
detonator

Venturi
tube

Closing
disc

Explosive
charge

Far right: The Pistol No 710 Proximity
Fuze appeared to be ideal for AA
rockets because it exploded either on
impact or when the photo-electric
cells came under a shadow. However
the No 710 could also be detonated if a
dark cloud or bird shadow passed
over it

carried out in great secrecy in Jamaica. The General Staff insisted on a closed-tube pattern of launcher with a breech similar to that of a gun, and the rocket's high-speed gas efflux, reflecting from the face of the closed breech, had a disturbing effect on the fins which led to erratic flight. By the middle of 1939 it was decided that the requirement for rockets was no longer pressing, though permission was given to continue research at low priority in the hope that the weapon's accuracy could be improved.

During all this time secrecy had been complete. The weapon was not referred to as a rocket but as an 'unrotated projectile' or 'UP', and the research establishment on the Welsh coast at Aberporth, was known merely as the Projectile Development Establishment.

After the outbreak of war the German dive-bombers appeared to pose a considerable threat and the Admiralty was soon asking the rocket scientists of PDE for a wire barrage device. This, known as the Apparatus, Air Defence, Type B was a cluster of 20 specially shortened 3-in rockets, each carrying a canister holding a mine, a parachute and a length of wire. The rockets were fired in a salvo, the canisters opened at about 2440-m (8000-ft) altitude, and the mines, suspended by the wire from the parachutes, were ejected into the path of the dive-bomber. This was the forerunner of a number of similar 'parachute-and-cable' devices used by the Royal Navy, most of which used the 2-in rocket for propulsion. A useful by-product of this development was the discovery that the rockets could be launched easily from simple open frames, provided that there was protection from the back-blast, and that firing in this way gave more accurate results than had the firings from closed tubes.

The next major design came from a request by the Chemical Warfare Staff for a weapon capable of discharging a heavy salvo of gas for a short distance. The requirement was to launch a 13.6-kg (30-lb) 127-mm (5-in) gas cylinder to 3600-m (4000-yards) range, and a short 5-in rocket motor was perfected by the end of 1940. However, since chemical warfare was not resorted to, the rocket lay dormant until 1943 when the navy replaced the chemical head with one carrying high explosive and turned it into a beach bombardment weapon, the Sea Mattress.

In the spring of 1940, as the military situation worsened, the dive-bomber threat to vital targets in Britain began to cause anxiety, and a project was put forward for a simple projector to fire a 3-in rocket equipped with a proximity fuze. This fuze, known as the Pistol No 710 had been under development at PDE since 1938, and relied for its action upon a bank of photo-electric cells

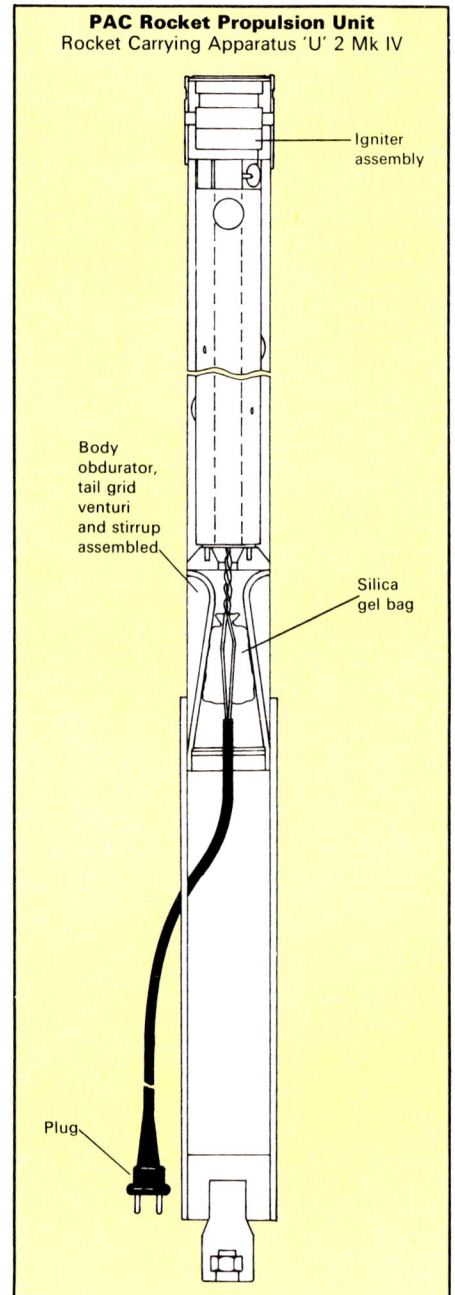

The Parachute and Cable Apparatus fired a 2-in (51-mm) rocket trailing a cable and mine assembly. It was a simple but effective means of attacking low-flying aircraft on bombing runs and did not need an elaborate mount

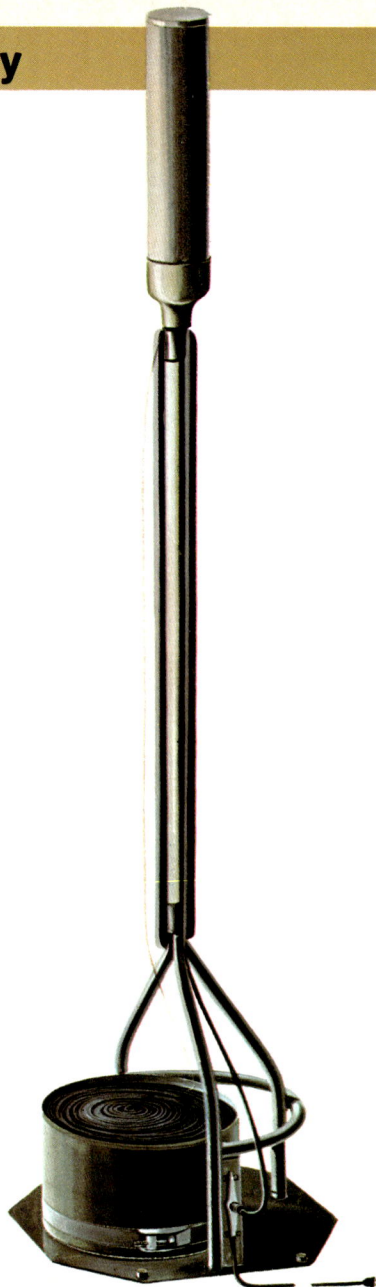

PAC Rocket Propulsion Unit
Rocket Carrying Apparatus 'U' 2 Mk IV

- Igniter assembly
- Body obdurator, tail grid venturi and stirrup assembled
- Silica gel bag
- Plug

'tuned' to normal daylight. As the fuze flew through the air, any shadow—such as that of an aircraft—which fell across the PE Cells would trigger the circuitry and detonate the rocket warhead.

This project was backed by both the army and the Royal Navy. Their prime requirement was for a projector cheap enough to be turned out in quantity and sufficiently simple

to be employed without elaborate facilities and by personnel with the minimum of training. The result was the Projector, Rocket, 3-in Mark 1, which was designed quickly and built by Harvey of Greenwich equally rapidly, known in the Royal Navy as the Harvey Projector. This was a very simple device consisting merely of a free-swinging pair of rails from which the rocket was

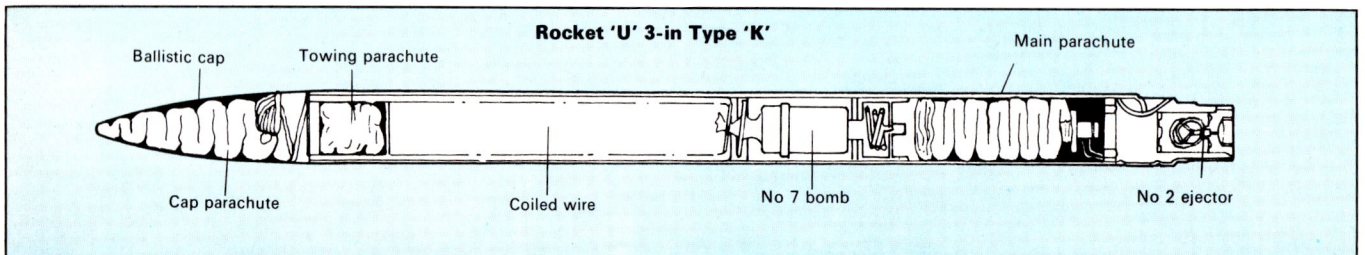

Rocket 'U' 3-in Type 'K'

- Ballistic cap
- Towing parachute
- Main parachute
- Cap parachute
- Coiled wire
- No 7 bomb
- No 2 ejector

Main parachute

Mine in position

Cable

Stabilising parachute released

Plane catches cable and causes towing parachute to open

The 3-in 'U' Type K AA Rocket was a development of the parachute and cable device. The cable hung from a large parachute which detached if the aircraft became entangled on the wire; a small stabilizing parachute deployed as a larger towing parachute hung below. The suspended charge was drawn into contact with the aircraft where its charge was sufficient to bring down its victim or severely damage it

Empty coil sheath falling clear

Towing parachute spilled from bag

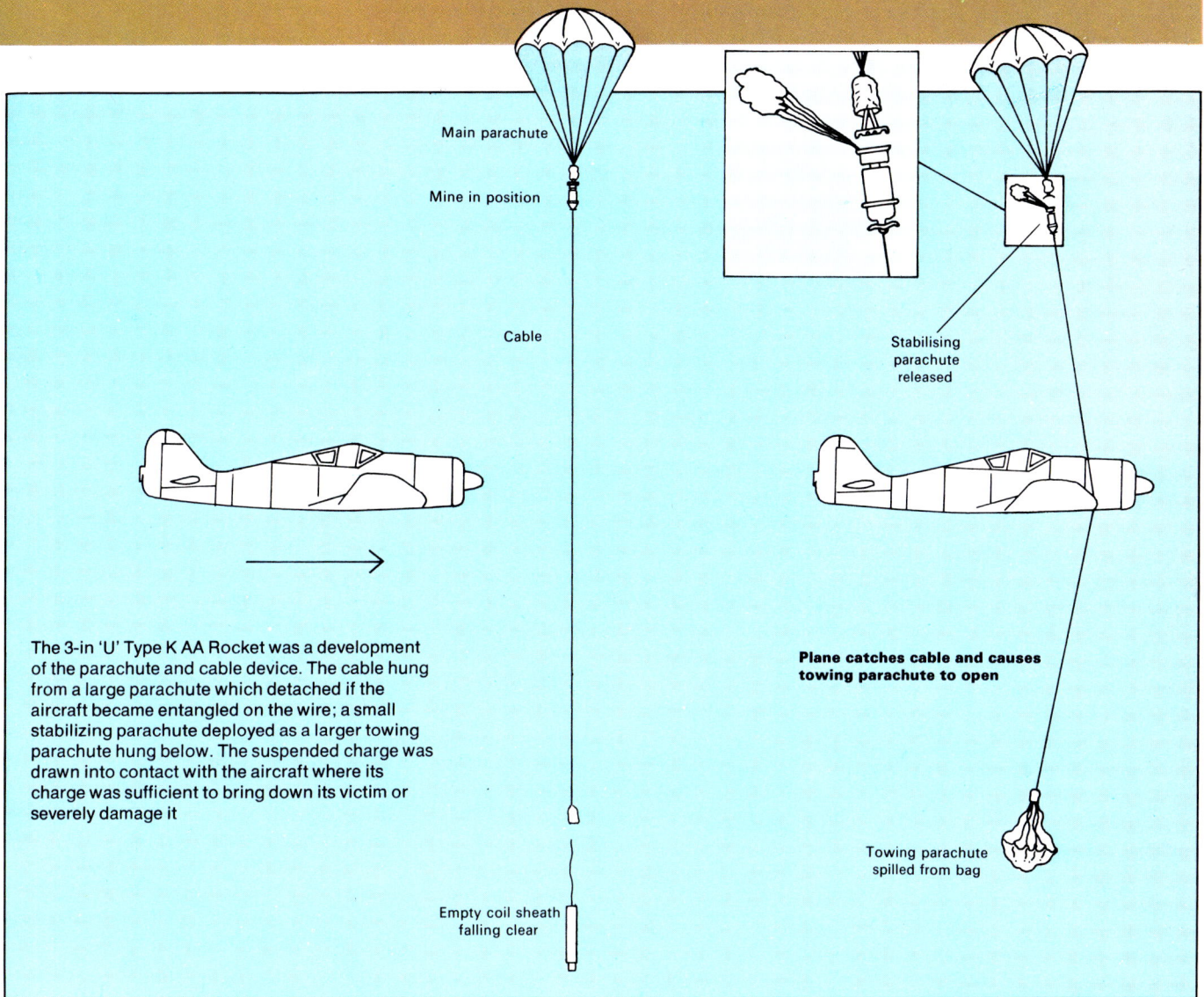

launched, shields at the sides to protect the operators, and an electric firing circuit. The first rocket battery was formed in October 1940 and many of these projectors were later to be manned by Home Guard antiaircraft batteries.

However, the Pistol 710 did not prove to be entirely satisfactory. It tended to over-react to flashes of sunlight and detonate prematurely, and, of course, it was useless at night. A conventional type of powder-burning time fuze had been designed and this replaced the Pistol 710 in service.

The shortage of manpower led to a review of projector design, and a double projector was developed, allowing the same number of men to fire twice as many rockets. This, the Projector No 2, was much the same as the No 1 but for having two sets of launch rails, and was also fitted with geared elevating and traversing mechanisms. Several thousand of these were produced and they became the standard equipment of the many 'Z Batteries', a security cover name for rocket AA batteries.

By the end of 1940 the dive-bomber threat had receded, but the peformance of rocket projectors during the Luftwaffe raids on south-east England had shown that they were very effective. These raids had exposed some weaknesses in AA fire-control systems of the day and showed that when aiming and prediction were in error, barrage fire had at least as

The No 7 Bomb was an ingenious device which armed itself as a small wind vane unwound a safety device. This would only happen if the bomb was being pulled down by an enemy aircraft

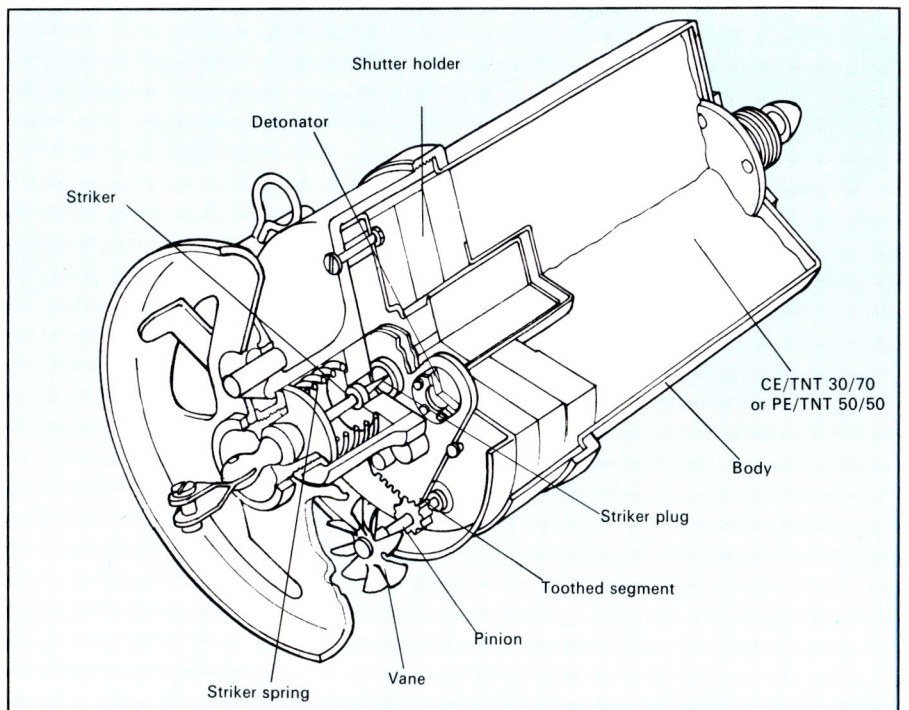

Shutter holder

Detonator

Striker

CE/TNT 30/70 or PE/TNT 50/50

Body

Striker plug

Toothed segment

Pinion

Vane

Striker spring

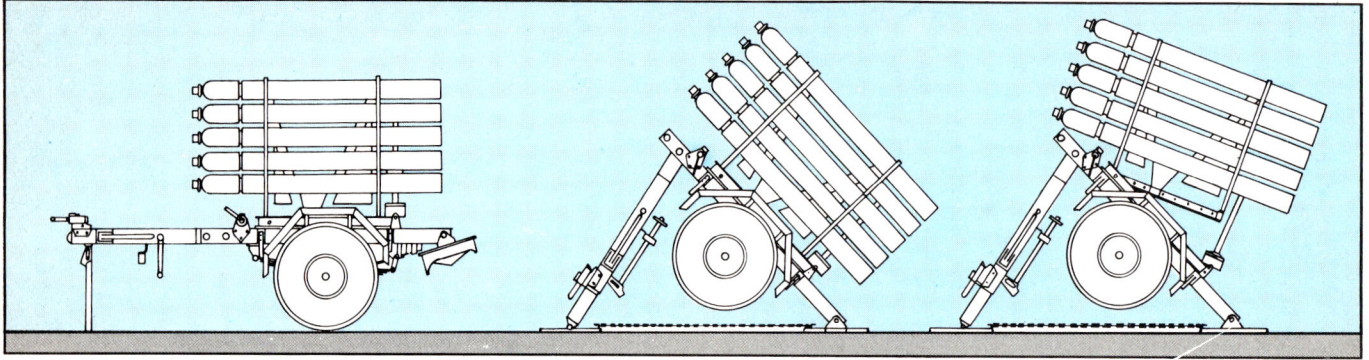

good a chance of hitting a target as aimed fire, and in these conditions the rockets gave an acceptable performance. A system was worked out of using a battery of projectors firing 64 rockets simultaneously to form a curtain of steel in the sky. This went into operation early in 1941 and soon scored some success. More batteries were formed throughout the country, most manned by the Home Guard, and in addition to a number of confirmed 'kills' they had a noticeable deterrent effect on formations of bombers.

The parachute-and-cable system was also revived for use with these batteries, with the adoption of the K Rocket. This was twice as long as a standard rocket and the over-length warhead carried two parachutes, 305 m (1000 ft) of cable, and a contact mine. A time fuze on the warhead ejected the contents at about 5800 m (19 000 ft) altitude; the main parachute opened and the wire was unreeled, the mine then hanging 305 m (1000 ft) below the parachute and the entire assembly falling through the air at about 4.6 m/sec (15 ft/sec). If an aircraft struck the wire, a weak link broke and the main parachute was disconnected, a smaller drag parachute then opening. This had sufficient pull to draw the cable across the aircraft wing until the contact mine struck the wing and detonated. While the 'K Rocket' was theoretically effective, it was clumsy and prone to damage while loading, and the debris that fell out of the sky after firing a salvo was a potential hazard to those underneath. It was, therefore, largely confined to batteries firing over the sea.

Further development of rockets continued and it was discovered that giving a small amount of spin to the rocket aided accuracy. This was known as 'roll stabilization' and was achieved by building the launcher with twisted rails which engaged the fins and imparted the desired roll. From this came the idea of adapting the rocket to a land-bombardment weapon, and a projectile was built up using a Naval 5-in head allied to a 3-

in motor. A simple multi-rail projector was built on a two-wheeled trailer and given the name Land Mattress. The launcher could only be elevated between 23° and 45°, giving the rocket a spread of range between 6125 m (6700 yards) and 7315 m (8000 yards). In order to be able to fire to shorter ranges, spoilers—discs of metal of various sizes which clipped around the percussion fuze and 'spoiled' the air-flow over the rocket head, thus altering the trajectory—were provided. These reduced the minimum range to 3265 m (3900 yds).

A particular feature of the war against Japan was the Japanese bunker, a strong earthwork which defied most infantry-accompanying weapons of the day, and in order to deal with these the Lilo rocket was developed. This used a 3-in motor with a 27.2-kg (60-lb) semi-armour-piercing type of

head, capable of penetrating 3 m (10 ft) of earth and a layer of logs, to burst inside the bunker. It was fired from a simple open tube capable of being carried and emplaced by one man. A light 9.5-kg (21-lb) head was also developed to give longer ranges. It does not appear to have been used very often.

Another project which arose out of the peculiar demands of jungle warfare was for a light spin-stabilized rocket of 60-mm (2.4-in) calibre. This was eventually developed, together with a magazine-fed launcher allowing a rate of fire of 240 rockets a minute, mounted on a Vickers machine-gun tripod. Development of this continued well after the war but eventually died out since none of the three services could see a use for it.

Since 1945, although several rocket designs have been investigated in Britain, no service artillery-type rocket has been introduced.

Above: **The Land Mattress was a 30-barrel rocket projector which first saw action in 1944**

COMPARATIVE DATA

Projectile	Weight complete (kg/lb)	Warhead weight (kg/lb)	Velocity (m/sec/ft/sec)	Maximum range (m/yards)	Launcher
3-in AA	18.82/41.5	4.62/10.2	640/2100	11 900/13 000	1-, 2-, 9- or 20-rail
5-in Chemical	27.82/61.3	14.17/31.2	204/670	3200/3500	1- or 6-rail
3-in Land	29.93/66	15.5/34.2	335/1100	7300/8000	16- or 30-rail
Lilo	36.28/80	27.6/60.8	102/335	100/110	single tube

The US 5-in Barrage Rocket was designed for a final barrage of support fire as the warships lifted their fire and the landing craft began their run in to the beach. It combined a 5-in HE impact-fuzed warhead with a 2.5-in rocket motor and was mounted in banks in special landing craft sailing with the invasion fleet

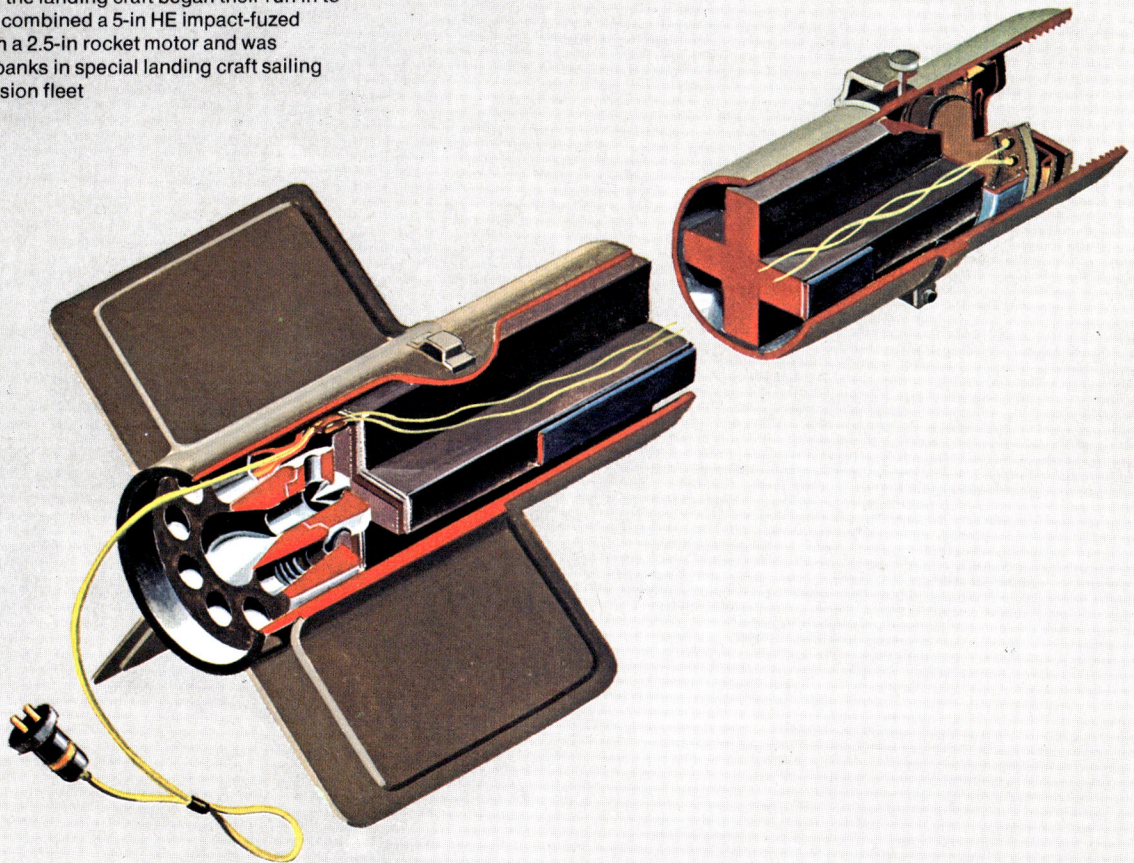

The most famous American rocket development was, of course, the Bazooka, dealt with in a separate entry under that title. Development of an artillery rocket began in 1941 and resulted in an extremely versatile 4.5-in (114-mm) model which was eventually used from field launchers, from landing craft in naval hands and as an air-to-air rocket

This rocket had four folding fins which jack-knifed out into the air after launch; the motor was of multiple sticks of nitrocellulose powder, and the warhead was in the front and also had a long stem extending into the centre of the motor so that upon detonation the motor casing was also fragmented. Known as the M8 series, these rockets were percussion fuzed, but experience showed that they were not as accurate as would have been liked, and they were eventually superseded by the M16 model which dispensed with the fins and

adopted spin stabilization, using a number of inclined jets at the rear to impart spin as well as thrust. A wide range of launchers was developed, ranging from single-tube models to multiple-tube racks mounted on trucks and DUKW amphibians.

For heavier and short-range bombardment a 7.2-in (183-mm) rocket was developed, using the British Hedgehog antisubmarine rocket as the basis. The motor was 57 mm (2.25 in) in diameter, and several experimental launchers were developed, but only one saw service. This was a multiple launcher known as the M17 or 'Whizz-Bang' which was mounted over the turret of a Sherman tank and discharged 24 rockets either singly or in salvoes.

The Japanese bunker problem also led the Americans to seek a rocket solution, and they developed the T53 8-in (203-mm) rocket, which was the standard 4.5-in rocket motor

allied to a special 8-in head. This was fired from a single-tube launcher very similar to that used with the British Lilo rocket, and small numbers were used in the Pacific theatre. In order to provide an even heavier warhead, the Multiple Rocket T13 was developed by strapping three 4.5-in motors together and attaching a 113-kg (250-lb) or 227-kg (500-lb) general-purpose aircraft bomb as a warhead. The launcher was a 105-mm (4.1-in) howitzer carriage with the barrel replaced by a simple trough. This device saw some use in the closing stages of the war.

In postwar years the spin-stabilized 4.5-in rocket remained in US service for several years but, as with the British Army, interest in bombardment rockets soon gave way to a search for effective long-range guided missiles. However, two long-range free-flight rockets were developed in the 1950s: Honest John and Little John.

Smoke billows over a landing ship as its cargo of 5-in bombardment rockets streak upwards. Up to 1000 rockets could be fired in ripple salvoes

Little John was a 354-kg (780-lb) rocket which was launched from a trailer-mounted rail and ranged up to about 15 km (9.3 miles). It used a solid-propellant motor and could be fitted with either an HE or a nuclear warhead.

Honest John was a similar weapon, but larger and with a maximum range of about 37 km (23 miles). As with the smaller weapon, Honest John can carry nuclear or conventional warheads, and is launched from a truck-mounted rail. Small auxiliary rockets give a degree of roll stabilization, and the weapon is travelling at supersonic speed before it clears its launcher.

During the war the Chemical Warfare Service expressed little interest in rockets, though chemical heads were developed for the 7.2-in bombardment rockets. After the war, however, the M55 rocket was designed to carry VX or GB gas warheads. This was a fin-stabilized 115-mm (4.5-in) solid-propellant rocket which was fired from a 45-barrel launcher mounted on a truck with a reported maximum range of about 12 km (7.5 miles). It is understood that the M55 rocket has been phased out of US service.

In the late 1970s both the US and Britain were said to be developing multiple field-artillery rocket systems, but little hard information was available.

COMPARATIVE DATA

Projectile	Weight complete (kg/lb)	Warhead weight (kg/lb)	Velocity (m/sec/ft/sec)	Maximum range (m/yards)	Launcher
4.5-in M8A2	17.32/38.2	7.25/16	256/840	3650/4000	1- to 60-tube
4.5-in M16	19.27/42.5	7.25/16	252/827	4850/5300	1- to 16-tube
7.2-in Chem	23.5/51.8	13.5/29.8	207/680	3020/3300	24-tube
M55 115-mm	30.4/67	15.2/33.5	—	12 000/13 000	45-tube
Little John	354/780	—	—	16 000/17 500	Single rail
Honest John	2040/4500	—	—	37 000/40 500	Single rail

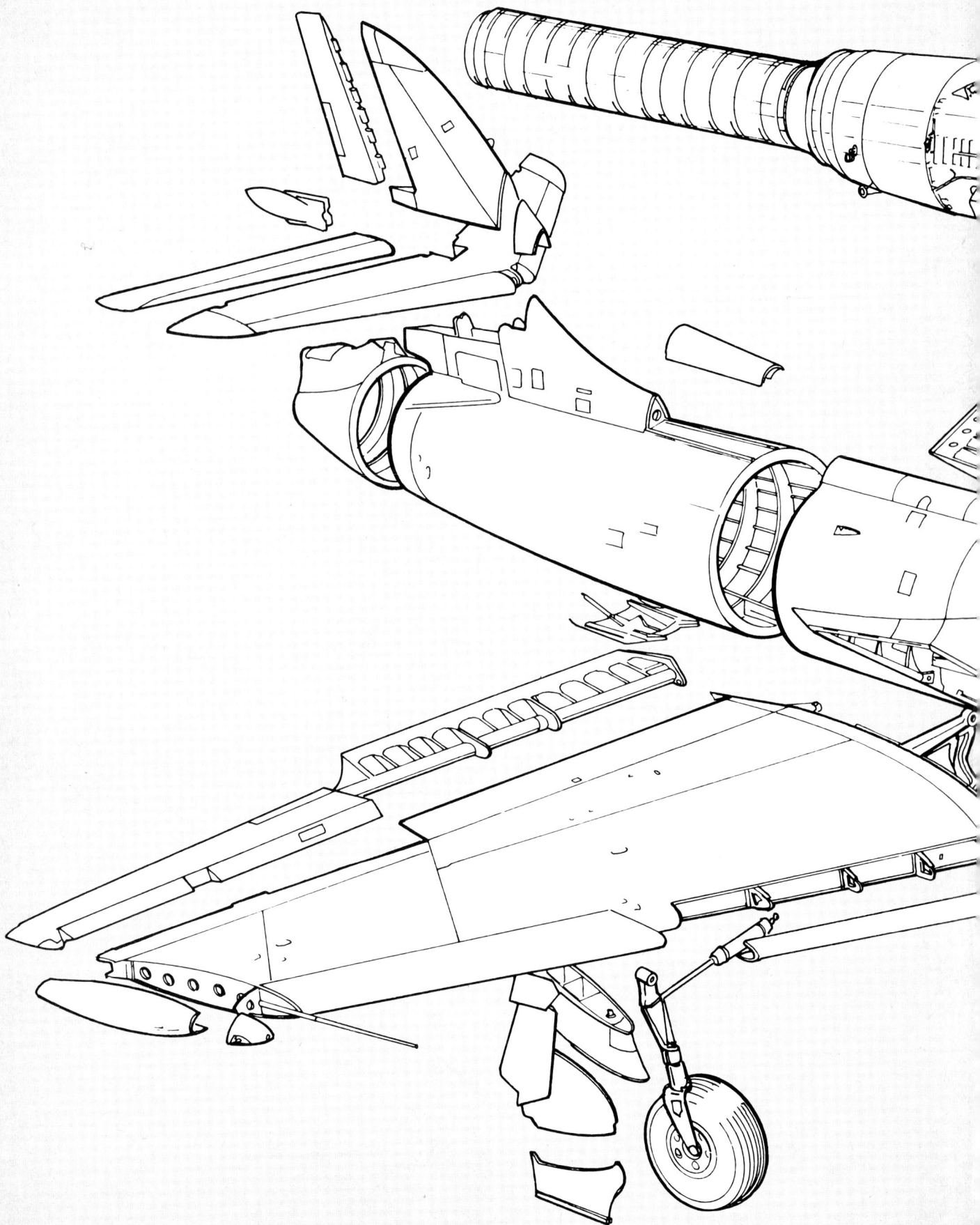